Praise for *Inside Out, Outside In: trans*

'This is a very welcome book. At a time informs the majority of mental health v ... ...across the planet is crumbling before our eyes, the need for positive examples of alternative approaches is great. The initiatives described in these diverse chapters are united by a commitment to a way of working in mental health that is based on relationships, values and finding meaning. They demonstrate that critical mental health practice is not simply about deconstructing current orthodoxies but is also about opening up new pathways to recovery and new ways of understanding mental health and healing.'
**Dr Pat Bracken, independent consultant psychiatrist**

'This book offers a real meaningful challenge to psychiatric services. It is a refreshing addition to the somewhat sparse existing literature. Through a compilation of engaging critical reflection on current practice, inspiring alternatives to mainstream mental health services and dynamic conceptual frameworks, the book challenges the current domination of the biomedical model of mental health difficulties. The engaging styles of the chapters draw on both private and public perspectives and are woven together with personal, professional and political threads. I would encourage anyone wanting to learn more about the limitations of current mental health care, and what to do about it, to read this book.'
**Bob Diamond, clinical psychologist**

'This is a significant addition to the critical literature on mental health. The editors introduce the wider socio-political context and ideologies constraining mainstream statutory services and the changes necessary to support people experiencing mental and emotional distress. Accounts of critical pedagogy in professional education, including a Mad-identified occupational therapist, offer hope that the next generation of workers will be more informed on survivor perspectives. It offers heart-warming and inspiring accounts of survivor/peer-led supports available alongside, and outside, mainstream services. This book deserves to be read by all who have an interest in transforming and humanising care of people in distress.'
**Liz Brosnan, survivor researcher**

'The mental health system is in crisis, starved both of funds and imagination. This is a time when we are in need of new ideas, and this book is full of them. The bulk of the book discusses practical alternatives like crisis services, Open Dialogue and peer support networks, with an emphasis on the "nuts and bolts", not just theory. Several chapters explore new approaches to professional training that should inspire the next generation. A final section focusing on the broader context includes some thought-provoking contributions on survivor histories, moving beyond diagnostic thinking and addressing the injustices experienced by service users. The editors are to be commended on producing such a timely contribution that will aid efforts to bring much-needed change to the mental health field.'

**Dave Harper, Professor of Clinical Psychology, University of East London**

# INSIDE OUT OUTSIDE IN

## TRANSFORMING MENTAL HEALTH PRACTICE

EDITED BY

## HARRY GIJBELS,
## LYDIA SAPOUNA
## AND GARY SIDLEY

First published 2019

PCCS Books Ltd
Wyastone Business Park
Wyastone Leys
Monmouth
NP25 3SR
United Kingdom

contact@pccs-books.co.uk
www.pccs-books.co.uk

**Inside Out, Outside In: transforming mental health practice**

British Library Cataloguing in Publication data: a catalogue record for this book is
available from the British Library.

ISBN  978 1 910919 49 1

Cover design by Jason Anscomb
Typeset in-house by PCCS Books using Minion Pro and Myriad Pro
Printed in the UK by ImprintDigital, Exeter

# CONTENTS

## PART 3: THE BROADER CONTEXT

## Acknowledgements

We would like to thank Heather Allen, former Marketing and Publicity Director at PCCS Books, who kickstarted a discussion with us a couple of years ago about what was to become the theme of this book. Pete Sanders, Director at PCCS Books, also deserves our thanks for being present and supportive in the background during the initial stages. We would also like to offer a sincere thank you to Catherine Jackson, Commissioning Editor at PCCS Books, for the insightful guidance and copyediting that brought the book to completion. We would like to extend our thanks also to Robert Whitaker for agreeing to write the foreword. Most importantly, we say a very big thank you to the contributors for their commitment, enthusiasm, time and energy in writing their chapters. We hope you like the book!

Finally, the editors would like to thank each other for the mutual support over the last two years in getting this book off the ground. We would like to think it was worth the effort and time.

# Foreword

## Robert Whitaker

For decades now, we have been prompted to think of 'mental health' as a medical affair. The individual is said to have a disorder (or disease) and needs to be treated for the symptoms associated with that ailment. Psychiatric journals are filled with articles telling of the 'effectiveness' of various therapies, with drugs the most commonly employed first-line treatment; providers of mental health services are expected to follow 'evidence-based' practices.

The evidence for the failure of this approach can now be found everywhere. Taking a public health perspective, the burden of mental disorders has dramatically increased over the past 40 years in societies around the globe that have adopted this approach. At the same time, the story of science has fallen apart: psychiatric diagnoses are understood to be 'constructs', as opposed to validated medical disorders; the efficacy of psychiatric drugs over the short term is marginal at best, and there is considerable evidence that drug treatment worsens long-term outcomes.

Yet the poor outcomes and the debunking of the science said to support current practices has not led to much change. We just keep on doing what we have been doing. As Jonathan Gadsby writes in this book in his wonderful chapter on nursing education: 'I had seen enough to know that you can let the air out of psychiatry's tyres and it still drives to work every morning.'

Which brings us to the structure of *Inside Out, Outside In*, and the reason that this book, with its collection of very fine essays, has such a powerful impact. It begins by laying out the reasons why current practices persist and the hurdles that stand in the way to radical change, and then sets forth ongoing efforts that show that such radical change is indeed possible. As such, it provides a blueprint for systemic change.

The first four chapters tell of the need to radically change the educating of the next generation of mental health professionals. They need to learn to be *critical* thinkers, and in all domains: about the research said to support current practices, the language we use to talk about mental health, social inequalities, power dynamics and a neoliberal agenda that locates psychiatric distress inside the head of the individual and gives a free pass to a capitalism that creates so much social injustice and hardship. This, of course, can be the foundation for enduring change – you can 'corrupt' the young while their minds are still open to new ideas.

The next four chapters tell of reform efforts that have originated from the *inside*, and in different settings: visiting teams to an inpatient psychiatric ward, the adoption of Open Dialogue approaches by a provider of community mental health services, the more-cautious prescribing of antidepressants in a GP setting, and the offering of trauma-informed care to women experiencing mental health crises. The common element to these efforts is that they all help people regain some degree of social footing and authority over their own lives.

The next section looks at radical change promoted from the *outside*. Three of the four chapters tell of survivor-led efforts, and the fourth tells of the creation of a residential community by a mother whose daughter suffered terribly within the conventional mental health system. All four are accounts of grassroots initiatives that promote radical change by creating something *new,* rather than amending an existing form of care.

The final chapters explore the 'broader context,' and thus the need for society to address larger philosophical and moral issues.

The overriding message is simply this: there is a long-running sentiment in Western societies that the 'mad' are unreliable witnesses to their own lives, and thus their voices – and the stories they may tell about society and their lives – are of little account. This is a sentiment that has walked hand in hand with societal oppression and violence toward the mad, and there can be no radical change as long as that sentiment rules the day.

It all leads to a final 'Aha' moment for readers: it's not enough just to let the air out of the tyres; you need to dismantle the car and build a new one.

Robert Whitaker, September 2019

---

**Robert Whitaker** is founder of *madinamerica.com* and author of *Mad in America* (2002) and *Anatomy of an Epidemic* (2010).

# Introduction

Human distress continues to be understood and responded to almost exclusively in individual terms, either as a biological disorder or as a psychological deficit. This has led to the development and maintenance of powerful structures, generally referred to as 'mental health systems', dominating thinking and practice, despite widespread recognition that such systems are often ineffective and harmful. The biomedical ethos, with its focus on 'mental illness' and corresponding drug treatments, has been particularly influential in this regard.

An increasing number of stakeholders – service users, activists, mental health professionals, academics, researchers, journalists – are striving for radical change towards approaches that explicitly acknowledge the significance of social and relational conflict, abuse, adversity and injustice as causal factors in human distress. Given this context, a central question is, 'How can we develop more effective, context-focused, sustainable ways of responding?' This book aims to inform this debate by showcasing a variety of projects and campaigns that are trying to change the orientation of dominant mental health systems and thereby offer something different.

After describing how the idea for the book was originally conceived, we will outline four important barriers often encountered when trying to offer meaningful alternatives to mainstream mental health provision: existing service culture; the political and legal context; the co-option and neutralisation of new ideas, and the often pernicious influence of traditional funding sources. To end, we will summarise the projects and campaigns described in these chapters – initiatives that aim to 'do things differently' while addressing some of these barriers – along three main themes: changing from the inside, changing from the outside, and changing the broader context.

## The original idea behind the book

The editors have been involved in critical mental health matters over many years, in the UK and in Ireland. Gary worked for 33 years in mental health services, mainly as a clinical psychologist, and, following his retirement in 2013, has been actively promoting alternatives to the dominant biomedical paradigm. Lydia comes from a social science/social work background and is involved in critical mental health education, research and activism. Harry comes from a mental health nursing background and has attempted to influence mental health practice and education both from the inside out and the outside in. Our respective backgrounds and histories have given us the motivation and the opportunity to produce this book.

The central theme of the book – a consideration of approaches to achieving meaningful and sustainable change in the way we respond to human distress – emerged in 2016 from a series of conversations between the editors and Heather Allen (at the time, a director at PCCS Books). We all recognised that there had been a number of books critical of dominant positions and systems – particularly with regards to biological psychiatry and the narrow options this paradigm offered to people in distress – but less had been written about projects and initiatives that had managed to offer something different. As our discussions progressed, we recognised it would be timely to compile a selection of initiatives that showcased innovative practice in the mental health arena – 'nuts and bolts' accounts of how people had striven to introduce alternative approaches to those currently available in mainstream services.

Further discussion ensued about the optimal focus of innovation: in which part of the current system should the change be located in order to maximise the likelihood of meaningful and sustainable alternatives to mainstream practice? Three broad themes were apparent to us. The first involves working from within the current system – an option referred to as 'inside out'. The rationale for this strategy is based on accepting that mental health services will always be there in some shape or form, and that enduring improvements to the way we respond to emotional distress can be realised by organic, evolutionary changes within these systems. This is based on the recognition that, despite the apparent rigidity of current mental health and education systems, there are possibilities to transform and humanise them on the basis of new knowledge, values and skills.

Our second theme considers alternatives to the dominant approach that take place outside of, or parallel with, mainstream mental health systems, often in the third or voluntary, charitable sector. A compelling argument in support of this approach is that innovation is only possible if it takes place at arm's length from mainstream provision, free from the constraints of dominant ideologies and funding restrictions. We refer to this form of change process as 'outside in'.

The third theme recognises that broader systemic factors, including socio-political and legal contexts, preclude the realisation of meaningful change in the way we respond to people experiencing distress. Therefore, broader interventions that directly challenge these systems – such as political activism, community education and different ways of conceptualising human response to trauma and overwhelm – would be essential precursors to innovation. We refer to this third theme as 'the broader context'.

The chapters in this book are structured around these three change processes: 'Inside out', 'Outside in' and 'The broader context'. While we believe that organising the accounts of the various projects in this way is informative, some of the projects are not so easily pigeon-holed. This is only a way of organising the content; what emerges is, we believe, a 360° image of initiatives that are genuinely making a difference, whatever their direction of influence.

The distinctive feature of the book is a consideration of innovative practice – in mainstream statutory services, in the third/voluntary sector, and in the wider socio-political context. Our aim is to enable the reader to:

- consider the opportunities for, and feasibility of, change in their areas of work
- initiate or participate in the delivery of change projects
- identify the complexity of bringing about cultural change in mental health systems and the challenges in this process
- recognise the processes, skills and resources required to maximise the likelihood of sustainable change.

This book aims to showcase innovation; we are not promoting a particular type of alternative as superior, and we are conscious that all the initiatives and approaches presented need to be critically examined. We are conscious too that, as we have drawn from our own knowledge and respective connections to identify potential contributors, a lot of significant innovative work does not feature here. Furthermore, we are not attempting to present a homogeneous approach to changing mental health systems. In that sense, the reader may identify contrasting ideologies and philosophies in this book. This reflects the reality and we hope to show the nuances and complexities of engaging with change. This is one snapshot in this moment in time; our hope is that it may engender more such innovations, and further volumes even of this book.

## Obstacles to sustainable change

Change rarely comes easily. Powerful systems have effective ways of sustaining themselves, responding to threats to their existing configuration and maintaining the status quo. Here we identify four common barriers to mental health innovation.

### 1. Service culture

Culture can be defined as 'the total of the inherited ideas, beliefs, values and knowledge, which constitute the shared bases of social action' (Collins English Dictionary, 2006). Informally, culture is a range of assumptions about 'how things are done around here'. This matrix of expectations, collectively held by members of a group or organisation, is often resistant to outside interference. The Western world is dominated by medicalised and individualised understandings of health – a mindset that is routinely deployed when making sense of and responding to human suffering and overwhelm. This prevalent culture can represent a formidable obstacle to innovation and meaningful change.

Mental health systems are dominated by biomedical assumptions about the basis of emotional distress, despite pervasive evidence that this 'illness like any other' approach is associated with a range of negative consequences for service users (see Sidley, 2015, for a review). In the UK and Ireland, psychiatric provision, under the auspices of the National Health Service (NHS) and the Health Service Executive (HSE) respectively, is a prominent example of this medicalised culture – one that privileges biological explanations and interventions; one where drug treatments are typically deemed to be essential, while alternative interventions are relegated to optional extras. The introduction of more context-informed approaches within such a milieu can present considerable challenges; the dominant ideology of an organisation will strongly influence decisions about which approaches to promote and which to let wither, particularly when resources are limited.

Meanwhile, it is important to reflect critically on whether interventions that are presented as 'alternatives' do indeed provide a meaningful alternative to the dominant culture of individual pathology. For example, there have been considerable critiques about how the use of psychological therapies does not counteract but, on the contrary, sometimes complements a medicalised approach by focusing on individual pathology rather than on addressing broader contextual factors affecting human experiences (see Harper & Speed, 2012; Friedli & Stearn, 2015; Moloney, 2013).

In the words of one American chief executive: 'Culture eats strategy for breakfast, every day, every time' (cited in Davies, 2002: 142). Such a formidable barrier raises questions for the potential innovator in these medicalised environments. Is it feasible to develop sustainable, context-informed approaches within biomedically skewed systems? Should we even try? Are all efforts at innovation in such a culture likely to be futile? Or can alternative approaches to human distress thrive alongside traditional mental health systems?

## 2. The neoliberal policy agenda

Experiences of and responses to distress take place within, and are influenced by, ubiquitous political and legal frameworks. Although mental health practitioners and innovators may often believe that their actions are apolitical and largely independent of such pressures, these contextual factors shape our assumptions about the way things are and the way things should be.

Current mental health systems, as well as mental health innovations, operate within the context of a neoliberal health and welfare agenda. In its broadest sense, neoliberalism refers to a political philosophy that emphasises the economic and societal benefits of free-market competition, as opposed to state intervention. Furthermore, neoliberalism represents 'the imposition of values of privatization, market freedom, and atomized individual responsibility to all spheres of human life' (Schiller, 2015: 12). For the purposes of our discussion about how to respond effectively to emotional distress, this neoliberal agenda encourages a focus on the individual rather than on the broader collectives to which we all belong. Consequently, explanations for human suffering and overwhelm are assumed to reside within the person – an internal flaw – rather than being the understandable consequences of adverse societal factors, such as discrimination, injustice, poverty and victimisation.

Neoliberal politics will privilege some types of mental health innovation over others. Bio-medical, 'illness-like-any-other' approaches – where brain abnormalities and biochemical imbalances are viewed as the primary cause of human distress – are a neat fit with neoliberal ideologies. Mental health laws across the Western world collude with this internal-deficit ideology when, for example, they are used to decide who should be subjected to involuntary restraint and treatment in a psychiatric hospital. The assumption is that the presence of distress and overwhelm – so-called mental disorder – is synonymous with an individual's loss of decision-making capacity (Szmukler, 2010).

It is important to note, however, that neoliberal health policies do not only encourage biomedical approaches. Person-centredness, self-management and patient choice are also emerging as key aspects of these policies, and can seem desirable alternatives to the view that 'mentally ill' people are lacking mental capacity. Nevertheless, the focus of these ascriptions remains on the individual's responsibility to achieve the desired changes in their lives; they do not address the structural conditions of inequality and adversity

(Harper & Speed, 2012). Furthermore, coercion is not the exclusive domain of biopsychiatry, as there is increasing evidence about the coercive, and often punitive, application of some psychological interventions in the context of securing welfare and unemployment benefits for people struggling to access employment (Friedli & Stearn, 2015; Cromby & Willis, 2014).

In light of this wider policy context, how can we introduce approaches to emotional distress that seriously address societal factors? In a context where individualistic approaches are branded as innovations, how can we ensure that alternatives that do not focus on assumed internal deficits can bed in and endure? Is a radical revision of the current legal and political contexts a necessary precursor to innovation in the way we address distress and overwhelm?

### 3. The risk of assimilation and co-option

A number of commentators have identified how maintaining the status quo of mainstream mental health provision involves an insidious dilution, assimilation and co-option of change ideas to the point where what remains is not appreciably different from the existing paradigm. For the purpose of this introduction, we draw on the work of Penney and Prescott (2016) and Boyle (2013), who offer useful frameworks for understanding how this nullifying of new approaches is achieved.

Movements for social justice by marginalised and oppressed groups often face the challenge of co-option by powerful institutions seeking to protect the status quo (Penney & Prescott, 2016). Co-option happens when dominant groups adopt the language of marginalised groups (eg. 'empowerment' and 'peer'), reducing once radical ideas to empty buzzwords. Co-option also happens when dominant groups appropriate and use service-user narratives in ways that diminish their power, or when they give the impression of supporting the rights of the marginalised group while, in fact, working to undermine their goals (Penney & Prescott, 2016)

Boyle (2013) argues that one strategy is for dominant groups to attempt to discredit innovation by 'invalidation' – resorting to personal attacks, such as accusations of ignorance or self-promotion. Another means of countering innovation is 'assimilation', involving the removal of the more radical aspects of the new idea so that what remains is little different from the accepted orthodoxy (Boyle, 2013). In large organisations, such as the UK's NHS, this neutering is often achieved by an editing process as the proposal for a different kind of service passes through governance forums and service development committees. Those seeking to maintain biomedical dominance within the mental health system can then claim that the 'new' idea is not really new and existing practices are already broadly consistent with it.

So how can those seeking meaningful change protect their innovations from these assimilation pressures? Boyle (2013) persuasively argues that the abandonment of language associated with physical illness – such as 'symptoms', 'treatments' and reference to diagnostic labels – may help to immunise new ideas from these dismantling forces. At a broader political level, co-option can be resisted when new initiatives are guided by principles of social justice, where redistribution of power and control are at the centre of the change process. Alternatively, some protection from assimilation and co-option may be realised by seeking operational distance from the currently dominant paradigm, either by establishing new initiatives outside of the current system ('outside', in the hope that the ideas will exert an influence and become 'in') or by securing alternative sources of funding.

## 4. Funding influences

Any discussion about the development of new initiatives needs to be located in the current context of the deep funding cuts in both state and voluntary services. Securing finance remains a key challenge. Funding applications need to reflect the agenda of the body providing the money. If funding is secured, then the values and priorities of the funding body will influence the shape and form of the change initiative, by setting clear parameters about how the money is to be used.

The various sources of funding for innovative projects (state, private, charitable and mutual) will each have distinctive advantages and disadvantages. State-funded initiatives, paid for by general taxation, are likely to benefit from the security of recurrent finance, thereby improving durability (although the current cutbacks in state funding of community and disability projects demonstrate that this, too, is vulnerable). But the dominant ideology held by the government department footing the bill will dictate the output of the project. Privately-funded projects might be more resistant to the influences of dominant ideologies, but the funders will be guided by market priorities, which will inevitably shape the values underpinning the project, potentially prioritising profit acquisition over the welfare and rights of service users.

Innovations that are paid for by charitable organisations and fundraising activities are arguably in a better position to maintain consistency with their explicit ethos and values, free from the neutralising pressures of state funding and the profit imperatives of private companies. The Hearing Voices Network (Longden, Corstens & Dillon, 2013) is a good example of a charitable organisation founded by its members and offering people who hear voices spaces to make sense of what they experience in a supportive environment, away from traditional psychiatric pressures to view such experiences as symptoms of illness.

The most radical way of nurturing innovation in mental health is through the development of mutual-aid co-operatives, organised and run entirely by survivors of the psychiatric system. By creating an alliance of shared support, immune to both the toxic influence of neoliberal policies and the self-serving intentions of the 'psy' industry, participants can reciprocally meet their individual and collective needs in an environment of equity and solidarity.

What is the most effective way to fund and organise change initiatives that are striving to offer alternatives to current mental health provision? To what degree does it matter who pays for the new initiative? Can inspirational leadership and comprehensive planning counteract the influence of the funder's ideology?

## Delivering something different

The contributors to this book were given a list of questions to guide them in describing and discussing their change initiative and ensure they maintained a critical perspective throughout: Why was the change needed? What is it and what does it involve? What are the complexities of the work involved? How are resistance and obstacles to change dealt with? What skills and resources are required for this change? How is the change initiative evaluated? What is the nature of evidence used in such evaluation? What are the future directions of the initiative? The reader will find that the authors have adopted a variety of approaches in their efforts to implement their projects and overcome the obstacles to sustainable change.

### Changing from the inside

The first section, 'Inside Out', begins with four chapters considering critical mental health education in the fields of social work, clinical psychology, occupational therapy and mental health nursing. Professional education is key in providing the conceptual and practice skills to change from the inside, to create opportunities for changes from the outside, and to acknowledge the importance of broader contexts and act on them. While recognising the challenges of working from inside formal, third-level education systems, contributors identify possibilities to disrupt, transform and broaden the way we understand and respond to distress.

Lydia Sapouna discusses social work education as a critical space to understand distress in life contexts through rethinking issues of power, language and identity. A key concern in this chapter is the co-option and appropriation of radical ideas by mental health systems, including education. The author suggests that we need to stay engaged with the unsettling question, 'Whose interests are we serving when innovating?', in order to recognise the nuances and complexities of changing mental health systems.

This is followed by Anjula Gupta's description of the innovative introduction of a community psychology placement to one university's clinical psychology course. This initial six-week placement in a third-sector community service provides students with the opportunity to be critical observers and to question taken-for-granted knowledge that locates problems within individuals rather than acknowledging the role of social inequalities that marginalise communities and maintain an unjust status quo.

Critical pedagogy in the context of occupational therapy education is then discussed through the use of a case study. Eoin Gorman explores his experiences as a Mad-identified academic of embedding meaningful survivor knowledge within the occupational therapy curriculum. He reports the criticisms he faced, the support from colleagues, and the benefits for students in gaining alternative understandings of 'Madness', as evidenced in their evaluation feedback.

In the next chapter, Jonathan Gadsby discusses the importance of philosophy and political ideology in the context of mental health nurse education. He argues that an analysis of ideological (and other forms of) power is essential in making sense of mental health nursing practice, and highlights the central components of a critical nursing education: ideologies of mental health, the contested nature of science behind common practices and re-politicising mental health.

Moving our focus from the educational domain to service provision, our exploration of 'Inside out' initiatives continues with Iseult Twamley's reflective account of introducing an Open Dialogue process into the mainstream work of a traditional community mental health team. Iseult describes the difficult transition from a psychiatrist-led, 'treatment'-of-symptoms approach towards an inclusive, dialogical stance, where each person's perspective is equally valued. She offers her personal perspective on the pain associated with such a cultural shift and the abandonment of traditional roles and attitudes.

Bryan McElroy then addresses the topical issue of antidepressant prescribing in general practice. Following a comprehensive audit of current practices, he used a combination of information sharing and collaborative discussion to try to influence how his fellow GPs responded to depressed patients who attended their surgeries. The intervention led to measurable improvements in several areas – not least, that patients were more often alerted to potential side effects and the risk of withdrawal symptoms. However, broadly, the change was not as great as he had hoped. To close, McElroy reflects on the range of influences – socio-economic, cultural and those related to the practitioners' own belief systems – that can shape GPs' antidepressant prescribing practices.

In the final chapter of this 'Inside Out' section, Anne Cooke, Shirley McNicholas and Andie Rose discuss Drayton Park Women's Crisis House, a state-funded project offering trauma-informed care to women experiencing mental health crises. A combination of outstanding leadership and a strong service-user presence in the organisation's management structure has enabled Drayton Park to sustain its distinctive provision of systemic, feminist-informed help for more than 20 years while operating within the UK's NHS.

### Changing from the outside

There are six chapters in the 'Outside In' section of the book. This section features projects that have deliberately maintained a separation from mainstream provision, while intersecting with it. The aim here is to try to capture both the struggles to achieve this and how these services exert an influence on mainstream services and make very real differences to service users' lives.

Joan Hamilton's passion and commitment shine through her description of the struggles and successes in setting up the Slí Eile residential community living project for people stuck in the revolving door of the psychiatric system. Her chapter tracks the history of the project, from its early days when attempts to transform a residential property were faced with hostility and sabotage from local residents through to the fully functioning farm and commercial enterprise it is today.

Next, Fiona Venner describes the Leeds Survivor-Led Crisis Service, which are nationally recognised as a beacon of excellence and innovation in mental health crisis care. The service provides a place of sanctuary and an alternative to hospital admission and statutory services for people in acute mental health crisis, together with therapeutic groups and a crisis line. Venner discusses the non-medical, non-diagnostic ethos that guides how this survivor-led, person-centred, third-sector organisation responds to distress. Of critical importance, she points out, is its separation from mainstream mental health services, especially its total lack of statutory power. People go there because they want to be there; they trust its workers and respect its ethos.

The following chapter, by Paul Brewer, describes a change project located at the core of the traditional mental health system: on an inpatient psychiatric ward. Paul details the development of 'ward visiting teams', comprising people with a wealth of personal experience of both mental health problems and hospitalisation, who regularly visit inpatient wards simply to talk with the patients, thereby bringing more compassion and humanity into the system. Paul details the perseverance required to gain the support of hospital managers to allow the visiting team routine access to these inpatient areas so that they can model humane interaction and, in so doing, prevent the culture of the ward from sliding towards 'regimentality'.

The importance of place also forms the focus for discussion in John Wainwright and Mick McKeown's chapter on the experiences of Black, Asian and minority ethnic (BAME) survivors of the mental health system who come to Mary Seacole House, a mental health resource centre in Liverpool 8 (more usually known as Toxteth) for the BAME community. Mary Seacole House is rooted in the history of its locality and of the Black community around it. The sanctuary it offers to BAME people is indissoluble from that central position at the heart of its own community.

Next, Stephen Normanton highlights the need for sustainable social support networks for people experiencing emotional distress. In his chapter, he describes the evolution of the PeerTalk Network, a third-sector organisation that offers informal groups, facilitated by trained volunteers, simply offering company and a place to talk to people who are unhappy, lonely, isolated or bereaved. These are essential spaces, he argues, missing from many people's lives. The chapter outlines the challenges that had to be overcome and the ongoing plans to develop the network to offer a truly national presence.

Finally in this section, Deirdre Lillis describes her work as an independent advocate, operating from within a community development project in Cork, Ireland. She outlines the current position of independent advocacy in mental health contexts in Ireland and the UK, and argues for its essential role in upholding the individual and collective human rights of marginalised and powerless groups. She also tackles the vexed issue of how to remain genuinely independent of influence by statutory bodies and mainstream services when they are the source of an organisation's funding.

## Changing the broader context

The final section of the book, 'The Broader Context', moves beyond inside and outside spaces to consider change at broader levels, including collective activism, conceptual reframing of distress, and how to heal the divide between those sanctioned by the state to provide mental health services and those who have suffered at the hands of the mental health system.

Anne O'Donnell and Kirsten Maclean discuss Oor Mad History, an innovative community history project focused on the mental health service-user movement in Lothian, south-east Scotland. The chapter argues for the need to record past activism in order to root, nourish and inspire current and future action to address the injustices still experienced by those in mental distress and within the mental health system. The chapter demonstrates how necessary it is that people who have experience of using services are able to record their own discourses, stories and alternatives to mainstream psychiatric narratives.

This is followed by John Cromby's chapter on re-conceptualising and identifying patterns in distress and troubled and troubling behaviour through the Power Threat Meaning Framework (PTMF) (Johnstone & Boyle, 2018). Published by the British Psychological Society, the PTMF is proposed as an alternative not just to diagnosis but also to how society regards mental health and mental 'disorder'. The framework addresses the wider, societal influences on our mental wellbeing and encourages the mental health practitioner to ask 'What happened to you?' and seek the person's own narrative of their experience, rather than 'What's wrong with you?' and diagnostic interpretations. John explains why PTMF is needed and summarises what it involves, why it is a better alternative to a diagnostic system and some of the criticisms it has provoked, before going on to consider some possible future developments.

The final chapter, by Mick McKeown and Helen Spandler, explores the power of collective action. Their discussion builds on earlier work towards establishing a truth and reconciliation process to repair some of the hurts and harms inflicted by mental health services on those in their care. The authors draw on the history of truth and reconciliation in other contexts – most notably in South Africa – to argue that collaborative ways forward are needed in which everyone works together to achieve a common aim. Recognition, apology, forgiveness and reconciliation are all part of a process, not a single act.

## References

Boyle M (2013). The persistence of medicalisation: is the presentation of alternatives part of the problem? In: Coles S, Keenan S, Diamond B (eds). *Madness Contested: power and practice*. Ross-on-Wye: PCCS Books (pp4–22).

Collins English Dictionary (2006) (8th ed). London: HarperCollins.

Cromby J, Willis M (2014). Nudging into subjectification: governmentality and psychometrics. *Critical Social Policy 34*(2): 241–259.

Davies HTO (2002). Understanding organisational culture in reforming the National Health Service. *Journal of the Royal Society of Medicine 95*: 140–142.

Friedli L, Stearn R (2015). Positive affect as coercive strategy: conditionality, activation and the role of psychology in UK government workfare programmes. *Medical Humanities 41*: 40–47.

Harper D, Speed E (2012). Uncovering recovery: the resistible rise of recovery and resilience. *Studies in Social Justice 6*(1): 9–25.

Johnstone L, Boyle M, with Cromby J, Dillon J, Harper D, Kinderman P, Longden E, Pilgrim D, Read J (2018). *The Power Threat Meaning Framework: towards the identification of patterns in emotional distress, unusual experiences and troubled or troubling behaviour, as an alternative to functional psychiatric diagnosis.* Leicester: British Psychological Society.

Longden E, Corstens D, Dillon J (2013). Recovery, discovery and revolution: the work of Intervoice and the Hearing Voices Movement. In: Coles S, Keenan S, Diamond B (eds). *Madness Contested: power and practice.* Ross-on-Wye: PCCS Books (pp161–180).

Moloney P (2013). *The Therapy Industry: the irresistible rise of the talking cure, and why it doesn't work.* London: Pluto Press.

Penney D, Prescott L (2016). The co-optation of survivor knowledge: the danger of substituted values and voice. In: Russo J, Sweeney A (eds). *Searching for a Rose Garden: challenging psychiatry, fostering mad studies.* Ross-on-Wye: PCCS Books.

Schiller N (2015). Liberalism, anthropology of. In: Wright JD (ed). *International Encyclopedia of the Social & Behavioral Sciences* (2nd ed). Oxford: Elsevier (pp11–17).

Sidley G (2015). *Tales from the Madhouse: an insider critique of psychiatric services.* Ross-on-Wye: PCCS Books.

Szmukler G (2010). *How Mental Health Law Discriminates Unfairly Against People with Mental Illness.* [Video.] Lecture, Gresham College, Oxford; 15 November. www.gresham.ac.uk/lectures-and-events/how-mental-health-law-discriminates-unfairly-against-people-with-mental-illness (accessed 29 August 2019).

# PART 1

Inside out

# Chapter 1

# Social work education as a critical space

## Lydia Sapouna

This chapter draws from my experience in mental health social work education. It is based on an earlier paper (Sapouna, 2016) discussing my contribution to innovative approaches in teaching for critical practice and the challenges in this process. Having become increasingly conscious of the need to challenge and problematise what is heralded as innovation and inclusion in mental health education and practice, I am now revisiting the 2016 paper to reconsider the way I teach in the pursuit of critical education. Some material of the original paper will be used to provide context to the discussion.

I started teaching mental health on professional social work programmes at University College Cork (UCC) in the mid-1990s. While, over the years, my thinking and approaches to education have changed considerably, some of the challenges I experience are ongoing and persistent. A key challenge is managing the tension between my commitment to social justice and the expectation to prepare students for practice in a predominantly biomedical context that is often experienced as coercive. At several points throughout these years, I found myself becoming frustrated with the apparent incompatibility between critical thinking and the 'reality' of practice, possibly feeding into the view that critical thinking is only suitable for the 'ivory tower' of academia but not for 'real life'. Indeed, I found my teaching becoming stagnant at times, as I was lacking resources to provide education for meaningful alternatives to the dominant way of thinking and practising in mental health (Sapouna, 2016).

Realising that a part of the problem was seeking resources inwards (ie. within existing systems), rather than outwards, in the early 2000s I started developing more systematic links with service users/survivors and activist and advocacy groups. I also started collaborating with other professionals who had identified the need for a more user-focused and democratic mental health practice. Through such links a pool of diverse resources was created, including enhanced input of service users in mental health education; conference co-organisation; co-authored publications; dissemination of user-led research, and service-user involvement in student selection and professional course accreditation processes. Such alliances also created possibilities to develop critical spaces inside and outside the university to consider mental health practice. An annual Critical Perspectives Conference, now fully integrated in the UCC social work mental health curriculum, and the emergence of the Critical Voices Network Ireland (Sapouna & Gijbels, 2016) are two examples of creating such critical spaces within and beyond professional education. I acknowledge that a lot of work remains to be done to develop meaningful partnerships with service users in the Irish social work education system. At the same time, I remain alert to and alarmed by the dangers of institutionalising service-user involvement. Nevertheless, these 'outside the box' alliances and the emerging critical forums have created opportunities for transformation, as I have had to rethink my ways of knowing and teaching.

I begin this discussion by briefly setting the context of mental health social work in Ireland and making an argument for the contribution of social work education in transforming dominant biomedical practice. I argue that such a transformation should involve rethinking issues of knowledge formation, power operation, language, narrative and identity, all of which are components of critical practice (Fook, 2002). Based on my 2016 paper, I will go on to discuss selective aspects of course curriculum and teaching approaches that can contribute to this process. These include:

- rethinking knowledge formation – reconsidering the 'social'
- rethinking narrative, language and identity – engaging with voice-hearing, reconsidering trauma
- rethinking power – engaging with critical spaces – the Critical Voices Network Ireland.

I will also discuss student feedback and student experiences from mental health placements to highlight the challenges of upholding social work values in hegemonic practice contexts. These approaches are not presented triumphantly as innovative alternatives to medicalisation in their own right. Taking a step further from the 2016 paper, I will problematise these aspects, questioning the appropriation of practices of innovation and inclusion in mental health systems. For the purpose of this chapter I focus on three examples of what I previously considered to be innovation in mental health education: recovery approaches, trauma-informed practice and user narratives. This problematisation involves asking questions such as: Whose interests do these practices serve? Do they provide a meaningful shift away from an individual pathology approach? Do they contribute to changing power imbalances in mental health systems, or do they ultimately serve dominant ideologies and practices? This is a rather unsettling consideration as I am confronted with my own contribution and role in such appropriation. Nevertheless, asking such questions recognises the nuances and messiness of changing mental health systems from the 'inside'.

## Articulating the 'social' in mental health social work – why is it needed?

In recent times we have seen possibilities for change in the field of mental health in Ireland through the adoption of community-based care, a recovery orientation and a commitment to user involvement in their care. However, despite the rhetoric of a bio-psycho-social approach, policy implementation has been slow and inconsistent across the country (Mental Health Commission, 2013; Mental Health Reform, 2015) and the main responses to people in distress remain medical/pharmacological in nature. Social work is located at the interface between the person and their social environment and is therefore ideally placed to engage with the context of people's lives – a long-neglected element in biomedical mental health services. While there are several examples of social workers in Ireland engaging with a social recovery approach to practice (Kelly & Donnelly, 2018), social work remains under-represented in mental health services, with several multidisciplinary teams still operating without a full-time social work post. Within a predominantly medical framework of thinking and practising, mental health social workers often consider themselves powerless to articulate a valid 'social' approach and to question coercive practices (Brosnan & Sapouna, 2015; Manchester, 2015; Allen, 2014). As a result, students on mental health placements do not often have the opportunity to witness a confident expression of a context-informed practice.

Within interdisciplinary contexts, there is still a tendency to view the primary role of social work as responding to practical concerns in people's lives, such as welfare benefits, housing and employment. While this focus is not an insignificant or a 'lesser' role for social workers, such a role does not in itself lead to a broader understanding of emotional distress. Students need to embrace an approach to practice that views emotional distress as a meaningful response to problems of living, trauma, injustice and adverse life experiences, rather than a chemical imbalance or individual pathology.

This is an approach in which context, relationships and meanings are put at the centre of our interventions (Bracken & Thomas, 2005). This is also an approach that addresses issues of oppression and injustice often experienced by people using mental health services. Such an approach involves a radical rethink of knowledge, power, language and identity. Social work education has a significant contribution to make in this process.

## Social work education as a critical space – what is it?

Social workers have distinctive skills in working alongside people and supporting them to overcome barriers to achieving their potential by adopting a community perspective, as well as an individual one. However, their potential to fully embrace this role can be seriously impeded by the identity social work has developed over the past two decades in Ireland. Social work as a profession seems to be increasingly defined by procedural and managerial guidelines for practice (McGregor & Quin, 2015) and is focused on individualised work and risk management rather than supporting people experiencing adversity (Cuskelly, 2013; Featherstone et al, 2018). Furthermore, in times of intensive neoliberalisation, social workers' commitment to social justice risks being continuously eroded (Conneely & Garrett, 2015; Garrett, 2018). In this context, there is a danger that the role of social work education can be reduced to preparing students for procedurally correct practice, with a primary focus on managing individual difficulties, while a consideration of broader contextual factors is often viewed as 'too abstract' to be useful in practice. In the area of mental health, such a trend is often witnessed in the argument of some social work students and practitioners that education focusing on critical or social perspectives does not adequately prepare students for practice in the current mental health system. Such education, it is argued, doesn't teach them 'how to do the job'. In increasingly corporate-minded university environments, critical education can become an endangered species.

I am not arguing for a 'broad social' education instead of a 'narrow medical' one. Such a binary is unhelpful and can feed into another battle to establish superiority. Social workers need to move beyond binaries and engage with the complexity and diversity of human experience while being cognisant of agency, culture and structural contexts. This can be facilitated by the creation of a critical space in social work education to rethink about (Fook, 2002):

- knowledge about experiences of human distress – this involves questioning dominant hegemonies in mental health knowledge formation and recognising that user/survivor knowledge is vital in exploring the context and the meaning of human distress

- operations of power – this involves understanding powerlessness and injustice as precursors of distress and the importance of empowerment, choice and dignity as cornerstones of a user-defined recovery process

- language and narrative – this involves a shift away from the language of symptoms and individual pathology towards locating people's narratives and meanings in the centre of social work practice

- identity – this involves a move away from the identity of the 'patient' to an understanding of the multiple and diverse aspects of people's lives. It also involves a validation of the emerging identities of user/survivors as equal partners in mental health practice.

A critical approach to education promotes knowledge formation beyond the domains of formal knowledge and self-reflection, towards critical action in the domain of the world (Barnett, 1997). Ultimately, a critical approach to mental health education can be transformative, as it seeks to change the way we understand and respond to human distress. To operationalise such a transformation, social work students require a value base that is informed by the principles of social justice, anti-oppressive practice and genuine partnerships that recognise the expertise of people with experiences of distress (Brosnan & Sapouna, 2015). Social work students also require a knowledge base that gives them confidence to advocate for a context-informed social approach. Social approaches are often considered to lack a coherent body of theory backed up by research in comparison with the medical perspective (Tew, 2011). Social work students need to be informed of the research evidence demonstrating the strong links between life adversity, injustice and emotional distress.

## Social work education as a critical space – what does it involve?

A mental health module is delivered separately to the undergraduate (BSW) and postgraduate (MSW) social work programmes in UCC. The curriculum encourages students to engage with critical questions in mental health and to understand the experience of distress beyond diagnostic categories. Community development approaches, anti-oppressive practice and person-centred, strength-focused and solidarity-based responses to distress are explored as the foundations of good practice. Service-user/survivor knowledge, issues of professional power, human rights, citizenship and working in genuine alliances with service users are central in this course. Teaching methodologies include experiential and interactive approaches to explore different ways of engaging with distress and unusual experiences such as voice hearing. The curriculum incorporates practice examples of democratic, recovery-focused approaches such as Open Dialogue and the Slí Eile social farm (see Chapters 5 and 8). The Annual Critical Perspectives Conference at University College Cork, discussed later in this chapter, is an integral part of the module.

### Rethinking knowledge formation: reconsidering the 'social'

The mental health curriculum includes a significant body of research challenging beliefs that madness can be explained without reference to the context of people's lives. This research problematises the excessive preoccupation with individual pathology, chemical imbalances and genetic predispositions as causes of human misery, including experiences that are labelled 'schizophrenia' (Rapley, Moncrieff & Dillon, 2011; Read & Dillon, 2013; Johnstone et al, 2018; Watson, 2019). Furthermore, the role of the pharmaceutical industry in promoting a narrow pharmacological approach to treating human distress has increasingly been called into question (Angell, 2005; Moncrieff, 2008, 2013; Whitaker, 2010).

Mental health education considers how life events and broader environments affect the likelihood of experiencing distress at some stage in our lives. Research confirms the relationship between inequality and poorer mental health, with particularly strong correlations between the incidence of distress and disadvantage, including unemployment, homelessness, lack of education and growing up in socially disadvantaged areas (Read, Johnstone & Taitimu, 2013; Rogers & Pilgrim, 2014). Furthermore, a considerable body of research has correlated membership of social groups that are subject to systematic experiences of oppression or disadvantage with higher rates of mental health difficulties (Thomas, 2014; Fernando, 2003, 2011). A 2009 World Health Organization (WHO) report concluded:

> ... levels of mental distress among communities need to be understood less in terms of individual pathology and more as a response to relative deprivation and social injustice, which erode the emotional, spiritual and intellectual resources essential to psychological wellbeing.
> (WHO, 2009: iii)

International research indicates that the experience of injustice and inequality may be more damaging to mental health than absolute levels of deprivation (WHO, 2009; Read, Johnstone & Taitimu, 2013). An influential contribution to this argument comes from the work of Wilkinson and Pickett (2009), which identifies the profound effects of living in unequal societies. Their research summarises multiple studies demonstrating that poverty leads to exclusion from community life and from a sense of belonging and being valued, all of which result in people suffering 'social pain'. This argument concurs with other evidence suggesting that inequality and injustice feed into a sense of 'otherness', worthlessness and shame (Janssen et al, 2004).

The challenge for education is to enable students to use this knowledge with confidence. Such knowledge should help practitioners develop context-focused assessments and interventions, rather than resorting to the dominant language of 'diagnosis' and 'treatment'. For example, rather than considering maternal mental health in clinical and risk assessment terms, we propose to look at women's life experiences, including experiences of inequality, powerlessness and abuse. On that basis, we define the primary social work role as family support and advocacy, rather than surveillance. Ultimately, it is about adopting a social justice approach to practice that can facilitate the consideration of explicit experiences of discrimination and injustice, such as sexism, racism, homophobia and ageism, and also more subtle experiences of being made to feel powerless, inadequate, inferior and left out. Within educational settings, it is important to acknowledge the evidence from both national and international research on distress within ethnic minorities, migrant populations (Fernando, 2011; Priebe, Giacco & El-Nagib, 2016) and lesbian, gay, bisexual and transgender groups (Higgins et al, 2011, 2016). This research can provide a useful framework for student social workers to consider the experiences of people from marginalised and/or disadvantaged groups on the basis of the personal story of the individual in the social context of their lives. Such a framework can help students think beyond individual pathologies, towards community development and social action approaches with groups that have been traditionally excluded. It can also help students think about recovery-conducive environments in socio-political, rather than merely individualised terms.

### Problematising recovery and the 'social'

At this point I would like to share some observations about recovery-informed teaching, as it has been a complex and nuanced learning curve for me. When the concept of recovery was first introduced in the Irish mental health strategy *A Vision for Change* (Department of Health and Children, 2006), I embraced it with considerable optimism and introduced it to students as a hopeful alternative to medicalisation. Recovery was (originally) a user-led concept, a move away from a pre-occupation with symptoms. It was about people taking control of their own lives, countering the pervasive, pessimistic references to 'severe and enduring mental illness' in traditional psychiatry. Recovery contested definitions of mental health and, because of that, was initially met with significant resistance from the mental health establishment. However, in less than a decade, most mainstream Irish mental health services now claim to be 'recovery oriented'. A sign of progress? Unfortunately not, as there is little evidence to suggest a significant shift from a focus on individual pathology. Furthermore, as Liz Brosnan's study on user involvement in Ireland found, recovery has been appropriated and assimilated into institutionalised practice: 'What they're actually talking about is the medical model redressed' (Brosnan, 2013: 221).

While I still teach about recovery, my teaching has become more critical of its application and its political implications. For example, we examine how recovery is increasingly becoming a neoliberal rationale to justify service cutbacks, as people who 'recover' have no need for support services (Wallcraft, 2014; Friedli & Stearn, 2015). We also examine how the current implementation of recovery remains focused on the individual's responsibility to change (Harper & Speed, 2012). Paradoxically, a focus on being autonomous, having a job and living in a decent house can overlook the structural conditions that impact on welfare, employment and housing. A key influence on my thinking is the service-user/survivor group Recovery in the Bin (RiTB),[1] formed in 2014 in response to what was increasingly being regarded as the ideological colonisation of the recovery model. RiTB argues for the right to 'unrecover', as its members are:

> ... fed up with the way… 'recovery' is being used to discipline and control those who are trying to find a place in the world, to live as they wish, trying to deal with the very real mental distress they encounter on a daily basis. (RiTB, undated)

This critique is captured in RiTB's 'Unrecovery Star' (Figure 1),[2] which was developed as a response to the Recovery Star™ (Figure 2)[3] used in traditional mental health services to plan and record service users' goals for 'recovery' and progress towards them. Comparing the two stars and critiquing recovery – a concept that is still heralded as innovative – can initially be confusing and unsettling for students. However, it is an opportunity to reclaim key social work knowledge, skills and values, such as social justice and anti-oppressive practice, in addressing the elements of the unrecovery star.

---

1. recoveryinthebin.org (accessed 6 August 2019).

2. https://recoveryinthebin.org/unrecovery-star-2 (accessed 26 August 2019).

3. Reproduced with permission from Triangle Consulting Social Enterprise Ltd. www.outcomesstar.org.uk (accessed 26 August 2019).

**Figure 1: Unrecovery Star** ((cc) RecoveryinTheBin)

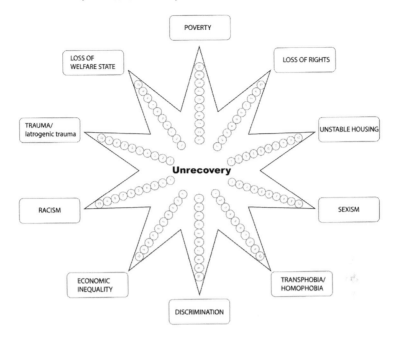

**Figure 2: Recovery Star**™ (© Triangle Consulting Social Enterprise Ltd)

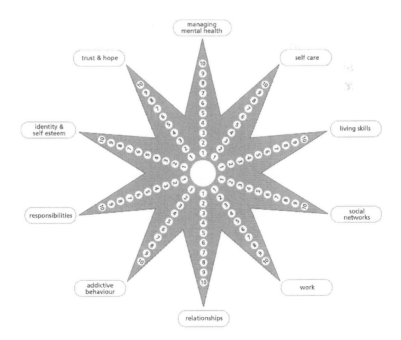

A critical look at recovery also offers an opportunity to reconsider what is presented as innovation and what can happen when movements become models. It can encourage students to think beyond the comfort of models and technical frameworks. Indeed, while I advocate for a social approach (as a broader knowledge base), I am becoming increasingly aware of the dangers associated with considering the social perspective as *the* solution to medicalisation. In that sense, I reiterate that a binary between a 'coercive' medical model and a 'progressive' social model is unhelpful. While social workers focus on people's life contexts, they are not experts in people's lives. Furthermore, a social approach is not in itself a meaningful alternative to biomedical hegemony. As Szasz warns:

> Nonmedical mental health and counselling professions are medicalisation cubed: as if to compensate for their lack of medical knowledge and qualifications, nonmedical mental-health 'professionals' are even more deeply committed than psychiatrists to their claim of special expertise in the diagnosis and treatment of mental illness.
> (Szasz, 2008: 31)

On a similar note, Manchester (2015: 150) argues that social perspectives have been assimilated into the prevailing bio-psycho-social paradigm and 'remain an adjunct to the view that people with mental health problems inevitably have some kind of pathological flaw that needs fixing, whether biological or psychological or both'. Rather than being preoccupied with the credibility of the social work role and perspective, it may be more helpful to take a grassroots approach in which survivors' language and narratives are the centre of education and practice.

### Rethinking narrative, language and identity: engaging with voice-hearing

In order to actively listen to service users' meanings and stories, it is important to engage with forms of expression and language that may be unconventional and perhaps unfamiliar to mental health professionals (Tew, 2002). In preparation for student engagement with such forms of expression, the curriculum draws from the work of the Hearing Voices Network[4] (HVN) and includes methodologies of working with people who hear voices and/or have other unusual sensory experiences. A key premise of this approach is that voice-hearing experiences are not viewed as pathological symptoms but rather

---

4. www.hearing-voices.org (accessed 6 August 2019).

as emotional responses to traumatic life events. The HVN, founded more than 30 years ago, is now an international movement and an influential example of people getting together as peers to share experiences and understandings of voice-hearing. Originating in the work of Dutch social psychiatrist Marius Romme and researcher Sandra Escher (Romme & Escher, 2000, 2005), the HVN challenges traditional biomedical practice and presents a new territory for mental health social workers who have been conventionally taught not to engage with 'auditory hallucinations', in the belief that such engagement may intensify psychotic symptoms. This radical shift from the pathologising language of *auditory hallucinations* to the ordinary language of *hearing voices* can be a mechanism to transform thinking and practice in mental health care.

Recent research shows HVN groups to be an important resource for helping people who have been primarily defined through their diagnosis to reclaim new identities through exploring their experiences and developing their own frameworks for coping and recovery (Longden, Read & Dillon, 2017). Awareness of and involvement in HVN groups also have benefits for professional practice. As Longden and colleagues suggest (2017: 188), such collaboration 'may help professionals gain knowledge and confidence for supporting voice hearers as well as enhance and inform their practice with the survivor-led and social psychiatric philosophies'.

Discussing the contribution HVN approaches can make to mental health social work, Sapey and Bullimore (2013: 624) suggest that social workers need to:

- develop a different understanding of voices to the traditional view of biomedical psychiatry that they are hallucinations indicating an underlying illness
- develop positive attitudes to voice hearers, respecting their expertise and experiences as valid
- understand the role of childhood trauma, particularly abuse and neglect, in hearing voices
- develop therapeutic skills so as to work with voice-hearers and with voices.

Helping social work students to understand the relationship between individual history and psychotic symptoms is of crucial importance. Perhaps the most influential body of evidence that has emerged over the past two decades in relation to life events and psychiatric diagnoses is the research linking childhood adversity and psychosis. Psychosis has been traditionally treated as a biochemical problem. During the past 15 years, however, there has been an avalanche of ground-breaking international studies showing that adverse life events, trauma, loss and neglect in childhood increase vulnerability to emotional distress (for example, Varese et al, 2012; Read & Bentall, 2012; Janssen et al, 2004). Yet, these research developments are only significant if mental health professionals act on them by asking people 'What happened?' in their lives and responding respectfully to the stories they hear. Hammersley and colleagues argue that:

> The current approach which asks people 'what is wrong with you?' rather than 'what has happened to you?' misses the crucial point that all distress and behaviour, however seemingly bizarre, is a meaningful attempt to survive maddening experiences in what for some of us can be a crazy world. (Hammersley et al, 2008: 19)

Social workers, as a profession carrying out psychosocial assessments, need to find a language to ask questions that haven't been asked before about people's lives, including questions about abuse, bullying, neglect and loss (Read, 2013). Through such questions, professionals can facilitate people to make connections 'between elements of experience that had previously seemed confusing or contradictory' (Tew, 2002: 146) and take control of their own recovery.

### Problematising trauma-informed practice

Nevertheless, making these connections is not in itself a remedy to medicalisation. Focusing only on the individual story of 'what happened' can be another form of pathologising. Friedli (2018) warns that, by only focusing on the individual story, we may lose sight of the broader context – the question of 'why it happened', which leads to a deeper engagement with the context of people's lives. In a culture where being trauma-informed has become the new 'big thing' for mental health professionals, we need to be aware of the critiques of trauma-informed practice. Approaching distress through a trauma framework seems like a 'feel-good' alternative to medicalisation. However, it can also perpetuate a disease model by focusing exclusively on adverse individual experiences at the expense of acknowledging adverse community environments (Ellis & Dietz, 2017). Indeed, looking at the widely used Adverse Childhood Experiences (ACE) questionnaire (Felitti et al, 1998), it is striking to note what is not included (eg. experiences of racism are not considered ACEs).

ACEs have helped to bring the language of trauma and adversity into mental health education and practice, but in a rather narrow way that, not unlike psychiatry, may fail to recognise what is not visible or measurable. Not all experiences of trauma are neatly articulated or easily identified as valid sources of distress. We need to be careful not to create a hierarchy of trauma where some types of trauma lead to justifiable distress and others don't (Hunter, 2018). This is a point I regularly discuss with students after listening to moving, well-articulated testimonies of trauma and psychosis. Not all people have words for their experiences; not all stories make sense. We therefore need to create spaces to listen, validate and explore diverse forms of expression, and this can be a long and messy process. In a service culture of evidence-based practice, quantifiable, rapid outcomes and performance indicators, teaching students about 'being with' confusion and uncertainty is not easy. Furthermore, it is important not to always assume the existence or denial of experiences of a particular type of trauma and abuse. As professionals, we can facilitate conversations about meanings, but we are not the makers of the meaning.

Nevertheless, I found that teaching about trauma and psychosis has helped students to contextualise human distress by seeing it as a meaningful human experience. Learning about voice-hearing is not presented as the only or best way to work with people experiencing psychosis. It is rather used as an example of challenging traditions of biological psychiatry in which the voice of the service user is primarily used to diagnose disorders. This learning has helped students to develop knowledge, skills and values in working with diverse experiences and expressions and listen to people in their own terms and language in all areas of practice. In Ireland alone, since 2012, more than 20 hearing-voices support groups have been set up, both within and outside mental health services, and some student social workers have had the opportunity to engage with these groups during their placements. Although they are a relatively recent arrival in the Irish context, international experience has demonstrated that hearing-voices groups are effective communal solutions that enable people to make profound, positive changes in their lives (Dillon et al, 2013).

Social workers should be active participants in seeking such communal solutions. This can be achieved by forming alliances with other voices of resistance, with forward-thinking stakeholders within and outside mental health systems, to facilitate the development of critical spaces for rethinking the way we understand and respond to distress. The following section discusses the development of the Annual Critical Perspectives Conferences at UCC and the Critical Voices Network Ireland (CVNI) as examples of such spaces which are also an integral part of social work education.

## Rethinking power, developing critical spaces

Over the past number of years, critical perspectives have emerged to raise concerns about the state of mental health systems in Ireland and to question dominant thinking and practice. Such concerns include coercive practices, lack of treatment choices, abuse of professional power, over-reliance on and excessive use of medication, discrimination and stigmatisation, inhumane physical conditions in hospital units and lack of meaningful community-based alternatives to hospitalisation (see also Mental Health Reform, 2015). Many of these have also been raised by Ireland's Mental Health Commission in its annual inspection reports. Questions have also been raised about the interests served by the adoption of so-called strategies of inclusion in mental health systems, such as 'user involvement', 'peer support' and 'co-production' (Brosnan, 2012; Costa et al, 2012; Voronka, 2016). These questions and concerns have been articulated in various ways by a diverse range of 'actors', including people who describe themselves as service users, survivors, patients, members of the mad community, carers, family members, professionals, academics and members of the public, all of whom are dissatisfied with current forms of care and its underpinning bio-medical philosophy (Sapouna & Gijbels, 2016).

In an attempt to provide a broader platform to discuss and debate concerns and share new initiatives and approaches, since 2009 an Annual Critical Perspectives Conference has been organised by the Schools of Applied Social Studies and Nursing and Midwifery at UCC.[5] Now in its 11th year, the conference, with an annual attendance of more than 500 delegates over two days, is considered one of the most significant events of its kind nationally and internationally, attracting speakers and delegates from across the continents. The Annual Critical Perspectives Conferences are unique, as they bring together people from diverse backgrounds (self-experience, survivors, professionals, academics and carers) to present, discuss and debate critical perspectives in mental health.

The Critical Voices Network Ireland[6] (CVNI) emerged out of these deliberations in 2010 as a coalition of service users, carers, professionals, academics, national campaigning and advocacy groups, all looking for a mental health system not based on the traditional bio-medical model. This network provides a democratic space with non-hierarchical structures that is open to everybody who wishes to join its discussions. An e-list and a Facebook page[7] have been established for people to begin to share, debate and discuss issues of concern and different ways of working. An important aspect of these developments is the beginning of a dialogue between stakeholders who have been separated in the past. Through the CVNI, a space has been created

5. See www.cvni.ie (accessed 6 August 2019).
6. www.cvni.ie (accessed 6 August 2019).
7. www.facebook.com/groups/Irishnetworkofcriticalvoicesinmentalhealth?_rdr=p (accessed 6 August 2019).

where different and sometimes conflicting voices and agendas can be heard and respected rather than silenced. Professionals, students and people with self-experience exchange views freely as part of this forum. This is not always an easy exchange. Challenging mental health practice can be unsettling as it may require positions of certainty to be reviewed and possibly relinquished. But the transformative potential of this space can also encourage participants to recognise that there are many truths, to shift from a position of certainty and to strive to understand the 'other'. Through these exchanges there is an opportunity to share stories, make sense of experiences and reconstruct meanings, particularly previously silenced meanings (Sapouna, 2012). The following section, informed by student evaluations and feedback, considers the student experience of engaging with critical mental health education.

## The educational impact of critical spaces – does it help?

The feedback of social work students who have attended the Annual Critical Perspectives Conferences has been overwhelmingly positive, with many saying that they are 'the best part of the mental health module'. Having such an event fully integrated in the educational curriculum provides students with opportunities to be in a space where different forms of knowledge formation, learning and exchange take place.

Students appreciate the opportunity to listen to survivor, carer and professional perspectives and the diverse approaches and languages used in the deliberations. They also enjoy being part of an environment that has been described by participants as egalitarian and democratic, with a positive 'buzz' in the atmosphere and lively discussions in university corridors and over coffee. As one student put it: 'I was sitting next to someone and didn't know whether they were a professional or a service user; it didn't matter and this was so refreshing.' Students also appreciate being in a space where survivor narratives are considered a valid way of learning about good practice.

On the other hand, critical comments suggest that, at times, services and professionals are portrayed in a negative way and this can be discouraging for students who are about to enter the world of practice. Over the years a few delegates, including students, have said that they found the expression of emotion and anger towards mental health services uneasy and unsettling. Others, however, recognise that such emotions should be respected as real parts of the lives of people they will be working with. Recognising the relationship between the emotional content of the issues debated and the capacity of dialogue within these spaces to achieve change is an important educational experience (Barnes, 2008). This process provides opportunities for capacity-building through learning how to deal with complex issues of practice and not avoid issues of injustice and oppression because they are emotionally charged. It is also an opportunity to be part of a process that models a shift in power and control as a way of transforming practice.

Feedback on classroom-based learning follows similar trends, while presenting some additional challenges. Overall, social work students tend to give positive feedback to the broader social perspective and the user-focused values embraced in the classroom, with many students describing the mental health module as 'thought-provoking' and an 'eye-opener', and as generating an interest in area of practice they have not considered before. However, some students also question the extent to which this module prepares them for practice by not covering enough 'mental health conditions' and by not providing enough information on the 'medical model'. For example, in the past six years when we have included more material on voice-hearing, some students have argued that there is too much emphasis on psychosis at the expense of other experiences, such as 'depression' and 'anxiety', which are considered to be more common in social work caseloads. Other critical comments suggest that the module does not provide a 'balanced' input on the medical and social approaches and, as a result, students may not be equipped to work in a predominantly biomedical practice setting.

The experience of UCC social work students who have undertaken a mental health placement[8] has not yet been systematically researched. In verbal feedback, many students report that they benefited from the value-base they developed through the mental health module, which allowed them to take an advocacy/human rights approach to practice. Other students argue that they struggled with what they describe as 'a requirement to speak the medical language' and the need to know more about diagnoses in order to have a voice in the multidisciplinary team. Most student experiences of placements suggest that discussions about service delivery are dominated by biomedical frameworks, a trend evidenced in clinical responsibility and leadership of the multidisciplinary team remaining with the consultant psychiatrist; criteria for intervention being based on clinical diagnosis; hegemonic views on mental 'illness' and subsequent 'cures' within the various disciplines, and the use of medical terminology in contemporaneous case notes/discussions, case conferences, team meetings and ward rounds (Clifford, 2014).

Some social work students who have completed mental health placements report that their education is not perceived as 'balanced' by their practice

8. Social work students in UCC undertake two 14-week placements during their studies in various statutory and community settings (eg. child protection, hospitals, disability, probation, mental health services, community family support). Not all students will have a mental health placement as part of their social work studies.

teachers, some of whom view it as disproportionately favouring a 'social model' and occasionally describe it as 'anti-psychiatry'. The problem with this view of 'balance', however, is that it assumes a binary between 'social and medical models', often described as 'two sides of the story', rather recognising that there are many stories. As argued earlier, advocating the superiority of a social model over a medical one fails to recognise that a model-based way of looking at human difficulties does not capture the complexity and messiness of human distress (Bracken, 2007). In that sense, social work education may be better framed as a *balancing*, rather than a *balanced*, act (Newnes, Holmes & Dunn, 1999; Read & Dillon, 2013); it aims to provide a *balancing* view to the hegemonic expert models that dominate professional education and practice.

### Problematising user narratives in education

The participation of service users/survivors in social work education is a key element of this balancing act in that it validates new ways of knowing about experiences of distress and, therefore, contributes to a shift in power imbalances. Over the years, survivor accounts through classroom, conference and video presentations have exposed students to some powerful stories. Students listened enthusiastically to these narratives; they appreciated the diversity of the experiences shared, and they saw the person beyond the symptom. These stories were an antidote to medicalisation. However, I soon became uncomfortable with some students' fascination with a 'brave individual's' story at the expense of an interest in structural change (O'Donnell, Sapouna & Brosnan, 2019). There is indeed a danger that a focus on and curiosity about the personal testimony can promote a culture of voyeurism (McFarlane, 2001, 2006) – a trend that Costa and colleagues (2012) describe as 'disability porn'. In an article on user narratives, Anne O'Donnell (community educator), Liz Brosnan (survivor researcher) and I have reflected on the commodifying of survivor stories, with mental health organisations and educational institutions using them primarily to promote their own agendas (O'Donnell, Sapouna & Brosnan, 2019). We discuss our disillusionment that something as powerful and transformative as telling stories can become neutralised and co-opted (see also Costa et al, 2012). We express our discomfort and rage with the unequal status of the service user as 'invited speaker', which gives no real recognition or power to those who share their stories within education. We also remain hopeful about the potential of stories to challenge mental health practices by 'seeking out more diverse individual and collective stories and listening carefully to those stories which challenge us to move beyond complacency' (O'Donnell, Sapouna & Brosnan, 2019).

User involvement is more than a narrative; it is a value for a more democratic way of working. Therefore, the issue of power needs to be addressed. Without this, as Cowden and Singh (2007: 15–16) argue, 'the voice of the user becomes a fetish – something which can be held up as a representative of authenticity and truth, but which at the same time has no real influence over decision making'. As user involvement becomes increasingly mainstreamed in professional service provision and education, it is important that social work education does not appropriate the user movement but recognises critical voices as essential contributors to the education process.

## Reflection

Working at the interface of academia and survivor movements is a personally challenging task. As an academic who works collaboratively with critically-minded survivors, I often have to take a step back while creating a platform for user/survivor voices to be heard – an act of disappearance that Church (2013) describes as political. While this discussion goes beyond the scope of this chapter, it is important to say that collaborating with survivors means that my work is not only complemented but also, at times, superseded by their dynamic, interesting and colourful insights. Over the years I am learning to become more comfortable with stepping back and enjoying the privilege of co-working, which has transformed my engagement with social work education. At the same time, I am becoming increasingly uncomfortable with the co-option of user involvement in educational institutions. Somehow these tensions help me to remain critically engaged with what I do!

## Conclusion

This chapter has considered the contribution of social work education in transforming dominant biomedical practice in mental health care. Within current practice contexts, social workers often find themselves powerless to articulate an alternative to the medicalisation of human distress and challenge practices of coercion. Social work education needs to support students to embrace a critical approach to practice that views emotional distress as a meaningful response to problems of living, trauma and adversity, rather than as individual pathology or chemical imbalance. This critical approach also addresses issues of injustice often experienced by mental health service users. In order to facilitate this process, education needs to become a critical space to:

- rethink issues of knowledge formation in mental health and recognise the importance of user/survivor knowledge in exploring the context and the meaning of human distress

- unlearn the language of symptoms and individual pathology – learn how to engage with people's unusual experiences and how to ask people 'What happened' rather that 'What's wrong' with them; learn how to ask why it happened, and therefore focus on wider life contexts and structures

- rethink issues of identity – move away from seeing people as 'patients' towards an understanding of the multiple and diverse aspects of their lives

- rethink issues and power – engage with critical spaces to consider different ways of responding to human distress and validate the emerging identities of users/survivors as equal partners in mental health practice

- stay engaged with and open to critiques of innovation and inclusion strategies, and keep asking the uncomfortable question, 'In whose interest is this?'

As this approach to education challenges current mental health ideologies and practice, it is at times criticised for not preparing students for the 'reality' of service provision. A further criticism of this approach is that it is 'not balanced', as it does not consider the medical model, often described as 'the other side of the story'. Moving beyond model-thinking, I propose that social work education may be better viewed as a *balancing* rather than a *balanced* act. This involves providing a balancing view to the hegemonic expert models that dominate professional education and practice.

A balancing act also implies that education is not an avenue for social workers to become the 'new experts' in the field of mental health. Rather, the voice of users/survivors becomes central to all practice. At the same time, such a balancing act requires us to constantly problematise the co-option and institutionalisation of innovation in mental health systems. By engaging in a paradigmatic shift and by forming meaningful partnerships with service users, survivors and people with self-experience, social work can reclaim its social identity and respond to human distress in a way that is user driven, respectful, context aware, and informed by human rights principles.

---

### References

Allen R (2014). *The Role of the Social Worker in Adult Mental Health Services*. London: The College of Social Work.

Angell M (2005). *The Truth About the Drug Companies: how they deceive us and what to do about it*. New York, NY: Random House Trade Paperbacks.

Barnes M (2008). Passionate participation: emotional experiences and expressions in deliberative forums. *Critical Social Policy* 28(4): 461–481.

Barnett R (1997). *Higher Education: a critical business.* Buckingham: Open University Press and Society for Research into Higher Education.

Bracken P (2007). Beyond models, beyond paradigms: the radical interpretation of recovery. In: Stastny P, Lehmann P (eds). *Alternatives Beyond Psychiatry.* Berlin: Peter Lehmann Publishing (pp400–402).

Bracken P, Thomas P (2005). *Postpsychiatry: mental health in a postmodern world.* Oxford: Oxford University Press.

Brosnan L (2013). *Service-User Involvement in Irish Mental Health Services: a sociological analysis of inherent tensions for service-users, service-providers and social movement actors.* Unpublished PhD thesis, University of Limerick.

Brosnan L (2012). Power and participation: an examination of the dynamics of mental health service-user involvement in Ireland. *Studies in Social Justice* 6(1): 45–66.

Brosnan L, Sapouna L (2015). Opportunities for social workers' critical engagement in mental health care. In: Christie A, Featherstone B, Quin S, Walsh T (eds). *Social Work in Ireland: changes and continuities.* Basingstoke: Palgrave Macmillan (pp159–177).

Church K (2013). Making madness matter in academic practice. In: LeFrancois B, Menzies R, Reaume G (eds). *Mad Matters: a critical reader in Canadian mad studies.* Toronto: Canadian Scholar's Press (pp181–194).

Clifford M (2014). A student's experience on a mental health placement. In: Sapouna L, Clifford M. Education beyond diagnosis: opportunities and challenges. [Conference paper]. *On and Beyond Psychiatric Diagnoses.* 6th Critical Perspectives Conference. School of Applied Social Studies and School of Nursing and Midwifery in association with the Critical Voices Network Ireland, Cork, 12–13 November.

Conneely E, Garrett PM (2015). Social workers and social justice during a period of intensive neoliberalization: a preliminary investigation from the Republic of Ireland. *Journal of Progressive Human Services* 26(2): 126–147.

Costa L, Voronka J, Landry D, Reid J, McFarlane B, Reville D, Church K (2012). Recovering our stories: a small act of resistance. *Studies in Social Justice* 6(1): 85–101.

Cowden S, Singh G (2007). The 'user': friend, foe or fetish? A critical exploration of user involvement in health and social care. *Critical Social Policy* 27(1): 5–23.

Cuskelly K (2013). Social work and the struggle for social justice in Ireland. *Critical and Radical Social Work* 1(1): 125–130.

Department of Health and Children (2006). *A Vision for Change: report of the Expert Group on Mental Health Policy.* Dublin: Stationery Office.

Dillon J, Bullimore P, Lampshire D, Chamberlin J (2013). The work of experience-based experts. In: Read J, Dillon J (eds). *Models of Madness: psychological, social and biological approaches to psychosis.* London: Routledge (pp305–318).

Ellis W, Dietz W (2017). A new framework for addressing adverse childhood and community experiences: the building community resilience model. *Academic Pediatrics* 17(7): 86–93.

Featherstone B, Gupta A, Morris KM, Warner J (2018). Let's stop feeding the risk monster: towards a social model of 'child protection'. *Families, Relationships and Societies* 7(1): 7–22.

Felitti VJ, Anda RF, Nordenberg D, Williamson DF, Spitz AM, Edwards V, Koss MP, Marks JS (1998). Relationship of childhood abuse and household dysfunction to many of the leading causes of death in adults. *American Journal of Preventative Medicine* 14(4): 245–258.

Fernando S (2011). Cultural diversity and racism. In: Moncrieff J, Ripley M, Dillon J (eds). *Demedicalising Misery: psychiatry, psychology and the human condition.* Basingstoke: Palgrave Macmillan (pp44–52).

Fernando S (2003). *Cultural Diversity, Mental Health and Psychiatry: the struggle against racism.* London: Routledge.

Fook J (2002). *Social Work: critical theory and Practice.* London: Sage.

Friedli L (2018). Recovery and resistance. [Conference keynote paper]. *On and Beyond 'Recovery': ten years on.* 11th Critical Perspectives Conference. UCC School of Applied Social Studies and School of Nursing and Midwifery in association with the Critical Voices Network Ireland, Cork, 13–14 November. https://ucc.cloud.panopto.eu/Panopto/Pages/Viewer.aspx?id=718325b8-12fb-46a7-a389-a9a100c95fa8 (accessed 7 August 2019).

Friedli L, Stearn R (2015). Positive affect as coercive strategy: conditionality, activation and the role of psychology in UK government workfare programmes. *Medical Humanities 41*: 40–47.

Garrett PM (2018). *Welfare Words: critical social work & social policy.* London: Sage.

Hammersley P, Langshaw B, Bullimore P, Dillon J, Romme M, Escher S (2008). Schizophrenia at the tipping point. *Mental Health Practice 12*(1): 14–19.

Harper D, Speed E (2012). Uncovering recovery: the resistible rise of recovery and resilience. *Studies in Social Justice 6*(1): 9–25.

Higgins A, Doyle L, Downes C, Murphy R, Sharek D, DeVries J, Begley T, McCann E, Sheerin F, Smyth S (2016). *The LGBTIreland Report: national study of the mental health and wellbeing of lesbian, gay, bisexual, transgender and intersex people in Ireland.* Dublin: GLEN and BeLonG To.

Higgins A, Sharek D, McCann E, Glacken M, Breen M, McCarron M, Sheerin F (2011). *Visible Lives: identifying the experiences and needs of older lesbian, gay, bisexual and transgender (LGBT) people in Ireland.* Dublin: Gay and Lesbian Equality Network.

Hunter N (2018). Trauma outside the box: how the 'trauma-informed' trend falls short. [Online]. *Mad in America.* https://www.madinamerica.com/2018/11/trauma-informed-trend-falls-short/?fbclid=IwAR1QbJHumX40L-EU5UDu_94Wzms1SJIRUxXBqzIG9VEMnePXgx2d4xaE1PI (accessed 7 August 2019).

Janssen I, Krabbendam L, Bak M, Hanssen M, Vollebergh W, de Graaf R, van Os J (2004). Childhood abuse as a risk factor for psychotic experiences. *Acta Psychiatrica Scandinavica 109*(1): 38–45.

Johnstone L, Boyle M, with Cromby J, Dillon J, Harper D, Kinderman P, Longden E, Pilgrim D, Read J (2018). *The Power Threat Meaning Framework: towards the identification of patterns in emotional distress, unusual experiences and troubled or troubling behaviour, as an alternative to functional psychiatric diagnosis.* Leicester: British Psychological Society.

Kelly L, Donnelly E (2018). Strengthening the evidence base for psychosocial interventions – the role of adult mental health social workers: a national survey. [Conference presentation.] *Psychosocial Interventions in Social Work: championing our therapeutic skills.* Social Workers in Adult Mental Health Special Interest Group conference, Dublin: 13 April 2018.

Longden J, Read J, Dillon J (2017). Assessing the impact and effectiveness of Hearing Voices Network self-help groups. *Community Mental Health Journal 54*(2): 184–188.

Manchester R (2015). Towards critical mental health social work: learning from critical psychiatry and psychiatry survivors. *Critical and Radical Social Work 3*(1): 149–154.

McFarlane J (2006). Paying attention to process: a lesson from the mental health user movement. In: Shaw M, Meagher J, Moir S (eds). *Participation in Community Development: problems and possibilities.* Edinburgh: Concept/Community Development Journal (pp87–90).

McFarlane J (2001). *Building on Common Ground: a report into mental health awareness training.* Edinburgh: Scottish Human Services.

McGregor C, Quin S (2015). Revisiting our history post 'Celtic Tiger': so what's new? In: Christie A, Featherstone B, Quin S, Walsh T (eds). *Social Work in Ireland: changes and continuities.* Basingstoke: Palgrave Macmillan (pp1–17).

Mental Health Commission (2013). *Implementation of a Vision for Change is slow and inconsistent across the country, according to the Mental Health Commission.* Press release. [Online.] www.mhcirl.ie/File/Press_Release_7th_Anniversary_AVFC.pdf (accessed 5 February 2019).

Mental Health Reform (2015). *A Vision for Change Nine Years On: a coalition analysis of progress.* Dublin: Mental Health Reform.

Moncrieff J (2013). *The Bitterest Pills: the troubling story of antipsychotic drugs.* Basingstoke: Palgrave Macmillan.

Moncrieff J (2008). *The Myth of the Chemical Cure: a critique of psychiatric drug treatment.* Basingstoke: Palgrave Macmillan.

Newnes C, Holmes G, Dunn C (eds) (1999). *This Is Madness: a critical look at psychiatry and the future of mental health services.* Ross-on-Wye: PCCS Books.

O' Donnell A, Sapouna L, Brosnan L (2019). Storytelling: an act of resistance or a commodity? *Journal of Ethics in Mental Health.* Special Issue: Disordering Social Inclusion, Ethics, Critiques, Collaborations, Futurities.

Priebe S, Giacco D, El-Nagib R (2016). *Public Health Aspects of Mental Health among Migrants and Refugees: a review of the evidence on mental health care for refugees, asylum seekers and irregular migrants in the WHO European Region.* Copenhagen: WHO Regional Office for Europe.

Rapley M, Moncrieff J, Dillon J (2011). *Demedicalising Misery: psychiatry, psychology and the human condition.* Basingstoke: Palgrave Macmillan.

Read J (2013). Childhood adversity and psychosis. In: Read J, Dillon J (eds). *Models of Madness: psychological, social and biological approaches to psychosis.* London: Routledge (pp249–275).

Read J, Bentall R (2012). Negative childhood experiences and mental health: theoretical, clinical and primary prevention implications. *British Journal of Psychiatry 200:* 89–91.

Read J, Dillon J (eds) (2013). *Models of Madness: psychological, social and biological approaches to psychosis.* London: Routledge.

Read J, Johnstone L, Taitimu M (2013). Psychosis, poverty and ethnicity. In: Read J, Dillon J (eds). *Models of Madness: psychological, social and biological approaches to psychosis.* London: Routledge (pp191–209).

Recovery in The Bin (undated). *RiTB Key Principles.* [Online.] Recovery in The Bin. https://recoveryinthebin.org (accessed 7 August 2019).

Rogers A, Pilgrim D (2014). *A Sociology of Mental Health and Illness.* Maidenhead: McGraw-Hill Education/Open University Press.

Romme M, Escher S (2005). Trauma and hearing voices. In: Larkin W, Morrison A (eds). *Trauma and Psychosis: new directions for theory and therapy.* London: Routledge (pp 162–192).

Romme M, Escher S (2000). *Making Sense of Voices: a guide for mental health professionals working with voice-hearers.* London: Mind Publications.

Sapey B, Bullimore P (2013). Listening to voice hearers. *Journal of Social Work 13*(6): 616–632.

Sapouna L (2016). Education for critical practice in mental health: opportunities and challenges. *Critical and Radical Social Work 4*(1): 59–76.

Sapouna L (2012). Foucault, Michel. Madness and civilization: a history of insanity (2001). *Community Development Journal 47*(4): 612–617.

Sapouna L, Gijbels H (2016). Social movements in mental health: the case of the Critical Voices Network Ireland. *Critical and Radical Social Work 4*(3): 397–402.

Szasz T (2008). *Psychiatry: the science of lies.* New York, NY: Syracuse University Press.

Tew J (2011). *Social Approaches to Mental Distress.* Basingstoke: Palgrave MacMillan.

Tew J (2002). Going social: championing a holistic model of mental distress within professional education. *Social Work Education: The International Journal 21*(2): 143–155.

Thomas P (2014). *Psychiatry in Context: experience, meaning and communities.* Monmouth: PCCS Books.

Varese F, Smeets F, Drukker M, Lieverse R, Lataster T, Viechtbauer W, Read J, van Os J, Bentall R (2012). Childhood adversities increase the risk of psychosis: a meta-analysis of patient-control, prospective-and cross-sectional cohort studies. *Schizophrenia Bulletin 38*(4): 661–671.

Voronka J (2016). *Researching the Politics of Inclusion.* [Online.] Vision Passion Action. https://radssite.wordpress.com/2016/03/14/researching-the-politics-of-inclusion (accessed 7 August 2019).

Wallcraft J (2014). Guide to Government Health and Social Care Jargon. [Online]. http://jwallcraft.wix.com/jan-wallcraft/health-and-social-care-jargon-a-guide/c1lqi (accessed 20 February 2019).

Watson J (ed) (2019). *Drop the Disorder! challenging the culture of psychiatric diagnosis.* Monmouth: PCCS Books.

Wilkinson R, Pickett K (2009). *The Spirit Level: why more equal societies almost always do better.* London: Allen Lane.

Whitaker R (2010). *Anatomy of an Epidemic.* New York, NY: Crown Publishers.

World Health Organization (WHO) (2009). *Mental Health, Resilience and Inequalities.* Copenhagen: WHO.

# Chapter 2

# Acknowledging social inequalities: developing competencies in community psychology in clinical psychology training

## Anjula Gupta

Professional training in clinical psychology involves a three-year doctorate programme, following an undergraduate degree in psychology. The programme involves three strands – academic, clinical and research – and includes placements in NHS or other qualified providers in the third and independent sectors.

This chapter will outline an innovation in clinical psychology training, introduced in 2013 on the clinical psychology training programme at Hull University and consisting of a set of experiences to develop community psychology competencies. The aim of this block is to provide trainees with an opportunity to develop their personal values, to be critical observers and to question taken-for-granted knowledge or systems. We anticipate that trainees will integrate these values into their clinical practice, thereby playing a crucial role in influencing traditional mental health systems and services and providing care that acknowledges the realities of social inequality and disadvantage and their impact on wellbeing.

More specifically, the community psychology block offers a foundation of values underpinned by the theory and principles of community and critical psychology and provides an understanding of the relationship between distress and wider social, political and cultural contexts.

## Rationale

Distress can be understood in different ways: spiritually, psychologically, biologically or socially. The way someone makes sense of their distress will depend on their lens – their life experiences, beliefs, culture, social class and political contexts (Burr, 2015). Our understanding of the world and 'knowledge' is not based on objective truths but is continuously co-created and constructed through social and relational processes (White, 2007). From a social constructionist perspective, all discourses are therefore equal, as there is no single truth.

Statutory health services, however, are organised in accordance with a dominant understanding (or truth) that distress is a sign of medical illness, and therefore they predominantly offer medical treatment as the first line of treatment. Although social or psychological understandings and interventions may co-exist with medication, it is often a medical model that denotes whether treatment is required and where this happens. The consequence is that other understandings of distress are marginalised and neglected by the system, as there is little room for a spiritual understanding of voice-hearing, for example, or an acknowledgement of the consequences of discrimination on wellbeing in a Western social and political context.

Community psychology is the field of psychology that is concerned with the interaction between people and society (Orford, 1992). The discipline is interested in the stories of strengths and resources in community settings, and in particular the move from oppression to resistance and from liberation to wellbeing. The focus is on collective understandings of distress – the shift from individualised concepts of cognition and behaviour to social processes and collective power (van Uchelen, 2000). The ideology of individualistic constructs of distress is argued to have an adverse impact on people in the form of internalised oppression (Smail, 2001). In addition, community psychology recognises that the use of diagnosis and the language of symptoms hide the social adversity that is often the root of distress.

Clinical psychology, by comparison, minimises the role that social injustice plays in the origin of distress, thereby perpetuating differences in social power and influence. As a profession that offers individual therapy, clinical psychology can perpetuate an individualised perspective and become invested in traditional psychological understandings or theories, meaning we may not always challenge the dominant discourses and practices that sustain the individualisation of distress. This means we can consciously or unconsciously neglect personal understandings of distress and, therefore, lose an opportunity to work with people within their explanatory framework, placing us in the uncomfortable position of telling someone what is happening to them. It is best understood as the difference between offering information and (psycho-)education, with the latter becoming a dominant intervention in mainstream clinical psychology. Psycho-education, although having empowering aims, can reinforce power imbalances between psychologists and service users: the psychologist holds the truth and knowledge and the service user needs education from the 'expert'.

Dominant models in clinical psychology practice are focused on the psyche and offer psychotherapy as the main alternative to medication in mainstream mental health services, thereby similarly pathologising and placing the fault with the service user for their perceived inability to cope with adversity (Smail, 2005). Traditional therapy models are based on a structuralist foundation of assumptions that assumes feelings and actions can be understood as internal mechanisms – for example, cognitions and schemas in cognitive behavioural therapy, and drives and defences in psychoanalysis (Harper & Spellman, 2006).

Mainstream models, therefore, are limited and risk sustaining unjust political, economic and societal structures (Fox, Prilleltensky & Austin, 2009) by neglecting the role of external factors, such as poverty, discrimination and social class, in the development and maintenance of distress. It is often argued that psychology should be apolitical, but the maintaining of marginalisation and injustice through positivist assumptions can be seen as a political act.

If therapy, as the dominant intervention offered in clinical psychology, doesn't work, then narratives in clinical practice suggest the client 'did not try hard enough', 'was not ready' or was 'ambivalent' about change. It does not question the premise of traditional psychology and the adequacy of therapy as a 'cure' for someone who, for example, is a single parent and living in poverty. This then risks people internalising a narrative that they are not good enough, which may be re-traumatising. Discussing the role of social adversity in distress can also cause suffering (Smail, 2001), but ignoring the role of these invisible social forces in a person's distress maintains the assumption that it is an illness that requires medical treatment. This discourse of distress being a symptom of mental illness rather than a response to external stressors leads to the medicalisation of suffering (Marecek & Hare-Mustin, 2009), which can result in the overuse of psychiatric drugs, legally enforced detention, and public and self-stigma. Internalised stigma may lead to loss of hope, and absence of hope can impede recovery. I vividly recall a young man in his 20s who I met in clinical practice. His psychiatrist had told him he was 'schizophrenic' and would never work again, so there was no point in trying to find a job. Not surprisingly, when I asked about his hopes and dreams, this young man was unable to tell me.

For these reasons, it is important that clinical psychologists should acknowledge social inequalities, promote an understanding of distress based on these assumptions and intervene at a wider societal level. Clinical psychology training programmes, as the gateway to the profession, seem the most logical place to encourage would-be practitioners to question mainstream practice.

An increasing number of clinical psychologists acknowledge the impact of austerity and inequalities on distress and question the medical model, recognising the limitations of clinical psychology in the face of social adversity. Reynolds (2013) provides a more empowering position for clinicians that privileges service users' truths about distress, and one where the role of professionals is to 'lean in as imperfect allies'. This poses the question of whether, as holders of psychological knowledge, clinical psychology training courses have a responsibility to ensure that trainees are thinking about the wider context, questioning taken-for-granted privileges and challenging unfair systems. This does not imply that individual therapy should not be offered by clinical psychology; rather, it proposes that, alongside developing therapy competencies, we provide an opportunity for trainees to be conscious of the invisible social forces that affect our wellbeing and equip us with different ways of being a clinical psychologist.

It is in this context that the clinical psychology training programme described in this chapter aims to equip psychologists with the capability to acknowledge social inequalities and understand how they contribute to and sustain injustice, so that they can avoid contributing to health inequalities. However, the programme also understands community and critical psychology as 'a truth' rather than 'the truth'. So the community psychology block offers trainees a set of experiences that provide a foundation of values and theories that can support them to develop their critical lens, while also acknowledging that individual therapy can be helpful for some people and has value. We hope that this allows trainees, as practitioners, to hear different narratives about distress.

## What does the community psychology component involve?

The six-week community psychology block comprises a placement in a non-statutory organisation. It constitutes the first placement of the training programme, and trainees are supported by the academic and clinical course tutors. The block also includes teaching and forums to support personal and professional development and an awareness of the principles and theory of community psychology with implications for clinical practice.

Trainees go on to complete a nine-month clinical placement in the first year, plus two placements of six months' duration each in their second year, and a further two six-month or 12-month placements running concurrently in their third year. Unlike the community psychology placement, these clinical placements are more usually in NHS services.

The general aim of the community psychology block is to provide trainees with a foundation for understanding the link between social adversity, inequality and psychological distress before they begin NHS clinical placements. It provides an opportunity for trainees to explore their personal values and to reflect on how they can combine the personal, political and professional in clinical practice. The overall objective is to ensure that trainees question the status quo in mainstream health services and contribute to models of understanding distress that do not marginalise. The learning outcomes for the block are outlined in Table 2.1.

**Table 2.1: Learning outcomes for the community psychology block**

- To develop an ability to reflect on your own social, cultural, and political context and how this influences your assumptions, values and beliefs about the world and different communities.

- To link theory and principles of social constructionism and critical and community psychology to practice within third sector contexts.

- To work and engage with socially marginalised communities, thinking about how power, environment, social status and invisible social forces play a role in maintaining an unjust status quo.

- To develop an awareness of difference and diversity and to work alongside people with similar or different social, cultural, historical and political contexts from you.

- To develop thinking about the implications of this for clinical practice and the relationship between power, privilege, and wellbeing.

- To develop an ability to reflect on and discuss these complex issues and subsequent emotional impact.

- To develop an understanding of supervision models and how to use supervision to reflect on experiences.

- To develop thinking about how social justice is constructed and maintained in society.

- To develop an understanding of the wider health economy and partnerships between statutory and third sector organisations.

These learning outcomes map onto the British Psychological Society (BPS) competencies required for clinical psychology training (BPS, 2017). These standards are used to accredit clinical psychology programmes, ensure consistent national standards for clinical psychologists and provide assurance that trainees are fit to practise once qualified.

There are different components to the six-week block that map onto the BPS training competencies for formulation, personal and professional development.

## Components of the community psychology block

### 1. Teaching

Teaching is an important component of the block, with sessions on social constructionism, critical psychology and community psychology before the placement starts. This teaching focuses on providing an introduction to and understanding of the principles of each theory and model, with a consideration of the implications for clinical practice. Following these preliminary sessions, the block includes one day a week of teaching on topics related to the fulfilment of the learning outcomes.

Teaching sessions include:

- power, inclusion and understanding difference
- supervision and self-care
- difference and diversity – race and ethnicity
- ethics and values
- endings.

The teaching sessions take the form of experiential workshops to provide a space for trainees to talk safely about their personal experiences and values, as well as learn about theoretical frameworks. Trainees are encouraged to be open and honest, to respect each other's values and to challenge or question the theories and concepts presented, in the same way that we encourage them to question taken-for-granted assumptions and knowledge in psychology.

### 2. Placement

The placement takes place in the autumn term of the first year of training. Trainees are assigned in pairs to a third-sector service for six weeks. The placements are three days a week and there is a clear understanding that trainees are there as volunteers, not as trainee clinical psychologists. The placement providers range from grassroots community projects to charities working with refugees/asylum seekers. They are chosen because they work alongside people and communities who are marginalised by mainstream society. A contract outlining and agreeing roles and legal responsibilities is signed between the university and the service provider. Trainees are expected to work according to the policies of the placement organisation, the university and their employing NHS organisation.

Although trainees are working as volunteers, the learning outcomes for the placement expect them to be reflecting on their experiences, using the principles of community and critical psychology as a framework. Trainees are encouraged to listen to people's stories, be curious, and consider the implications of power and privilege through, for example, the way that language or systems might be used to continue to marginalise or to 'other'.

Placements can be powerful experiences and can also be challenging to trainees, who may be facing for the first time the reality of their own privilege. A mentor is allocated to each placement pair, to provide support and maintain contact with the course team. Trainees and their mentors meet weekly and for an initial, mid-, and end-of-placement review. These meetings allow the trainees and mentor to agree placement goals aligned to the learning outcomes and review them, using the programme's placement documentation. Trainees are required to complete their placement logbook with experiences that align to the BPS competencies for clinical psychologists. Placement mentors have a named course tutor they can contact if they have any concerns about the placement.

BPS requires that trainee clinical psychologists are supervised by a clinical psychologist on all placements. The academic and clinical tutors on the course team, all of whom are clinical psychologists, provide clinical supervision for the placement.

### 3. Clinical supervision

A course tutor is assigned to each trainee to provide weekly individual clinical supervision. This fulfils the BPS requirements but also provides opportunities for learning and development and a governance structure. Trainees are expected to use supervision to identify any gaps in learning and development in terms of the community psychology learning outcomes.

At mid-placement, the supervisor contacts the placement mentor to gain an understanding of the trainee's progress and discuss any concerns. In the last week of the block the trainee and clinical supervisor meet to review the placement documentation and how well they have achieved the goals and learning outcomes. Any continuing development needs or competencies are identified and agreed by the trainee and supervisor and are added to the documentation for the next placement.

This ensures that strengths and development needs from the first placement are embedded in the core training, and acknowledges the importance of community and critical psychology competencies in the development of a clinical psychologist.

## 4. Reflective practice

In order to develop reflexivity and reflective skills, trainees are encouraged to begin a reflective journal about their experiences, within a community and critical psychology framework. They are encouraged to reflect on the impact this has on them personally, using the community psychology learning outcomes as a guide.

The reflective journals are not submitted as an assessed piece of work; they remain a private record of trainees' development, although it is expected that the journal will provide themes for discussion in the weekly reflective practice groups (RPGs).

The RPGs are facilitated by two course tutors. The trainees use this forum to share their experiences on placement, reflect on the impact and demonstrate their understanding of theoretical models. The experiences they draw on from placement are discussed generally, without disclosing confidential or identifiable information about particular people trainees have worked with.

## 5. Assessment

The community psychology block is formative but trainees must complete a portfolio of work at the end to demonstrate their learning. This portfolio comprises:

- a community psychology poster – each trainee pair makes a poster presentation at the end of the block that is open to the course team and faculty colleagues in the university. In addition, the trainees invite two people from their placements to attend. The presentations focus on an exploration of their reflections and the impact on their personal and professional development. They are expected to relate these reflections to theory and demonstrate their ability as reflective practitioners. Written formative peer feedback is provided for each poster on presentation skills, content of poster and personal and professional development.

- a community psychology presentation – each trainee presents a diagrammatic formulation and discussion of the psychological processes identified to demonstrate theory–practice links to peers and the course team. The formulation must attempt to capture factors such as power, difference, justice and a wider consideration of the social, political and cultural contexts of the placement service/organisation or the individuals, community groups and populations that they work alongside. This should be linked to community and critical psychology but should not focus on a specific individual; the emphasis is on trainees' ability to conceptualise systems, not a clinical problem.

The presentation aims to demonstrate trainees' abilities to articulate complex psychological theories and constructs while locating them within wider contextual factors, indicating how these might be presented in a formulation diagram. The presentation also assesses trainees' understanding of the core competencies of assessment, formulation, intervention and evaluation by describing an event or specific experience on placement that has made them more aware of the wider social/political context and its relationship with health and wellbeing. All information about individuals and services is anonymised.

Trainees have used a number of formulation models:

- **Social GRRAAACCES** (Burnham, Palma & Whitehouse, 1993) – a framework representing aspects of difference in beliefs and power that is visible/invisible, voiced/unvoiced. The 'social graces' have developed over time to represent gender, geography, race, religion, age, ability, appearance, class, culture, ethnicity, education, employment, sexuality, sexual orientation and spirituality.

- **Social constructionist formulation** (Harper & Spellman, 2006) – an exploration of one construction of someone's story, completed through a series of dialogues, that refrains from locating any 'deficits' in the individual and recognises there may be a number of ways that their 'problems' might be conceptualised. The authors describe it as a process of ongoing collaborative sense-making, rather than an objective description of the 'problem'.

- **Social inequalities formulation** (Miller & McClelland, 2006) – based on the premise that traditional psychological formulations can hide oppressive power processes that are implicated in abuse and trauma experiences. The social inequalities formulation allows abusive experiences to be explicitly presented by being concerned with the social forces that have influenced the person's life, the discourses that are in play and where the power lies in relationships.

- **Power map** (Hagan & Smail, 1997) – a tool that maps people's proximal resources with four main domains: home and family life (parents, relations, spouse/partner, children, love life); social life (friends, leisure, associations); material resources (education, work, money, health, housing, physical environment), and personal resources (confidence, understanding of past, intelligence). The power map can be used to make sense of a person's distress, relating it to negative and positive social power in their life (either past or present) and to identify areas for potential change.

- **Societal case formulation** (Burton & Kagan, 2008) – this interview schedule was designed as a teaching tool and aims to widen individualistic formulations with a focus on five domains: the individual in the economy; the person in the family; the person and the state; the person in the community, and cultural and historical context.

All the presentations are video-recorded and written formative feedback is provided by course tutors, focusing on:

- the appropriate identification of an issue that captures the impact of wider social/political/cultural factors
- the ability to use formulation to understand the role of these factors on health and wellbeing
- the presentation of a relevant theory with evidence of theory–practice linking
- critical reflection skills related to placement experiences and professional issues
- awareness of ethical issues – awareness of own values, attitudes and professional ethical issues.

Trainees have a study afternoon each week to work on their portfolio.

## Managing resistance and overcoming obstacles to change

The community psychology block began as a personal and professional development (PPD) placement six years ago. It consisted of the same components as described above but the emphasis was on PPD. Many trainees reported that they valued the placement, as it provided a good introduction to the training programme, but there was also some evidence that it was not being valued as much as the subsequent placements, which are mainly in the NHS. Trainee feedback suggested that it was not seen as a placement that delivered the core competencies they thought they needed to be a clinical psychologist; mainly, it seemed, because they were not developing therapy competencies or working individually with service users, and there was a strong sense that trainees felt they were being disadvantaged by, from their perspective, 'missing out on a clinical placement'.

Trainees who are more aligned to a traditional position of clinical psychology as a therapy profession have been critical of the community psychology placement, feeling that training should be supporting their role as therapists. As a course team, we do not feel that we have to challenge this view but aim instead to model curiosity and invite trainees to consider community and critical psychology as a strong foundation of principles and values for all clinical psychologists.

The course team reflected on the feedback, which strengthened our commitment to provide a placement that might challenge the view that a clinical psychologist should be a provider of individual therapy in an individualistic system that locates problems within individuals and fails to acknowledge the role of social inequalities in marginalising communities and maintaining an unjust status quo. It affirmed our belief that the community psychology placement was essential to challenge this limited model of clinical psychology and provide a basis for supporting critical psychologists in the system.

However, we also recognised trainees' concerns and, in response, relaunched the PDD placement as a community psychology placement. This helped to explicitly highlight the theoretical knowledge trainees would be developing in the six weeks and provided further legitimacy by anchoring it more firmly with the BPS competencies for clinical psychologists. The introduction of formally assessed work also helped trainees to recognise in a more tangible way the learning they had acquired over the six weeks. The community psychology block continues to evolve in response to feedback from trainees and the local NHS trust.

This innovation originally developed from the shared values within the course team about distress and its relationship with social inequalities. There was a mutual understanding of our important role as training providers to ensure that the NHS is able to employ clinical practitioners who recognise that not all distress can be alleviated by interventions that focus on the individual, to the exclusion of wider social, cultural and political contexts.

In addition, we found the community psychology block aligned well with the Health and Care Professions Council (HCPC) standards for clinical psychologists (HCPC, 2015 ) – 'to understand social approaches such as those informed by community, critical and social constructivist perspectives' – and the BPS (2017) standards for accrediting clinical training courses under personal and professional skills and values:

- appreciating the inherent power imbalance between practitioners and clients, and how abuse of this can be minimised
- understanding the impact of difference, diversity and social inequalities on people's lives, and implications for applying in practice
- understanding the impact of one's own value base upon clinical practice.

Although BPS endorses competencies in understanding the relationship between social inequalities and distress, we are aware that clinical psychology has a history of the 'colonisation of psychic space' (Oliver, 2004) and that we could be criticised for 'colonising' community psychology. For this reason, it is important that we clarify that we are not aiming to train clinical psychologists to be community psychologists. Our aim is to provide an alternative discourse within the profession that does not simply define distress in intrapsychic terms that blame the oppressed for their mental health difficulties. To focus on the potential for divisions between clinical psychology and community psychology serves only to divert energies from our shared aim and purpose to acknowledge the role of social inequalities in emotional distress.

We have been careful to demonstrate the importance of these competencies and knowledge in clinical psychology, but evaluation of the community psychology block has shown us that training critical clinical psychologists in community psychology competencies can pose a challenge for traditional systems. Qualified psychologists in the region have been supportive of the placement, but some trainees have reported difficulties in NHS placements when they discuss critical and community principles or try to include them in their clinical work. Some have found they are unable to talk about the wider societal context in supervision, either because this is not how their supervisors talk about distress and, as trainees, they feel powerless to bring this into the room, or because there is resistance to their attempts to integrate these models into their clinical work with service users. This can lead to a silencing of these discourses, paralleling the silence around social injustice in society.

This resistance and schism in the profession became apparent with the recent publication by BPS of *The Power, Threat, Meaning Framework* (Johnstone & Boyle, 2018). For some, the framework presented in this report seems to pose a threat to the established psychiatric diagnostic system, the unquestioned assumptions underlying it, its positivism and the ideological power of individualising distress. Others have used social media to make personal and professional attacks on the authors (Johnstone et al, 2019). While in some ways this has opened up a discussion, it has also drawn a spotlight to the ideological power in the profession and the vested interest in maintaining the status quo. The risk of these negative responses is that the perspective offered becomes dismissed or marginalised rather than seen as an opportunity for meaningful discussion in the profession.

It can be risky to question the status quo or present an alternative model, and this can lead to isolation or being viewed as a 'troublemaker' or as 'obstructive'. This can have a toxic impact on the practitioner, especially if they are still in training. In my own experience, the antidote is to connect with other local clinicians with the same values and principles and join regional or national networks to find allies among wider professional groups. As a course team, we recognise the responsibility we hold in introducing trainees to a critical and community perspective, knowing that they may experience being similarly marginalised or silenced throughout their training and following qualification.

Another challenge to the community psychology placement is the reality of the consequences of austerity. Some of the third-sector services with which we have developed partnerships have had to close, due to loss of funding. This is a powerful reminder of what local people are losing when services that make a difference to marginalised communities have to close their doors. Trainees have often retained a link with their placement providers, either by continuing to volunteer with them or by supporting fundraising events. The reality of the economic climate and its specific impact on local services has further highlighted social and health inequalities for them. Additionally, the clinical psychology course team values the partnerships we have developed with local organisations through these placements, as they link the university to the community, and the closure of services affects these relationships.

## Evidence that it helps

This section will report on outcomes from the community psychology (CP) block for the trainees, taken from the personal account of two trainees and feedback from online surveys. The evidence presented is limited and there is a need to understand other aspects of the impact of the block, including the effect on course tutors and placement providers.

## A personal statement of the impact of the CP block

'If a tree falls in the woods and nobody is around to hear it, does it make a sound?'

Your immediate response to this question perhaps mirrors how our own minds transitioned from dumbfounded to critical thinker during our experience of the community psychology placement. From the introduction of a lens during teaching, to the application of academic principles during our placement, we were able to view systems, health services and ourselves through alternative perspectives.

The introduction to critical psychology, social constructionism, concepts of power, privilege and diversity in teaching was the first step to reflecting on my experiences and how they shaped my pursuit of this career. Exploration of these topics raised my awareness of the wider contextual issues of society, statutory and third sector organisations.

After consecutive teaching, going into a six-week placement allowed for a smooth transition from academic learning to developing our inner reflective practitioner. During this time, I delved into a systemic way of working and my eyes were opened to the experiences of communities that are socially marginalised and the powers that operate to maintain these injustices. This experience was moving and I felt privileged that clients were willing to share their lives and discourses with me outside of a therapy room.

Going forward, my experience on the community psychology placement will undoubtedly shape my future career as a clinical psychologist. The experience challenged a lot of taken-for-granted information and put me in a prime position to begin thinking, 'What kind of psychologist do I want to be? And how can I make that happen?'

Your immediate response to the profound question asked above may have failed to look beyond previous experience. As a society, adopting an open dialogue to discuss the many facets of societal marginalisation and distress can foster the liberation to allow us to become vessels for social change.

**Abigail Oluwatimilehin Daniels and Alexander Gibson**

### Trainee evaluation

The programme sends an online survey to trainees six months after the community psychology block. The aim of the survey is to evaluate trainees' satisfaction with the block and explore its continuing influence on learning and development. A qualitative study has also been conducted with trainees, using focus groups. Themes from both the online surveys and focus groups are summarised here.

The community psychology block is valued by the majority of trainees, supporting them to think about the impact of wider systems on distress and systemic factors within healthcare:

> The placement I was on for six weeks gave me a very real insight into the wider systemic background and lives of people I saw. Without this experience, I would not have understood the extent of poverty, neglect and wider issues relating to housing, families, finances and substance abuse, and how it impacts people's lives very differently.

Trainees described how the RPG provided them with a safe space to learn and share with peers. They recognised their development as reflective practitioners through this process and the space it provided to think about the application of diversity perspectives in their teaching and placements. One trainee stated that they had a 'responsibility' to bring issues relating to diversity into teaching that did not address this explicitly:

> Really helpful to be able to share experiences and have other viewpoints/questions to aid personal reflection.

Reflexivity was highlighted as a benefit of the experience, and specifically how it prompted trainees to recognise their privilege, acknowledge values and cultures different from their own and build resilience:

> As a White, English-speaking male, it was insightful to look at the world from a different lens to my own and address my own privileges that could affect how the clients respond to me as a clinician.

> I've definitely learnt how privileged I am and the extent of injustice [and] poverty that people experience in the same city as me. The most moving experience was a home visit to a client who lived within a mile of where I live and how very different our lives are.

Trainees particularly valued the RPG as a forum of peer support and a significant contributor to their confidence to hold the critical position developed during the community psychology block. They missed it when they completed the block:

> … you are in more of a contained space in a reflective practice group that is more… confidential… I still feel like I need to talk to someone about it that maybe isn't my supervisor who is on placement with me all the time.

An additional aim of the evaluation is to measure whether trainees transfer learning from the community psychology block to other parts of the course: clinical placements, teaching, academic work and research. Trainees recognised the importance of a community and critical psychology perspective in understanding and meeting clients' needs:

> The context around that person and things that can help maintain their difficulties that you've kind of picked up on placement… like housing or just things like that and employment, how they can affect mental health and how they can contribute towards their difficulties and their life at the moment.

> I think it's understanding that therapy isn't everyone's number one priority as well is really important.

However, this perspective could be hard to maintain in mainstream clinical placements:

> I didn't get the most overwhelming response… you can't turn around as a trainee six months in and be like 'Yeah, but have you considered this'… it's really difficult to maintain that critical… so I'm saying now in supervision I'm less willing to do that, I'll just go with it.

The NHS system itself and traditional professional roles, models of clinical care, service referral criteria and policies also prevented trainees from integrating community and critical psychology principles in clinical practice on placement:

> Yeah… sticking to policy and things that you have been told you need to do and I would like to do that but I don't think I can… which is difficult when you have taken things from community placement

and you are thinking I need to involve all these people… everything interacts with each other and everything in their system is maintaining these factors and you can only work with the individual.

It is important to still hold what I have learnt in my head but there are not that many opportunities to put it into practice on my current placement.

Trainees suggested that more teaching in these areas across all their training would assist in maintaining their position and provide more opportunities for discussion. Being in individualistic systems prevented them from retaining learning about the role of wider social factors:

[There needs to be] some continued teaching on community psychology theories. The presentation that we had to do also helped to remind me of what was learnt from community placement. Other tasks get in the way of retaining some of the learning. However, I feel that the course helps to remind us of what we might have learnt in academic teaching and presentations.

As a course team, we are interested in how the structure and content of the teaching after the community psychology block aligns to trainees' learning from the block and its role in supporting them to retain this learning. There were mixed opinions about this, some thinking that the teaching was aligned and others that the focus became more individualistic:

While I believe the teaching is important and interesting, there is often no referral to our community psychology placements besides when I make my own links in my reflective journal. The focus shifts to teaching being focused on clinical placements.

The teaching builds on the frameworks of community psychology teaching and placements.

In summary, it seems from the online questionnaires that the trainees appreciate what they have learned from doing the community psychology block: that it provides a framework to consider their values, the impact of poverty and social inequalities on health and how to apply this to their clinical practice.

A significant concern is that trainees feel unable to hold onto this learning and critical perspective in their subsequent clinical placements, due to the culture of services and the NHS. This poses an important question for us as a course team: how do we continue to support trainees' critical perspective through their training and in professional practice without them becoming professionally isolated?

The evidence presented is limited as the sample size for the online survey and the focus group was around 50% of all trainees, so there may be trainees who did not have a good experience of the community psychology block, or who hold different values but did not feel comfortable sharing this.

## Future directions

There is scope for the course team to think about the barriers trainees face after the community psychology block in integrating their learning in clinical practice on the remaining NHS placements. How do we support trainees to maintain their learning in critical community psychology? Currently we are discussing developing open conversations with clinical supervisors through existing university forums such as the Board of Supervisors, planning joint CPD events/seminars around critical and community psychology, and identifying and developing alliances with like-minded clinicians. This last might include supporting the development of a regional special interest group for community psychology, aligned to the community psychology faculty within the BPS Division of Clinical Psychology and the regional Psychologists for Social Change group.

Another step would be to maintain contact with trainees after qualification as a valuable source of supervisors who have experienced the community psychology placement and may be trying to practise by these principles. These clinicians will then have a significant role in reinforcing the learning from the community psychology block in NHS clinical practice. Finally, maintaining contact with trainees after qualification will help us to understand the challenges they face in maintaining critical and community psychology practices in their work, as well as keep us in touch with valuable allies who are modelling a professional identity with a critical and community psychology perspective.

### Acknowledgements

With thanks to the clinical psychology programme team at Hull University for supporting the community psychology block; to Nick Hutchinson for material from the focus groups with trainees; to all the trainees who have taken part in the community psychology block and provided feedback about their experiences and all the non-statutory services that have hosted placements over the years.

## *References*

British Psychological Society (BPS) (2017). *Standards for the Accreditation of Doctoral Programmes in Clinical Psychology*. Leicester: BPS.

Burnham J, Palma D, Whitehouse L (1993). Learning as a context for differences and differences as a context for learning. *Journal of Family Therapy 30*: 529–542.

Burr V (2015). *Social Constructionism*. London: Routledge.

Burton M, Kagan C (2008). *Societal Case Formulation*. [Online.] Community Psychology UK. www.compsy.org.uk/Societal%20case%20formulation%20expanded%20version%202008.pdf (accessed 8 August 2019).

Fox D, Prilleltensky I, Austin S (2009). *Critical Psychology: an introduction*. London: Sage Publications.

Hagan T, Smail D (1997). Power-mapping – I: background and basic methodology. *Journal of Community and Applied Social Psychology 7*: 257–267.

Harper D, Spellman D (2006). Social constructionist formulation. In: Johnston L, Dallos R (eds). *Formulation in Psychology and Psychotherapy: making sense of people's problems*. London: Routledge (pp98–125).

Health and Care Professions Council (HCPC) (2015). *Standards for Proficiency for Practitioner Psychologists*. London: Health and Care Professions Council.

Johnstone L, Boyle M, Cromby J, Dillon J, Harper D, Kinderman P, Longden E, Pilgrim D, Read J (2019). Reflections on responses to the Power Threat Meaning Framework one year on. *Clinical Psychology Forum 313*(Jan): 47–54.

Johnstone L, Boyle M, with Cromby J, Dillon J, Harper D, Kinderman P, Longden E, Pilgrim D, Read J (2018). *The Power Threat Meaning Framework: towards the identification of patterns in emotional distress, unusual experiences and troubled or troubling behaviour, as an alternative to functional psychiatric diagnosis*. Leicester: British Psychological Society.

Marecek J, Hare-Mustin R (2009). Clinical psychology: the politics of madness. In: Fox D, Prilleltensky I, Austin S (eds). *Critical Psychology: an introduction* (2nd ed). London: Sage (pp75–92).

Miller J, McClelland L (2006). Social inequalities formulation. In: Johnstone L, Dallos R (eds). *Formulation in Psychology and Psychotherapy: making sense of people's problems*. London: Routledge (pp126–153).

Oliver K (2004). *The Colonization of Psychic Space: a psychoanalytic social theory of oppression*. Minneapolis, MN: University of Minnesota Press.

Orford J (1992). *Community Psychology: theory and practice*. Chichester: Wiley-Blackwell.

Reynolds V (2013). 'Leaning in' as imperfect allies in community work. *Narrative and Conflict: explorations of theory and practice 1*(1): 53–75.

Smail D (2005). *Power, Interest and Psychology: elements of a social materialist understanding of distress*. Ross-on-Wye: PCCS Books.

Smail D (2001). *Why Therapy Doesn't Work and What We Should Do About It*. London: Constable & Robinson.

van Uchelen C (2000). Individualism, collectivism, and community psychology. In: Rappaport J, Seidman E (eds). *Handbook of Comunity Psychology*. Doprdrecht: Kluwer Academic Publishers (pp65–780).

White M (2007). *Maps of Narrative Practice*. New York, NY: WW Norton & Co.

# Chapter 3

# Critical pedagogy in occupational therapy

## Eoin Gorman

'Occupation' is the core of the profession of occupational therapy, and there are many researchers who have attempted to define this term (Clark et al, 1991; Yerxa et al, 1990; Carlson et al, 2014; Christiansen et al, 1995; Wood, Towers & Malchow, 2000; Humphry, 2002; Spitzer, 2003). Frank (2012) suggested that the lack of a concrete definition of 'occupation' does not hamper the discipline of occupational therapy, but rather serves to highlight the dynamism of the term. For the uninitiated, and for the purpose of this chapter, I propose that occupation be interpreted as the 'stream of activities that compose the realm of daily life' (Zemke, 2016: 510). These streams of activities, or daily occupations, are invested with form, a sense of purpose, meaning, cultural style and social significance (Nelson, 1988; Christiansen et al, 1995; Christiansen & Townsend, 2014).

In the practice of occupational therapy, health and wellbeing are approached as occupational issues. When an issue arises, whether physical, psychological, social, cultural or spiritual, that affects a person's engagement in occupation, an occupational therapist can focus on subsequent changes in their identity, wellbeing and participation in society (Christiansen & Townsend, 2014). Occupational therapists work with individuals and populations across the life-span, from newborns to older adults, in a variety of settings. Occupational therapists work to address the occupational needs of individuals and populations. In doing so, occupational therapy endeavours to influence the health and wellbeing of individuals and populations.

## Affective learning

The culture of occupational therapy education is becoming one that gives primacy to technical knowledge and practical skills rather than the humanistic aspects of the profession (Battaglia, 2016). An increased focus on technical skills can lead to a decrease in affective learning – learning that seeks changes in attitudes, beliefs and values through the teaching of transformative topics. Transformative topics, such as occupational justice and Mad-positive knowledge, are concepts underpinning the example of critical pedagogy explored in this chapter.

### *Occupational justice*

Critical pedagogy recognises that teaching and learning are not ahistorical, apolitical or value-free activities (Doughty, 2016). The view of 'occupation' as an inherently political concept (Pollard & Sakellariou, 2014) is evident in occupational therapy's focus on the enablement of the person's full participation in their chosen occupations in any environment (Rebeiro Gruhl, 2009). Consequently, the education of occupational therapists is intended to equip graduates with knowledge, skills and attitudes necessary to work collaboratively with people, at an individual, community or societal level, to bring about positive life changes.

A political perspective on occupational therapy embraces the goals of occupational justice – that is, 'enabling, mediating and advocating for environments in which all people's opportunities to engage in occupations are just, health promoting and meaningful' (Hocking, 2017: 33). Occupational justice extends notions of social justice by recognising that everyone has occupational rights and emphasising the need to enable universal participation in meaningful occupation (Wilcock & Townsend, 2009; Stadnyk, Townsend & Wilcock, 2010).

Occupational injustices refer to the outcomes of social policies and other forms of governance that restrict people's participation in the everyday occupations (Nilsson & Townsend, 2010: 58). There are five forms of occupational injustice (Table 3.1) (Kronenberg, Pollard & Sakellariou, 2011). Adopting a critical pedological approach in occupational therapy can begin to address these injustices.

**Table 3.1. Occupational injustices (Kronenberg, Pollard & Sakellariou, 2011)**

| Occupational alienation | A prolonged experience of disconnectedness, isolation, emptiness, lack of a sense of identity, a limited or confined expression of spirit, or a sense of meaninglessness (Townsend & Wilcock, 2004: 80) in relation to participation in occupations viewed as meaningless or purposeless (Stadnyk, Townsend & Wilcock, 2010; Wilcock, 2006). |
|---|---|

| Occupational apartheid | Occupational apartheid occurs in situations where opportunities for occupation are afforded to some individuals and restricted to others based on personal characteristics such as race, disability, gender, age, nationality, religion, social status, sexuality and so forth (Kronenberg & Pollard, 2005). |
|---|---|
| Occupational deprivation | A state of preclusion from engagement in occupations of necessity and/or meaning due to factors that stand outside the immediate control of the individual (Whiteford, 2000: 201). |
| Occupational imbalance | Occupational imbalance refers to occupational patterns that lack balance between self-care, leisure, work and rest occupations, thereby failing to meet a person's unique physical, social or mental health needs (Hocking, 2017). |
| Occupational marginalisation | Occupational marginalisation refers to social exclusion, due to invisible expectations, agreements and/ or social and cultural norms, which restricts the occupational participation of individuals or populations (Durocher, Gibson & Rappolt, 2013). |

The task of critical pedagogy is to facilitate members of an oppressed group to develop a deep awareness of the social structures that oppress them both individually and collectively, resulting in resistance and emancipation through a counter-hegemony (Giroux, 1983). Ragumondo's (2011) concept of 'occupational consciousness' strengthens the presence of critical pedagogy in occupational therapy education. 'Occupational consciousness' promotes an awareness of the dynamics of hegemony by challenging taken-for-granted exclusionary social practices, by recognising how everyday personal and collective occupations perpetuate hegemonic practices, and by appraising consequences for individual and collective wellbeing (Ragumondo, 2011).

### Mad-positive counter-knowledge

In the same way that the word 'queer' represents a resistance movement, transforming the oppressive nature of the term into a positive, political and preferred description of the self (Pinar, 2005), the term 'Mad' is used by anyone who has chosen this as a politised form of self-identification (LeBlanc & Kinsella, 2016). The knowledge and experiences of Mad people are habitually disregarded in professional education, which favours a 'broken brain' (Webb, 2010) approach to understanding distress and unusual emotional or mental experiences. This exclusion of the Mad person's experiences and knowledge is a product of sanism – a form of discrimination and oppression affecting those who experience Madness (Fabris, 2011) – and psychocentrism, whereby mental health difficulties are considered to be rooted in the mind and body rather than being the product of social factors (Rimke, 2011).

LeBlanc and Kinsella (2016) argue that the acquisition of Mad-positive counter-knowledge is an action of resistance by the Mad community. As a self-identified Mad occupational therapist and educator, it is my belief that occupational therapy has the potential to foster and support a Mad-positive culture committed to advocacy and activism. This requires occupational therapy educators and practitioners to reflect on their power and positioning within oppressive systems. Adopting a Mad-positive approach in occupational therapy education and practice can lead to reflexive practice and action on reflection, resulting in acknowledgement of the experiences and needs of Mad people. Adopting a critical approach to teaching and learning in occupational therapy offers opportunities to embed Mad experiences and knowledge within the programme and ignite a resistance to sanist and psychocentric models of understanding distress and diverse mental experiences.

## Critical pedagogy in occupational therapy

The BSc in occupational therapy at University College Cork (UCC) is a four-year programme educating future practitioners in the knowledge, skills and attitudes necessary to deliver traditional occupational therapy and prepare future leaders in policy development and emerging areas of practice. The first year of the programme introduces the foundations of occupational science and occupational therapy. In the second and third years, a life-span approach is adopted. Students learn paediatric and family-centred practice in the second year, and the focus shifts to adults and older adults in the third year. The final year of the programme integrates previous learning and is concerned with developing role-emerging or non-traditional practice, adopting a human rights-based approach to healthcare and completing a research project.

The case study in this chapter is taken from a third-year module of the programme, called Person Environment Occupation V (PEO5). The module is designed to continue the development of the student's skills as a therapist and apply their knowledge from previous years to occupations related to adults and older adults. The module is split into two streams – psychosocial and physical. Commonly, students expect the psychosocial stream of the module to focus on mental 'illness' and diagnosis, with an emphasis on a standardised prescription of occupational therapy interventions.

However, in the psychosocial stream of the PEO5 module, a conscious decision was made to shift the focus from 'mental illness' to psychosocial health and wellbeing, incorporating mental, emotional, social and spiritual health. Reframing the module brings together the personal, social and inner and outer worlds, which combine in unique and complex ways (Woodward, 2015). The processes of connection and disconnection are explored throughout the module to encourage students to critically examine the limitations of binary thinking, such as nature/nurture, male/female, Mad/sane, good/bad and personal/social, from an occupational perspective. An occupational perspective is a 'way of looking at or thinking about human doing' (Njelesani et al, 2014) that applies at the level of individual doing through to societal doing. Such a perspective considers contextual factors, assumes occupation is connected to health and wellbeing, attends to the form, function and meaning of occupation and contributes to being, becoming and belonging (Njelesani et al, 2014).

Throughout the PEO5 module, a variety of topics are explored from an occupational perspective, including sanism, Madness, death and dying, spirituality, cultural diversity, sexuality and gender, and social and political injustices. The interconnectivity of the person, the occupation and the environment are used as a perspective to explore these various topics and how they are interwoven when manifesting as trauma, distress or unwellbeing.

The aims of the PEO5 psychosocial stream module are to:

- understand adults and older adults as occupational beings in terms of mental, social, emotional and spiritual health
- explore and critically assess dominant models of practice (and explore alternative approaches)
- understand key concepts and beliefs underpinning anti-oppressive practice
- develop an occupational perspective on current social and political issues
- explore the relevance of cultural diversity to occupational participation, including influences of hegemony, ethnocentrism and theoretical imperialism on health services and occupational therapy practice
- critically engage with visiting lecturers from various occupational practice settings
- reflect on and engage with 'difficult or taboo' areas of practice.

## Madness and mental illness in Ireland

There isn't space here to share all the examples of critical education from the module. One example exemplifying critical educational practice in occupational therapy is a lecture entitled 'Madness and Mental Illness in Ireland', which covers the following themes:

- madness and civilization – a brief overview
- psychiatric diagnosis – a historical perspective
- normal and abnormal.

### Setting the scene

As an academic who has been a mental health service user and has worked as an occupational therapist in mental health settings, I consider myself as providing my students with both an insider and an outsider perspective on mental health services. In addition to my professional experiences, I also share my experiences of being a mental health service user. But instead of using my assigned diagnosis, I explain that I self-identify as Mad, but also as gay and Catholic – not to label myself, but to problematise these labels and challenge the assumptions of what each of them represents, especially when some could appear to be in opposition with one another. Positioning myself as both a health professional and health service user, I endeavour to create an open-dialogical space within the class. My approach is designed to challenge students to recognise me as not only their lecturer but also a human with complex needs when presenting my professional and personal insights into the mental health services in Ireland. I share and use my experiences to bring a personal dimension to what could, sometimes, be experienced as abstract and theoretical content.

As outlined previously, the PEO5 psychosocial stream adopts a psychosocial perspective on health and wellbeing. Classes delivered before the lecture discussed below include an overview of psychosocial health as opposed to mental illness, an exploration of the building blocks of the spectrum of mental health, a critical analysis of stigma and anti-stigma campaigns, an introduction to the concept of sanism, an exploration of the underpinnings of anti-oppressive practice and an introduction to the concept of occupational justice. In each of these sessions I use personal and professional experiences to elucidate key points.

### Madness and civilization – a brief overview

To build on the information covered in the preceding lectures, students are introduced to Foucault's classic text, *Madness and Civilization* (1988). An overview of the concept of Madness is provided, covering the Renaissance, the Classical Age and the Modern Experience. Tracing the development and understanding of Madness exposes students to epochal perspectives on Madness. In each phase, Madness is explored through an evolution of how it is understood, how it is treated and how this influences the personal, environmental and occupational lives of people at that time.

Human rights and social justice issues are embedded in the discussions. Students are asked to reflect on the current treatment of mental health service users and to consider how future generations may judge us, in much the same way that we are reviewing this history of Madness.

I share with students some of the occupational issues I experienced, and continue to experience, as a user of mental health services in Ireland. I never share with students the diagnostic label given to me; to do so would give it credence and legitimise its power. Instead, I share with students the occupational injustices that affect me in my day-to-day life and the way in which people perceive and treat me differently on the basis of my 'diagnosis'. This portion of the lecture ends with a quote from Foucault warning against the dangers of silencing the dialogue between Madness and reason, and specifically the resulting domination of the language of psychiatry.

### *Psychiatric diagnosis – a historical perspective*

The lecture segues into a critical review of psychiatric diagnoses. Students have been encultured in the language of psychiatric diagnosis, which has been exalted as truth through socialisation, education, literature, social media, the entertainment industry and social campaigns. This indoctrination into a binary perception of Mad/sane and normal/abnormal is rarely contested by students without prompting. My decision not to teach diagnoses in what students understand as the 'mental health' module can oftentimes meet resistance. As a compromise, I now include four diagnoses in this lecture and engage students in a critical review of historic context and impact on the lives of those who received the diagnosis.

### Diagnosis 1

| Drapetomania | | | |
|---|---|---|---|
| Description | Symptoms | Treatment | Oppressive outcomes |
| An overwhelming urge to run away (from home, a bad situation, responsibility etc.)<br><br>A 'mental illness' that caused black slaves to flee captivity<br><br>Literally translates as 'Crazy Runaway Slave' | 'Sulky and dissatisfied without cause'<br><br>Prone to take flight | Whipping | Scientific racism |
| Cartwright, 1851 (cited in White, 2017) | | | Rutledge (1995) |

The way science is misused to give power and credence to prejudice is explored with students. Although drapetomania (Cartwright, 1851, cited in White, 2017) is defunct as a diagnosis, its message remains relevant today. A critical examination of *The Bell Curve* (Herrnstein & Murray, 1994), an American political work of scholarship drawing on fields of sociology, psychometrics and history, is presented to students. It is an example of scientific oppression through occupations (researching, writing, and publishing) to oppose multiculturalism and governmental programmes to alleviate poverty. Students learn that antiquated and malignant concepts of cultural and scientific racism can be disguised in contemporary academic fashions that are warmly received and championed by conservative intellectuals.

### Diagnosis 2

| Nymphomania | | | |
|---|---|---|---|
| Description | Symptoms | Treatment | Oppressive outcomes |
| Women with sexual insatiability, performing lewd advances towards men and the practice of self-pleasure | Too much coitus<br><br>Too much desire<br><br>Too much masturbation | Surgical removal of clitoris and ovaries<br><br>Leeching of the vagina<br><br>Cold baths<br><br>Enforced bed-rest<br><br>Vaginal application of cocaine | Medicalisation of female sexuality<br><br>Used in defence against charges of rape and incest<br><br>Accused of imagining sexual assaults or inciting sexual acts with lewd behaviour<br><br>Exoneration of sexual violence |
| Groneman (2000) | | | Ussher (2013) |

Students are asked to identify various occupations associated with this diagnosis. Sexual intercourse and masturbation are easily identified. However, when prompted to a more critical review and reflection with questions concerning how this diagnosis would have influenced other intimate occupations, such as displays of affection, dating or flirting, students astutely identify the inherent patriarchal and overt misogynistic subjugation of women inherent in this diagnosis.

## Diagnosis 3

| Homosexuality | | | |
|---|---|---|---|
| **Description** | **Symptoms** | **Treatment** | **Oppressive outcomes** |
| Sexual preference for a partner of the same gender<br><br>(Evident throughout history but not always named) | Attraction to members of the same sex<br><br>Engaging in sexual activity with members of the same sex | Chemical castration<br><br>Aversion therapy<br><br>Masturbatory re-conditioning | Internalised and external<br><br>Homophobia<br><br>Violence<br><br>Marginalisation<br><br>Human rights abuses<br><br>Substance abuse<br><br>Reparative therapy |
| *DSM-II* (APA, 1968) | | Smith, Bartlett & King, 2004 | Banks, 2003 |

The controversy and history of this diagnosis is typically well known among the students. However, my choice in using it is multifaceted. There has been a paradigm shift in queer issues in Ireland. Representation of gay people has increased; however, this perceived acceptance can create an illusion of equality, particularly among non-queer people. Students tend to be complacent when presented with this former diagnosis, suggesting it is no longer an issue, that we live in a 'post-gay Ireland'. I share with students my own experiences of systemic, institutional and everyday homophobia in Ireland, such as my fear of personally engaging in public displays of affection with my husband. While I have been fortunate not to experience overt violence, I regularly experience social situations where the underlying threat of violence or being 'othered' is present. Unfortunately, there are plenty of examples of homophobic violence to share with students. Global examples of homophobia are also shared with students, affirming that it is still treated as a mental disorder in parts of the world and that the human rights of gay people, from an occupational perspective, are still under threat. Even in societies where gay people are free to marry, the existence of and debate surrounding 'conversion' or 'reparative therapy' illustrate the intersection between sanist attitudes and homophobia.

**Diagnosis 4**

| Heterosexuality | | | |
|---|---|---|---|
| Description | Symptoms | Treatment | Oppressive outcomes |
| 1901<br>'An abnormal or perverted appetite towards the opposite sex'<br><br>1923<br>'A morbid sexual passion for one of the opposite sex'<br><br>1934<br>'A manifestation of sexual passion for one of the opposite sex; normal sexuality' | None sourced | None sourced | Heteronormativity<br><br>Heterosexism |
| Ambrosino (2017) | | | GLEN & BeLonGTo (2016) |

This diagnosis is deliberately presented last to challenge students on the concept of what is considered 'normal'. Students tend to react in disbelief to this 'diagnosis', having never questioned or contemplated the origin of 'heterosexuality' and its position as a dominant norm of sexual orientation. As such, heterosexuality tends to be immune to critique. It is summarised for students that heterosexuality is not normal, it is just common.

### *Normal and abnormal*

'Normal' and, by association, 'abnormal' are loaded words that have been misused throughout history but are still freely and frequently used in everyday conversations. While there is no universally accepted definition of 'abnormality' (Bergner & Bunford, 2014; Pierre, 2010), most definitions have certain features in common, often referred to as the four Ds: deviance, distress, dysfunction and danger. The aim of this session is for students to acknowledge that behaviour must be viewed in the context in which it occurs, and to consider how the concept of (ab)normality depends on who holds the power to make these judgements and the norms and values of the society in question. Students are encouraged to consider that oppression and abnormality, or diagnostic labelling, are bedfellows, interconnected in a hierarchical ordering that leads us to accept certain 'truths' about occupational beings as normal and abnormal. I challenge students to reframe 'normal' as an illusion based on the perception of reality, not a universal truth.

In terms of mental illness, students are encouraged to reflect that certain disorders are not sufficiently rare to be defined as abnormal, such as phobias or even depression. Students are asked to critically reflect on the effect of the social value or desirability placed on normality – that, for example, both intellectual disabilities and genius-level intellect are rare, but only the former is regarded as abnormal.

## Deviations from social norms

To capture the essence of the lecture's key message, an allegorical story is shared with students. Students are asked to describe and list the characteristics of a carrot. A consensus is agreed and, as expected, students describe a vegetable that grows in the ground. Its leaves are green, the carrot is orange and it is cylindrical in shape but ends in a point. I then share with the students an image of a 'purple carrot'. Some students will know about it already, or will have heard of it, but no one in the class will consider it a 'normal carrot'. I then tell them about the history of the carrot (Stolarczyk & Janick, 2011). Before the 17th century, almost all cultivated carrots were purple. The modern, orange carrot wasn't cultivated until the late 16th century. Dutch farmers took mutant (or abnormal) strains of the purple carrot and gradually developed them into the orange variety that is now widely accepted as a normal, average carrot. The occupation of story-telling is identified and highlighted to students in this scenario, which I use to exemplify the cultural specificity of social norms. I propose to students that social norms can differ between generations, ethnic groups, socio-economic groups and so forth. Too much reliance on understanding 'mental illness' as a deviation can reify 'normal' and result in the oppression of people's occupational rights and negatively impact their psychosocial well-being.

## Occupational injustices

It is only by questioning the foundations of a consensus (common sense) view that 'normal' phenomena are dethroned from their privileged positions. Racism, prejudice, misogyny and homophobia are examined as issues of occupational rights and participation. The concepts of occupational injustices, occupational deprivation, occupational alienation, occupational apartheid and occupational marginalisation are embedded throughout the lecture and students engage with, and reflect upon, these concepts in class. I share examples of my own experiences and provide others to ensure that occupational injustices are named, framed and debated.

## Student feedback

The Student Evaluation of Educational Quality (SEEQ) is a research-based instrument for collecting students' evaluations of university teaching (Coffey & Gibbs, 2010). Reliability of the SEEQ is considered good when based on the responses of 10 to 15+ students, which is ideal for my class sizes of 30 students. Below are some examples of student feedback.

### *Use of personal experiences as strength*

> Loved to hear lecturer's personal experience. Wasn't so interested in mental health or didn't know much about it but now I can really see myself working there.

> Lecturer's use of personal experiences was my favourite feature. Before these lectures I didn't have a great interest in mental health and now my views have completely changed. Lecturer created a relaxed atmosphere and focused on each of our opinions and experiences instead of focusing on marking and exam side.

> Really enjoyed the module – never really saw OT having a concrete role in mental health but my view has changed. Personal experiences used throughout lectures were interesting and illuminating. I've been inspired to question more of my own values and beliefs!

### *Developing critical thinking skills*

> Really enjoyed this module. It was eye-opening. I left each class with new knowledge, concepts and dilemmas to consider. I am beginning to question my moral thinking and how I view mental health 'diagnoses' etc… I was really challenged… which I think will stand me in good stead.

> I feel it's the first time we have really been challenged to think for ourselves and make up our own minds. I've developed an outlook which is not diagnosis driven in mental health. Lecturer was consistently competent, prepared, interested in topic and made me really consider working in this area.

> Every day I went home after class and opened discussions, which lasted for hours, about what I learned in class. I have had heated discussions with people around topics which I am now passionate about and defend to the last. I was afraid of going into a mental health placement and now I can see myself working there when I graduate.

Lecturer was first to make me question my thoughts, made me really think about the topics and encouraged me to discuss topics with peers and at home. Will take what I have learned with me in the future.

## Opportunities and challenges

There has been little resistance, and few challenges, from colleagues to embedding critical perspectives in this occupational science and occupational therapy module. When I first designed the content of the module, there were some concerns from a small number of occupational therapists working in mental health that diagnoses would not be taught explicitly and in sufficient depth. Concerns were raised that students were not being adequately prepared to work in mental health.

In defence of my decision, and with the support of my department, I explained that my teaching focus centres on occupation and the occupational issues experienced by people who have been affected by mental health and social, spiritual and emotional issues. A focus on symptoms and diagnosis reduces a person to a label and encourages a reductionist and prescriptive approach aligned with the medical model of mental illness. Students are learning to be experts in occupation, and to be critical and clinical thinkers with skills that can be used in any setting and in addressing a variety of needs.

A key opportunity integrated into my module is student attendance at the Annual Critical Perspectives Conference on mental health held in UCC. Each year, students are registered for the conference and allotted time to attend the two-day event. Students must attend a minimum of two presentations and complete a reflection on their learning experience. I review these reflections and gather and collate the information to feed back in class. The student reflections enable me to identify any areas that require further exploration or clarification.

Attending this conference provides opportunities for critical self-reflection and the identification of professional development goals. Personally, I find it reassuring to meet people who share my thinking and who are motivated to continue to  promote Mad-positive culture in a professional programme.

## Reflections

Most of my experience as a mental health service user can be understood in a single word: compliant. I was the 'good patient'. I was 17 when I received and embraced my first diagnosis. I accepted the explanation that I was chemically imbalanced and inherently disordered. I swallowed every tablet given to me, I engaged in every group and individual therapy offered to me. I completed every task and assessment asked of me. I obeyed every rule set out for me, whether by society, education, religion or medicine. I did not answer back, and I did not question. I deferred to the knowledge of experts. I was invited to share my 'success' narrative with other patients and was complicit in convincing them to trust my words, fostering their obedience and compliance. As a mental health occupational therapist, I transitioned from the 'good patient' to the 'good worker'. I followed institutional and professional rules and in turn ensured these rules were implemented. I remained silent when conversations about patients supported oppressive power dynamics. I never questioned whether beneficence could be oppressive.

I am no longer the 'good patient' or the 'good OT'. I embrace my identity as a Mad man. I may still experience mental health difficulties, but I am also angry, or Mad, at how I was treated, and continue to be labelled and treated, and also how I acquiesced to and supported dominant practices. Mad studies, critical thinking and feminism are embedded in my life and my teaching. I use my life to teach the next generation of occupational therapy students through sharing my personal experiences; the 'good patient' is now reframed as the Mad occupational therapist. I firmly believe in the power and value of occupation as it relates to a person's identities and health and wellbeing. By writing this chapter, I hope to reach more occupational therapists and other disciplines and find new allies, so we may work together to contribute and participate in these emerging fields.

## References

Ambrosino B (2017). *The Invention of Heterosexuality. [Online.] BBC Future; 16 March.* www.bbc.com/future/story/20170315-the-invention-of-heterosexuality *(accessed 21 August 2019).*

American Psychiatric Association (APA) (1968). *Diagnostic and Statistical Manual of Mental Disorders* (2nd ed) (DSM-II). Washington: APA.

Banks C (2003). *The Cost of Homophobia: literature review on the human impact of homophobia in Canada.* Saskatoon, Canada: Gay and Lesbian Health Services.

Battaglia J (2016). Toward a caring curriculum: can occupational therapy be taught in a caring context? *International journal of Teaching and Learning in Higher Education* 28(2): 265–270.

Bergner RM, Bunford N (2014). *Mental Disorder is a Disability Concept, not a Behavioural One: an empirical investigation.* Athens, OH: Ohio University.

Carlson M, Park D, Kuo A, Clark F (2014). Occupation in relation to the self. *Journal of Occupational Science* 21(2): 117–129.

Cartwright S (1851). Report on the diseases and physical peculiarities of the negro race. *The New Orleans Medical and Surgical Journal* May: 691–715. Cited in: White K (2017). *An Introduction to the Sociology of Health and Illness* (3rd ed). London: Sage (46).

Christiansen C, Clark F, Kielhofner G, Rogers I, Nelson D (1995). Position paper: occupation. *American Journal of Occupational Therapy* 49(10): 1015–1018.

Christiansen C, Townsend E (2014). *Introduction to Occupation: the art of science and living* (2nd ed). London: Pearson.

Clark F, Parham D, Carlson M, Frank G, Jackson J, Pierce D, Wolfe R, Zemke R (1991). Occupational science: academic innovation in the service of occupational therapy's future. *American Journal of Occupational Therapy 45*(4): 300–310.

Coffey M, Gibbs G (2010). The evaluation of the Student Evaluation of Educational Quality questionnaire (SEEQ) in UK Higher Education. *Assessment & Evaluation in Higher Education 26*(1): 89–93.

Doughty HA (2016). *Critical skills and critical pedagogy in an era of 'permanent crisis' in postsecondary education.* Paper presented at the Higher Education in Transformation Symposium, Oshawa, Ontario, Canada.

Durocher E, Gibson BE, Rappolt S (2013). Occupational justice: a conceptual review. *Journal of Occupational Science 21*(4): 418–430.

Fabris E (2011). *Tranquil Prisons: chemical incarceration under community treatment orders.* Toronto: University of Toronto Press.

Foucault M (1988). *Madness and Civilization: a history of insanity in the Age of Reason.* New York, NY: Vintage Books.

Frank G (2012). The 2010 Ruth Zemke lecture in occupational science occupational therapy/ occupational science/ occupational justice: moral commitments and global assemblages. *Journal of Occupational Science 19*(1): 25–35.

Freire P (1970/2005). *Pedagogy of the Oppressed* (30th anniversary ed) (Ramos MB, trans.) New York, NY: Continuum.

Gay Lesbian Equality Network (GLEN), BeLonGTo (2016). *The LGBT Ireland Report.* Dublin: Gay Lesbian Equality Network/BeLonGTo.

Giroux H (1983). *Theory and Resistance in Education.* Westport, CT: Bergin and Garvey Press.

Groneman C (2000). *Nymphomania: a history.* New York, NY: WW Norton.

Herrnstein RJ, Murray CA (1994). *The Bell Curve: intelligence and class structure in American life.* New York, NY: Free Press.

Hocking C (2017). Occupational justice as social justice: the moral claim for inclusion. *Journal of Occupational Science 24*(1): 29–42.

Humphry R (2002). Young children's occupations: explicating the dynamics of developmental processes. *American Journal of Occupational Therapy 56*(2): 171–179.

Kronenberg F, Pollard N (2005). Overcoming occupational apartheid: a preliminary exploration of the political nature of occupational therapy. In: Kronenberg F, Algado SS, Pollard N (eds). *Occupational Therapy Without Borders: learning from the spirit of survivors.* Toronto, ON: Elsevier Churchill Livingstone (pp58–86).

Kronenberg F, Pollard N, Sakellariou D (2011). *Occupational Therapies Without Borders: towards an ecology of occupation-based practices.* London: Churchill Livingstone.

LeBlanc S, Kinsella EA (2016). Toward epistemic justice: a critically reflexive examination of 'sanism' and implications for knowledge generation. *Studies in Social Justice 10*(1): 59–78.

Nelson DL (1988). Occupation: form and performance. *American Journal of Occupational Therapy 42*: 633–641.

Nilsson I, Townsend E (2010). Occupational justice – bridging theory and practice. *Scandinavian Journal of Occupational Therapy 17*(1): 57–63.

Njelesani J, Tang A, Jonsson H, Polatajko H (2014). Articulating an occupational perspective. *Journal of Occupational Science 21*(2): 226–235.

Pierre JM (2010). The borders of mental disorder in psychiatry and the DSM: past, present, and future. *Journal of Psychiatric Practice* 16(6): 375–386.

Pinar W (2005). Queer and queer theory. In: Sears J (ed). *Youth, Education, and Sexualities: an international encyclopedia*. Westport. CT: Greenwood Press (pp673–675).

Pollard N, Sakellariou D (2014). The occupational therapist as a political being. *Cadernos De Terapia Ocupacional Da UFSCar* 22(3): 643–652.

Ragumondo EL (2011). Occupational consciousness. *Journal of Occupational Science* 22(4): 488–501.

Rebeiro Gruhl KL (2009). The politics of practice: strategies to secure our occupational claim and to address occupational injustice. *New Zealand Journal of Occupational Therapy* 56(1): 19–26.

Rimke H (2011). The pathological approach to crime: individually based theories. In: Kramar K (ed). *Criminology: critical Canadian perspectives*. Toronto: Pearson Education Canada (pp78–92).

Rutledge D (1995). Social Darwinism, scientific racism and the metaphysics of race. *The Journal of Negro Education* 64(3): 243–252.

Smith G, Bartlett A, King M (2004). Treatments of homosexuality in Britain since the 1950s – an oral history: the experience of patients. *BMJ* 328: 427.

Spitzer S (2003). With and without words: exploring occupation in relation to young children with autism. *Journal of Occupational Science* 10(2): 67–79.

Stadnyk R, Townsend E, Wilcock A (2010). Occupational justice. In: Christiansen CH, Townsend EA (eds). *Introduction to Occupation: the art and science of living* (2nd ed). Upper Saddle River, NJ: Pearson Education (pp329–358).

Stolarczyk J, Janick J (2011). Carrot: history and iconography. *Chronica Horticulturae* 51(2): 13–18. https://hort.purdue.edu/newcrop/pdfs/ch5102-carrot.pdf (accessed 28 August 2019).

Townsend E, Wilcock AA (2004). Occupational justice and client-centred practice: a dialogue in progress. *Canadian Journal of Occupational Therapy* 71(2): 75.

Ussher J (2013). What makes a woman a nymphomaniac? [Online.] *The Conversation*; 24 December. http://theconversation.com/what-makes-a-woman-a-nymphomaniac-20306 (accessed 8 August 2016).

Webb D (2010). *Thinking about Suicide: contemplating and comprehending the urge to die*. Ross-on-Wye: PCCS Books.

Whiteford G (2000). Occupational deprivation: global challenge in the new millennium. *British Journal of Occupational Therapy* 63(5): 200–204.

Wilcock AA (2006). *An Occupational Perspective of Health* (2nd ed). West Deptford Township, NJ: SLACK.

Wilcock A, Townsend E (2009). Occupational justice. In: Crepeau EB, Cohn ES, Schell BAB (eds). *Willard and Spackman's Occupational Therapy* (11th ed). Philadelphia, PA: Lippincott Williams & Wilkins (pp192–199).

Wood W, Towers L, Malchow J (2000). Environment, time-use, and adaptedness in prosimians: implications for discerning behavior that is occupational in nature. *Journal of Occupational Science* 7(1): 5–18.

Woodward K (2015). *Psychosocial Studies: an introduction*. London: Routledge.

Yerxa EJ, Clark F, Frank G, Jackson J, Parham D, Pierce D et al (1990). An introduction to occupational science: a foundation for occupational therapy in the 21st century. In: Johnson JA, Yerxa EJ (eds). *Occupational Science: the foundation for new models of practice*. New York, NY: The Haworth Press (pp2–17).

Zemke R (2016). Extending occupational science education. *Journal of Occupational Science*. 23(4): 510–513.

# Chapter 4

# Critical mental health nursing education

## Jonathan Gadsby

In 1999 I was one of a small cohort of mental health nursing students at the University of the West of England to take Lucy Johnstone's third-year psychology module. Over several sessions, Lucy taught us why psychiatry is not good science, undermining notions of diagnosis and showing how correlation and causation are grossly misused. She explored alternative perspectives about 'treatments' (everything was now in inverted commas) and described how mental health services could compound the trauma that so many people experience by using approaches that deny their experiences and invalidate their feelings. She introduced us to the Hearing Voices Network (Longden, Corstens & Dillon, 2013). My subsequent experience and further study have confirmed everything she told us back then. Things haven't much changed. I am still recommending her books. She set me on a path that has totally changed my career.

Fifteen years later, by then a PhD student, I was asked to teach a class of third-year mental health nursing students 'about anti-psychiatry, and make sure there is lots on what they can do about it'. I was initially allowed two hours, but now have five. I felt I had to teach some of the same but also some different material. The continued relevance of everything Lucy taught us required explanation after so much time. The science is crucially important but I had seen enough to know that you can let the air out of psychiatry's tyres and it still drives to work every morning.[1] Over the years I have been

---

1. From this distance I do not remember if Lucy confined herself to scientific critique only; it was what 'sank in' and stayed foremost in my mind over the next few years.

teaching critical ideas about mental health, I have come to realise that, without more philosophy, students just wonder if the root problem with mental health services is stupidity – a view that can breed arrogance, rather than understanding. What they need, and I believe it is urgent to share with them, is that this version of the bio-psycho-social, and its accompanying hopes, has existed for a long time and has not led in the direction desired by its original author (Engel, 1977; 1997). In fact, it seems to have witnessed (facilitated?) an against-the-odds increase of indefensibly one-sided views and practices.

Another reason for my desire to do more than explore the poor science of psychiatry is that I had begun to see that, while I had fought against being used to further unscientific practices, I was nevertheless being used for another purpose. I have described this realisation elsewhere (Gadsby, 2015; Bull, Gadsby & Williams, 2018); essentially, I now feel my motivation to see a new kind of mental health nursing was channeled into being the vanguard of a neoliberal 'recovery' model that, in the words of Harper and Speed (2012), is 'founded on a model of identity politics which displaces and marginalises the need for social, political and economic redistribution to address many of the underlying causes of emotional distress'. Had I understood a little more about the relationship between political ideology and health, I feel I would have been less naïve. Less medical is not necessarily more neutral. However, while I feel confident that the sequence of learning I am going to describe is unusual in mental health nursing education, it is not right to call the ideas new (see Coles, Diamond & Keenan, 2013; Harper, 2013; Moncrieff, 2010).

## Part one: three steps to critical mental health nursing

I want to take students through three main steps. Listing them separately hides two important factors. The first is that students have guided this way of structuring my teaching, through their questions and difficulties – something that I will return to below. The second is that the three steps can't really be separated out so distinctly. The steps comprise learning about:

1. Ideologies of mental health
2. Bad science of mental health
3. Re-politicising de-politicised mental health.

### 1. Ideologies of mental health

So, first I introduce thoughts about the ideological nature of knowledges within mental health services. This is not where students expect to start, yet I have found it helps for (I suspect) two reasons. The first is that it fits with their experience. They have all seen, at least sometimes, how medical approaches to distress seem to help some people (perhaps within the narrow and often self-serving terms of reference of which they have so far been aware). They have also found (when they think about it) that psychological explanations frequently vie with medical ones, rather than complementing them. They have experienced that certain colleagues are able to steer the team's understanding from more straightforward illness explanations towards more psychological ones (or vice versa) by emphasising particular details or invoking certain narratives, sometimes just with a couple of sentences. Perhaps some have already noticed that they themselves can steer a team's understanding in this way. Yet, although you might think that this just illustrates that working in bio-psycho-social ways is possible, what it really shows is that a person, be they professional or service user, can be drawn in (my favoured term for this is 'recruited', taken from the work of Michael White) to one ideology or another, via different language or differently emphasised details (White, 1995; White & Epston, 1990).

The resulting approach will call upon its own evidence, select details to be salient, and imply a matching solution. As far as most nurses are concerned, both psychiatry and psychology are 'evidence-based' (they do not generally seem to know much about sociology), and so with this step I am really just giving them a name for something they already experience: *incommensurability* of evidences – that useful word I first read in Thomas Kuhn's famous work (Kuhn, 1970) – and the role of certain uses of language or certain stories in connecting to them. I draw their attention to the way that 'evidences' have now become plural.

Another reason that I believe this to be a helpful start is that it sets up what will be an important understanding later – that critical thinking about mental health is not a separate school of thought, as the 'anti-psychiatrists' were characterised as being (Moncrieff & Middleton, 2019). I feel this point often needs to be underlined; I teach them 'critical mental health', but there seems to be a pressure to slip back to calling it 'critical psychiatry'. I want to show students that there is no profession in the field of mental health that can escape these patterns of ideology. I draw their attention to the fact that what I am exploring with them is the kind of 'critical' for which every university essay awards marks, across many faculties, not just connected to the current module and specific to mental health. If I had the time, I would show them that the very same schools of thought – Marxism, post-structuralism, feminism, post-colonialism, neocolonialism etc – drive the critique in those other departments too, and the philosophy-of-science questions raised are not at all special to psychiatry (although mental health is a particularly fascinating arena for them).

## 2. Bad science of mental health

The second step is to show that the science behind common practices and beliefs in mental health services is highly contested. I call this section (taking inspiration from Ben Goldacre (2008)) 'Bad Science of Mental Health'. I will not provide much detail for this section as this is the most readily available critique; most of it could be gleaned from Moncrieff (2009), Johnstone (2014) and Read and colleagues (2004).

I introduce a small selection of serious problems with biomedical psychiatry, including issues of reductionism and anti-reductionism. Here we talk about genes and I tend to draw on the seminal work of Stewart and Cohen (1994), along with others such as Thomas and Longden (2013), who provide a succinct explanation of how genes and trauma can be viewed together in a non-reductive way. Without going into a lot of detail and using a lot of technical phrases, I hope to give students the general understanding that it is no longer considered safe to assume that 'emergent' properties and their attendant sciences may be better explained by a more 'fundamental' science. By this I aim to unsettle their received sense that biology can adequately explain systems of human meaning and interactions, without in any way suggesting that biology is irrelevant. This enables the class to consider Joanna Moncrieff's views (2009, and elsewhere) about pharmaceuticals. I add to this discussion the controversy surrounding the rejection of the phrase 'chemical imbalance' by the American Psychiatric Association (eg. Pies, 2011).

Next is an exploration of the *Diagnostic and Statistical Manual of Mental Disorders (DSM)* (American Psychiatric Association, 2013) and issues of reliability and validity. After this section, I hope students will recognise that notions of diagnosis are fraught with difficulty, and I generally draw on Burstow's analysis that psychiatry uses reliability *as* validity (Burstow, 2015). I explain to them that the US National Institute for Mental Health, a mainstream institution by any reckoning, has rejected the latest edition of the *DSM (DSM-5)* (Cromby, 2018). Finally, I open up some questions about drug company influence on psychiatry, especially drawing on the work of Cochrane Institute specialist, Peter Gøtszche (2013). (The Cochrane Institute is an organisation devoted to scrutinising the quality of published research. When the Cochrane uses strong language (the phrase used by Gøtszche is 'organised crime'), then everyone should take note.)

By this stage I hope that an irreversible learning may have taken place. Students' beliefs about mental health services could not remain unaltered by the end of this session; it necessitates radical change. We have a striking improvement on hegemony; much more is required than the claim that it is 'evidenced', since many viewpoints can be evidenced. That being the case, then any *dominance* attracts attention and requires justification. This is especially true if you discover that dominant views are maintaining their prominence not by having the best evidence but by aggressively making other views less visible – 'decontesting' themselves (Freeden, 1994; 2005) – and I believe that is precisely what the students see clearly before them in the practice of biomedical psychiatry. This understanding of ethical deliberation of narratives I mostly take from Arthur Frank (2012);[2] students are not only connected with the question 'What is true?' but now also with questions such as 'Why does this truth get heard the most?' Without realising it, they have begun to see the inter-permeation of values and facts. As a result, questions about what constitutes quality have shifted to questions about moral philosophy, as well as evidence.

In addition, in a service where the law is used to force 'treatment' on people under the belief that it is a 'last resort', in the person's 'best interests', to undermine the supporting evidence for diagnosis and treatment (and to demonstrate the existence of alternatives) is to make it hard to imagine the moment at which mental health law could be honestly applied – which is precisely one of the arguments made by a recent UN report I share with the students (Pūras, 2017). Indeed, a focus on the Mental Health Act as 'legalised discrimination' is important in critiques of psychiatry (Sidley, 2015). Troublesome knowledge indeed!

I need here to convey something of the pain that students experience, which usually begins in earnest at this juncture. Some students seem crushed, even nauseated. I ask if there are any questions and, not infrequently, look out at a sea of shocked faces.

### 3. Re-politicising de-politicised mental health

The third step is to show that political perspectives are needed to understand mental health services. A problem I encounter when teaching students this material is that they very often lack the basic political language they need to begin to think about this. Occasionally, nurses insist they do not need to know anything about politics, and some have even become surly, although less often now that I present this section last. I understand this inertia as part of the way in which medical narratives work to create notions of health that are falsely depoliticised (Metzl & Kirkland, 2010). This reluctance is worse if I try to approach the political content first, rather than last, which I have done.

---

2. Indeed, I wonder if it is likely that the dominant views within a contested field will be among the most poorly evidenced, because dominance is so often the result of rhetoric and rhetoric is so seldom the basis of good science.

In some ways I feel it is a companion to my first section, but it seems that, without first seriously undermining the status quo (step 2), students may be less willing to think politically. Educationalist Stephen Brookfield notes that critical examination of a paradigmatic assumption only occurs with resistance and 'a considerable amount of contrary evidence' (Brookfield, 2017: 6).

However, mostly students are not resistant. Many make the leap from bio-psycho-social to a map of political views like a light being switched on. There are three diagrams I use repeatedly to help me teach this section and they seem to hold a lot of explanatory power for students. The first I drew myself. It falls into the category of material that sometimes seems profound and sometimes just obvious. We begin with a blank whiteboard and I draw a horizontal line across the middle. On the left side I write 'Fully internal' and on the right, 'Fully external'. I call this a 'map of experience' and say that the words represent where distress (or happiness) is located. Some students find it easier to think of this as where the cause of distress lies.

We start to fill in the kinds of terms, professions and interventions one associates with each position. Working across the board, we talk about genes, neurons, hormones, chemicals, thoughts, emotions, behaviour, meanings, relationships, abuse, social networks, geography, economics, demographics and oppressions. I then point out that what we have is nothing more and nothing less than the word 'bio-psycho-social' laid out in a kind of map. Key realisations to be had from this map at this stage are that a) what we think of as 'mainstream' mental health services are very firmly located towards one side of the map, sometimes strikingly close to the extreme edge and b) something interesting happens at the centre, a place in which views are divided by whether distress is derived from 'inside outwards' (everything to the left of the diagram) or 'outside inwards' (everything to the right).

The second diagram is David McCandless' 'Left and Right' (2012).[3] It is diagram that describes typical political and social views of left- or right-wing politics. It suggests general positions towards authority and a sense of what being a successful and moral adult is for left- or right-wing thinkers. This is a fascinating diagram and we spend some time exploring it. Quite quickly, someone will notice that, really, the left of my map ('internal') is rather like the right of McCandless' diagram, and my right ('external') contains a lot of similarities to the left of his. We allow this to sink in. I tell them that this suggestion contains some very interesting questions. Are mental health services, and especially psychiatry, connected to right-wing politics in some way? I ask

---

3. You can find this online at https://informationisbeautiful.net/visualizations/left-vs-right-world (accessed 26 August 2019).

them to think about what they know of the dominant politics in the UK and to continue to speculate: if concepts of mental health reflect or in some way map onto political ideologies, what kinds of influence might we expect to see between mental health services and the wider political landscape? I always wish we had more time here.

The famous trouble with any map is that *it is not the territory*, and McCandless' brilliant depiction of left and right is useful but ultimately limited, as is a division of political views into left and right. For a better understanding of political ideologies and mental health, arguably students need the improvement brought about by a third diagram, the 'Political Compass'.[4] This confines left and right to their economic features only and places them as an *x* axis, intersecting with an authoritarian-libertarian *y* axis. In some ways, this *y* axis is even more important when thinking about mental health services.

However, no matter how I have used this improved map with students, I have run into significant problems. I have tried asking them to imagine what 'mental health looks like' from each quadrant, but typically this falls rather flat. Currently, I feel that I simply do not have time in my sessions to try to open up all of the promised further understandings that could arise from the Political Compass. Sometimes I try to tell the story of the word 'recovery' over the last 20 years (Watts, 2016), showing that its shift from peer-to-peer empowerment (left-libertarian?) to the recovery model of services (left/centre-authoritarian?) and now through to privatised 'Recovery Colleges', with a concurrent change in the power of the Jobcentre and the 'Work Capability Assessment' (right-authoritarian). Others have noted Peter Sedgwick's prediction that, if the Left were successful in showing the social determinants of 'mental illness', the Right would use that to remove or deny services (Sedgwick, 2015; McKeown & White, 2015).

Yet, with or without the Political Compass, I think it is enough for students to have noticed that these maps begin to explore and answer the question posed by our first understanding about the role of ideologies in mental health: *Why does this truth get heard the most?* The thought that they are being encultured to work in a service that almost inevitably serves as a conduit to political views is, once again, new and distressing to many students, especially those who tend towards left-libertarianism.

### Caring in a political landscape

This is an important moment for the class. Students are vulnerable and I could try to persuade them that psychiatry is bad *because* it is right wing or *because*

---

4. See www.politicalcompass.org/crowdchart2 (accessed 23 January 2018).

it is authoritarian. A lazy critique of mental health services is that they are *de facto* wrong because they represent views that value order as a prime good in society. Order always comes with a heavy price: diversity becomes problematic. However, it is simply not the case that this means less or no order is better. My aim is not to undermine authoritarianism by calling it authoritarianism but by showing that, once mental health services are understood to be interlocked with political ideologies, everything changes and the need for debate is now constant, urgent and the only acceptable form of practice, just as it should be in any political arena. Suddenly we become aware that history is full of examples of that which should in any case be obvious: it suits those in authority to narrow the band of accepted diversity in society, and psychiatry is one of several key tools at their disposal to achieve this. Like all such tools, it takes difference and describes it, often with quasi-scientific rhetoric, as *being of nature* (Harari, 2014). Given this, there is an extraordinary and ongoing burden of proof on psychiatry to show that their own stated Platonic aim of 'carving nature at the joints' is genuine apolitical science; yet by now students have already seen that it is very unlikely to succeed in this.

I lead students to notice that, rather than simply being 'an evidenced-based profession', they are arguably on a 'bandwagon' and that other bandwagons are available and under-represented. Critical thinking is not a bandwagon, however, which is why a) I am so keen to stress that we are not 'doing anti-psychiatry' and b) I explicitly warn them that *all* ideologies are dangerous (Frank, 2012) – very much a Foucauldian perspective – because they work by the selective exclusion of detail. This is something I feel entitled to say as someone who has been susceptible to several. I therefore define critical mental health as the study of the creation, interactions and maintenance of bandwagons within mental health. If critical mental health writing in the UK currently appears to contain a predominance of left-wing or libertarian content, it is because of the need to provide a *balancing* position. Right now, a critical stance often rightly begins with questions about neoliberalism, but if pushed too far with Marx – perhaps via the genius of David Smail (2001) – I will start to raise arguments in favour of self-discipline and autonomy, and in doing so I will be being consistent, not duplicitous. I am learning that only this kind of criticality is defensible as an educator. Just as a critical understanding of ideologies leads one to become more fully appreciative of the need for democratic political processes, so a properly re-politicised understanding of mental health leads one to see the need for democratic mental health practices. What I mean by this is most close to what many refer to as 'dialogical' practice (Grant, 2015; Frank, 2012), but I hope that the word 'democratic' is harder-hitting; one could easily speak of *dialogue* between service users, carers and various professions and not imply a massive alteration in the balance of power between these groups. However, speak of democracy and I understand that rights must be upheld and hierarchies must convincingly justify themselves or be toppled.

The final part of my time with students is taken up with introducing them to 12 (regularly updated) texts I pick to demonstrate some of the wealth of writing about mental health from critical perspectives. These include the work of Joanna Moncrieff, Anne Cooke, Recovery in The Bin, the Hearing Voices Network, Psychologists for Social Change, Lucy Johnstone, the British Psychological Society's Division of Clinical Psychology, Richard Bentall, Gary Sidley, Stephen Coles, the Critical Psychiatry Network, Angela Sweeney and others. Students discuss these in small groups, all writing notes on the same online 'Padlet', which they can access after the lesson. After this, we spend a ludicrously tokenistic few minutes asking what they might like to do about all they have learned.

## Part two: emotions

When I began teaching as a PhD student, I admit that I was aiming for the 'killer lecture'. Part of me wanted to leave in tatters the complacent, uncritical and culturally-received nursing knowledge already growing within these students. Thankfully, I quickly saw that this was punitive and hypocritical. It was my background in nursing that helped: I knew that this kind of adversarial positioning was useless for creating change conversations within therapeutic relationships, so why would it be different in the classroom? I then moved into another stage with my teaching. I began to redesign the class so that students spent a little more time exploring the ideas for themselves and articulating their responses. It was only a year later, after being employed by the university as a teacher, that I studied pedagogical theories that support this change (Pratt, 1993; Holton, Swanson & Naquin, 2001), and was struck by how many parallels there were between therapeutic values and educational ones. I started to treat my students a little more respectfully.

As class participation increased, I began to experience student emotions more directly. There were some who found that any perspectives that challenged the medicalisation of distress challenged ideas that they needed themselves, personally, in order to present themselves to the world and get the support that they needed. Whether it was a 'fight against depression', 'generalised anxiety syndrome' or something else, this was part of a story that had brought the student to the class and enabled them to *hold their own* (Frank, 2012) in some way. In one memorable class, two students became so enraged that they could barely speak and, when they did, they started to accuse me of saying that all 'mental illness' was 'just socially constructed' (a phrase I would not dream of using because it clings to the other extreme, opposite biomedical psychiatry, of a false dichotomy). Both were heavily recruited into an 'illness like any other' narrative. I was left with a very uncomfortable feeling that two people I would have wanted to take care of in the classroom really suffered (yet all I had done was to explain that alternative, viable perspectives are available).

There are also students who have had to fight to get a child diagnosed in order to have their difficulties recognised and adequately supported. It seems to me that bound up with the parent who does this are all the awful choices (or lack of them), questions about responsibility, relationships with authorities and their categories, questions about communities (often viewed through the lens of classrooms), difference versus deviance, cavalier prescribing, high emotions and hard calculations that make up the landscape of critical mental health, and, unsurprisingly, such a parent can arrive at a class ready to snap. As a parent of three children myself, my heart goes out to them (and their children).

I therefore began to be very careful when introducing the sessions. I wanted students to know that I was an experienced nurse and not just a critical academic. This seemed to help them see that I was part of their struggle, rather than just heaping up problems, thereby further reducing the 'adversarial problem'. I also began to make some more general suggestions about education, all aiming to illustrate that education is much more than learning how to do a job and involves exploring new and troubling perspectives.

However, I can see now that emotions were something I still hoped to avoid in the classroom and that these strategies were mostly designed to 'head them off'. In this is irony; one of the effects of being exposed to survivor knowledges is to see that mental health services, far from being the place in which strong emotions receive the expert help a lay person might expect, are often the places in which emotions are most suppressed. Yet here I was, setting up a classroom atmosphere in which my main approach to emotions seemed avoidant, containing or deflecting. Students, some of whom now began to talk with me seriously outside of class about their emotional struggles, also noticed that, in effect, the university was a conduit of the conceptual confusion of services, passing it on to them without giving them what they needed to process or overcome it. This also felt like another mirroring of ways in which we mental health professionals can treat users of our services, as did the excuse that the size of class made anything else impossible.

I think the most enlightening description of the kind of difficulties students have is by Alec Grant (2018). He improves on Leinhardt's view of the problem of a gap between university knowledge and professional knowledge (cited in Biggs & Tang, 2011), and finds that all student nurses in the UK are under the influence of at least three curricula. First, there are the series of standard modules found at universities to meet the bureaucratic requirements of the Nursing and Midwifery Council (NMC, 2018), characterised as 'competencies'. This is in conflict with what Grant (2018: 34) describes as the 'alternative/practice-based curriculum', encapsulated by 'the way things are done around here/forget all that shit they teach you in uni'. However, there is also the third 'university' curriculum. This is the curriculum in large part driven by our marking scheme: students are required to think critically to pass, and more critically to get higher marks. Many would argue it is this third curriculum that changes mental health nursing courses into education, rather than mere training.

Dainius Pūras, the UN special rapporteur for health, argues that mental health professionals have a duty to prevent all forced treatment (Pūras, 2017). Yet the job descriptions of nurses and their daily reality is that they must collaborate and even instigate it. This intense conflict of perspectives is exhausting. We nurses need the Hearing Voices Network's approach to voices for our emotions: *'Don't shoot the messenger'*. I have found a new personal catchphrase, *'Critical thinking is emotional labour'*, in order to make it clear that it is not merely an intellectual exercise and that emotions are not getting in the way of the work, *they are the work*. My next step towards meeting the emotions of students in a positive way was to start my set of sessions by showing them that they already have turmoil before they meet me. I now ask them to predict the kinds of things we might explore together. They are quick to suggest over-prescribing, doubts about the efficacy of medication, questions about the corrupting role of pharmaceutical industries, doubts about diagnostic classifications, the Rosenhan Experiment (Rosenhan, 1973), and even the possibility that there is 'no such thing as mental illness'. Sometimes they say something about labelling theory (referring to the work of Thomas Scheff (1990)). I ask them how they are coping with this degree of uncertainty just a few months before qualifying. This approach allows me to increase the sense that I am coming to help them meet head-on and gain clarity over a situation that is already painful and confusing, rather than arriving towards the end of an otherwise peaceful training to undermine certainties and create distress.

I am satisfied that this more accurately reflects reality, and as a strategy it is more like White and Epston's (1990) 'externalizing the problem narrative' – we get it out onto the whiteboard and look at it together, separate from us. I think this begins to voice some of the very complicated feelings that students have about their experiences. For example, I think that many find that the violence and coercion they witnessed on arrival on their first acute ward placement is very hard to process and the ways in which it alters their imagined relationships are a series of dashed hopes. As it becomes clear to them just how few service users would choose to meet them if they were not under compulsion, student nurses begin to hope that, despite it all, they will be different and that somehow this violence can be shown to be necessary, no matter how tragic. These hopes drive connections to other stories (for example, 'best interests', 'no alternative', 'tragedy of the mental illness lottery' and 'working to change the system from within') that this exercise indicates are not working.

Then comes a new phase: students begin to meet with me outside of lessons, communicating that their feelings of bewilderment about poor science and concern about coercion has started to feel very personal. Some express a fear that they are going to be seriously hurt by working as a mental health nurse, either by finding that they must conform to actions they may now find very questionable, or by the systems that exist to ensure that refusal will be viewed as professional negligence. They fear for their integrity and they fear for their registration. They see before them the task of taking the contested field into their own bodies and suffering. I believe that suffering is common to many nurses.

## Part three: what have I learned? Where do we go next? What are the positive results of this learning for students?

I have come to see that everything I have done to date, including all of the critical material and recognition of the emotional labour, is merely a first step. Once again, I think that Alec Grant's 'three curricula' can help me think about the current situation more clearly. We have arrived at a moment in mental health in which these three curricula are in terrible and acute conflict. This has become so serious that I think it is sometimes impossible to mark student essays. The implications driven from one curriculum can lead to failing another. For example, following through the implications of the UN report (Pūras, 2017), which, by 'critical curriculum' standards, is great scholarship, could lead to being sanctioned by the 'alternative service curriculum' and struck off the NMC register, the guiding light of the 'bureaucratic curriculum'. Our nursing lives are full of impossibilities. This is how the ideological powers at play meet within the body of the nurse.

In the most immediate future, I believe there is a very simple answer. Without needing to resort to arguments for pragmatism and the needs of stakeholders and even justifying my teaching on positive student outcomes, there is a basic fact: *mental health nursing is taught in universities*; it is a degree course, and all university marking schemes make critical thinking the basis on which marks are awarded. As I have already said, none of what I teach is extra to a standard set of critical perspectives you would find in many faculties (I expect most would be pretty scandalised by my current omission of explicitly feminist, post-colonial or neocolonial critiques of mental health). Without the following changes I do not think that we can claim to be worthy of university education:

1. decolonisation of language
2. a new engagement with the emotional experiences of critical mental health nursing, not merely as 'support' but as education
3. a new commitment to dialogue (leading to democratic ideals), but not to uncritical acceptance of all ideas
4. a focus on skills that the current de-politicised ideologies have made less visible and less relevant.

Further explanation below is necessarily introductory.

## *1. Decolonisation of language*

For me, this idea is the least controversial. If nurses want to think critically, be ethical and score marks in university essays, they cannot unreflectively use language that evokes hidden ideologies and poor science and shuts down alternative explanations, especially in ways that can be described as self-serving. We must strive for a very careful and inclusive language, decolonising it of reductionist medical overtones, and especially remove pathologising[5] and 'totalising' terms. Thankfully, this is remarkably easy and, far from making nurses seem contrary and divisive, makes them appear precise and practical. The instant you remove illness-speak, you understand what a poor replacement it was for genuine description of experience – experience that is very often highly explanatory. You also gain new opportunities to notice that pathologisation itself is more often a social than a natural fact.

This one change alone would utterly transform our course and it would take just one staff meeting to begin the process. My experience is that, although language may be changed quickly, the processes of decolonisation

---

5. Categories of illness all fail validity and reliability tests (Burstow, 2015). However, they also internalise problems in ways that some psychological and most sociological perspectives show to be highly problematic (Smail, 2001). Survivor groups also show us what is to be gained by welcoming and working with experiences (such as hearing voices) using non-pathologising frameworks (Corstens, Escher & Romme, 2008; Corstens et al, 2014). We *can* talk about distress and suffering, even utter torment, without assuming individual pathology; it is *less* controversial to do so. Any claim for the pragmatic functions of illness language can be countered with equally pragmatic reasons for non-pathologising (Cromby, Harper & Reavey, 2013).

it helps to drive are hard, ongoing work and will certainly expose different staff members' individual understandings of the word 'critical'. What could be better? A university should be at the forefront of this.

### 2. Engagement with emotions

A senior member of a local mental health trust has described my efforts as 'very sad' and told me that I would create cohorts of angry nurses. Others fear that teaching like this is 'not pragmatic'. A consultant nurse scoffed at the name 'Foucault', as if no one could be so naïve as to read him. As I suggest above, I do not see critique as optional if we want to have university degrees, and in any case, many students have grave concerns before they come into my class and some are already traumatised by the coercive elements of mental health services (Gadsby, 2018). If we want nurses to learn critical perspectives, if the kinds of emotions I witness are the result of this learning, and if practising mental health nurses find this kind of education threatening, then we have to help student nurses understand the strong emotions they feel and use them as both instruction and motivation. We have to help them to make plans that include genuinely good, practical, skills-based, positive nursing, if we want them to survive long enough to get into positions of influence.

My department has been involved in setting up a programme of group clinical supervision for students; existing personal tutor relationships remain but additional groups are now run for each set of personal tutees. A few other universities have similar schemes, but my impression is that they tend to be focused only on issues to do with clinical placements. The contested nature of mental health requires this kind of small group work to explore emotions arising from the course, too – the gaps between the curricula. This presupposes that personal tutors are familiar with a depth of critique of mental health and have themselves been engaged in the emotions the students are experiencing. The critical material described in this chapter should also come earlier in the course, instead of its current position in the third year, especially if we have hopes for the implementation of the language-change I suggest above. I believe there are some students who are gaining in criticality *and* confidence about their future as a result of this approach. One further development is that I notice more students drawing on critical perspectives in the research module assignment that runs concurrently with the module in which I teach this material, pushing up the marks.

### 3. Commitment to dialogue

As stated above, it is clear to me that, if we need complex processes of representation and rights in order to live fairly and productively as a country –

processes we call 'democracy', driven from the understanding that ideologies are legitimately diverse (Morgan et al, 2015) – then we need at least the same for the field of mental health. Democratic mental health recognises the legitimate diversity of ideologies that permeate the evidences we draw upon, but it also provides the platform and debate that is required if we are to notice the rhetorical work of those ideologies. This is alien to mental health professionals. A class of psychiatrists I taught recently thought that 'democratic' simply meant 'majority rule'.

### 4. New skills

In many ways, the above suggestions *are* the new skills. Working through the implications of the loss of hegemony that a democratic critical outlook requires and noticing the effects of ideological power is hard work and takes time. However, such changed perspectives should also lead to an interest in several new/neglected skill sets. One of the most important might be 'trauma-informed approaches' (Sweeney et al, 2016; 2018) and work that could be described as 'narrative competence', which touches too on the work of the Hearing Voices Network (Corstens, Escher & Romme, 2008; Corstens et al, 2014).

I hope that mental health professionals will see the Power Threat Meaning Framework, launched in 2018 (Johnstone & Boyle), as a watershed in our history. Undoubtedly, acceptance of this framework will imply a) a requirement for a more political 'public health' understanding of distress and b) greater acknowledgement that biologically observable 'symptoms' and psychological phenomena are embedded in personal and cultural narratives. With this new framework, nurses who continue to view low mood simply as contingent upon a causal biological illness, for example, will be seen to be reductive and even colluding with personal and societal abuse. In short, acceptance of this framework will drive a wedge between mental health nurses and psychiatric frameworks, bringing into sharp focus the allegiance problems we already have. Yet the new framework does not imply that the current divisions between professions are supportable, and the vast paradigmatic distance between this scholarly framework and mental health nursing in 2018 only underlines the gap between curricula already described.

## Conclusion

I have worked to produce a learning sequence that fits with the critical perspectives that should characterise every university degree. Brookfield (2017: 9) makes it clear that education and uncovering hegemony are the same project. I do not have to balance critique with 'pragmatism' or keep silent if I cannot provide a coherent vision for the future. The process has revealed the ways in which the intense conceptual conflict of the field becomes personally traumatic for student nurses, revealing the vast gaps currently existing between conflicting curricula and the educational aspirations and practices of mental health nurses.

Students who attend my classes learn that, without engagement with an analysis of ideological (and other forms of) power, little about contemporary mental health nursing practice makes sense. I hope they are challenged to recognise the falsehoods behind commonly used phrases such as 'evidence-based practice', and prefer to work towards a democratic practice that prizes rigorously explored evidences. In this, I hope they will be drawn to new frameworks such as the Power Threat Meaning Framework.

## References

American Psychiatric Association (2013). *Diagnostic and Statistical Manual of Mental Disorders* (5th ed). Washington, DC: American Psychiatric Association.

Biggs J, Tang C (2011). *Teaching for Quality Learning at University* (4th ed). Maidenhead: Open University Press.

Brookfield SD (2017). *Becoming a Critically Reflective Teacher* (2nd ed). San Francisco, CA: Jossey Bass.

Bull P, Gadsby J, Williams S (2018). *Critical Mental Health Nursing: observations from the inside.* Monmouth: PCCS Books.

Burstow B (2015). *Psychiatry and the Business of Madness: an ethical and epistemological accounting.* New York, NY: Palgrave Macmillan.

Coles S, Diamond B, Keenan S (eds) (2013). *Madness Contested: power and practice.* Ross-on-Wye: PCCS Books.

Corstens D, Escher S, Romme M (2008). Accepting and working with voices: the Maastricht approach. In: Moskowitz A, Schäfer I, Dorahy MJ (eds). *Psychosis, Trauma and Dissociation: emerging perspectives on severe psychopathology.* Chichester: Wiley-Blackwell (pp319–332).

Corstens D, Longden E, McCarthy-Jones S, Waddingham R, Thomas N (2014). Emerging perspectives from the Hearing Voices Movement: implications for research and practice. *Schizophrenia Bulletin* 40(4): S285–S294.

Cromby J (2018). An alternative to psychiatric diagnosis? An innovative framework provides new ways of understanding mental health. [Online.] *Psychology Today*; 30 January. www.psychologytoday.com/blog/the-bodies-we-re-in/201801/alternative-psychiatric-diagnosis (accessed 14 August 2019).

Cromby J, Harper DD, Reavey DP (2013). *Psychology, Mental Health and Distress.* Basingstoke: Palgrave Macmillan.

Engel GL (1997). From biomedical to biopsychosocial. *Psychotherapy and Psychosomatics* 66: 57–62.

Engel GL (1977). The need for a new medical model: a challenge for biomedicine. *Science* *196*(4286): 129–136. https://doi.org/10.1126/science.847460 (accessed 14 August 2019).

Frank AW (2012). *Letting Stories Breathe: a socio-narratology*. Chicago, Ill: University of Chicago Press.

Freeden M (2005). What should the 'political' in political theory explore? *Journal of Political Philosophy 13*(2): 113–134.

Freeden M (1994). Political concepts and ideological morphology. *Journal of Political Philosophy 2*(2): 140–164.

Gadsby J (2018). Nursing violence, nursing violence. In: Gadsby J, Williams S, Bull P (eds). *Critical Mental Health Nursing: observations from the inside*. Monmouth: PCCS Books.

Gadsby J (2015). The Recovery Star meets the UnRecovery Star. [Online.] *Critical Mental Health Nurses' Network*. https://criticalmhnursing.org/2015/10/19/the-recovery-star-meets-the-unrecovery-star/ (accessed 14 August 2019).

Goldacre B (2008). *Bad Science*. London: Fourth Estate.

Gøtzsche P (2013). *Deadly Medicines and Organised Crime: how Big Pharma has corrupted healthcare*. Boca Raton, FL: CRC Press.

Grant A (2018). Moving around the hyphens: a critical meta-autoethnographic performance. In: Bull P, Gadsby J, Williams S (eds). *Critical Mental Health Nursing: observations from the Inside*. Monmouth: PCCS Books.

Grant A (2015). Demedicalising misery: welcoming the human paradigm in mental health nurse education. *Nurse Education Today 35*(9): e50–e53. https://doi.org/10.1016/j.nedt.2015.05.022 (accessed 16 August 2019).

Harari YN (2014). *Sapiens: a brief history of humankind*. London: Harvill Secker.

Harper DJ (2013). On the persistence of psychiatric diagnosis: moving beyond a zombie classification system. *Feminism & Psychology 23*(1): 78–85. https://doi.org/10.1177/0959353512467970 (accessed 16 August 2019).

Harper D, Speed E (2012). Uncovering recovery: the resistible rise of recovery and resilience. *Studies in Social Justice 6*(1): 9–25.

Holton EF, Swanson RA, Naquin SS (2001). Andragogy in practice: clarifying the andragogical model of adult learning. *Performance Improvement Quarterly 14*(1): 118–143. https://doi.org/10.1111/j.1937-8327.2001.tb00204.x (accessed 16 August 2019).

Johnstone L (2014). *A Straight Talking Introduction to Psychiatric Diagnosis*. Ross-on-Wye: PCCS Books.

Johnstone L, Boyle M, with Cromby J, Dillon J, Harper D, Kinderman P, Longden E, Pilgrim D, Read J (2018). *The Power Threat Meaning Framework: towards the identification of patterns in emotional distress, unusual experiences and troubled or troubling behaviour, as an alternative to functional psychiatric diagnosis*. Leicester: British Psychological Society.

Kuhn TS (1970). *The Structure of Scientific Revolutions* (2nd ed). Chicago, IL: University of Chicago Press.

Longden E, Corstens D, Dillon J (2013). Recovery, discovery and revolution: the work of Intervoice and the Hearing Voices Movement. In: Coles S, Keenan S, Diamond B (eds). *Madness Contested: power and practice*. Ross-on-Wye: PCCS Books (pp161–180).

McCandless D (2012). *Information is Beautiful*. (New ed). London: Collins.

McKeown M, White J (2015). The future of mental health nursing: are we barking up the wrong tree? *Journal of Psychiatric & Mental Health Nursing 22*(9): 724–730. https://doi.org/10.1111/jpm.12247 (accessed 16 August 2019).

Metzl J, Kirkland A (eds) (2010). *Against Health: how health became the new morality*. New York, NY: New York University Press.

Moncrieff J (2010). Psychiatric diagnosis as a political device. *Social Theory & Health* 8(4): 370–382.

Moncrieff J (2009). *A Straight Talking Introduction to Psychiatric Drugs*. Ross-on-Wye: PCCS Books.

Moncrieff J, Middleton H (2019). Critical psychiatry: a brief overview. *BJPsych Advances* 25(1): 47–54.

Morgan A, Felton A, Fulford B, Kalathil J, Stacey G (2015). *Values and Ethics in Mental Health: an exploration for practice*. London: Palgrave.

Nursing and Midwifery Council (NMC). *The Code for Nurses and Midwives*. [Online.] https://www.nmc.org.uk/standards/code/ (accessed 16 August 2019).

Pies R (2011). Psychiatry's new brain-mind and the legend of the 'chemical imbalance.' [Online.] *The Psychiatric Times*; 11 July. www.psychiatrictimes.com/articles/psychiatrys-new-brain-mind-and-legend-chemical-imbalance (accessed 16 August 2019).

Pratt DD (1993). Andragogy after twenty-five years. *New Directions for Adults & Continuing Education 1993*(57): 15–23.

Pūras D (2017). *Special Rapporteur on the Right of Everyone to the Enjoyment of the Highest Attainable Standard of Physical and Mental Health*. United Nations Human Rights: Office of the High Commission.

Read J, Bentall R, Mosher L (eds) (2004). *Models of Madness: psychological, social and biological approaches to schizophrenia*, (2nd ed). London: Routledge.

Rosenhan D (1973). On being sane in insane places. *Science 179 (4070): 250*–258.

Scheff TJ (1990). *Being Mentally Ill: a sociological theory* (3rd ed). New Brunswick: AldineTransaction

Sedgwick P (2015). *Psycho Politics*. London: Unkant Publishers.

Sidley G (2015). *Tales from the Madhouse: an insider critique of psychiatric services*. Monmouth: PCCS Books.

Smail DJ (2001). *The Nature of Unhappiness*. London: Robinson.

Stewart I, Cohen J (1994). *The Collapse of Chaos: discovering simplicity in a complex world*. London: Penguin.

Sweeney A, Clement S, Filson B, Kennedy A (2016). Trauma-informed mental healthcare in the UK: what is it and how can we further its development? *Mental Health Review Journal* 21(3): 174–192.

Sweeney A, Filson B, Kennedy A, Collinson L, Gillard S (2018). A paradigm shift: relationships in trauma-informed mental health services. *BJPsych Advances* 24(5): 319–333. https://doi.org/10.1192/bja.2018.29 (accessed 19 August 2019).

Thomas P, Longden E (2013). Madness, childhood adversity and narrative psychiatry: caring and the moral imagination. *Medical Humanities* 39(2). https://doi.org/10.1136/medhum-2012-010268 (accessed 19 August 2019).

Watts J (2016). Recovery: compromise or liberation? [Online.] *Mad in America*. https://www.madinamerica.com/2016/02/recovery-compromise-or-liberation/ (accessed 19 August 2019).

White M (1995). *Re-Authoring Lives: interviews and essays*. Adelaide: Dulwich Centre Publications.

White M, Epston D (1990). *Narrative Means to Therapeutic Ends*. London: WW Norton & Company.

# Chapter 5

## Reluctant revolutionaries: implementing Open Dialogue in a community mental health team

### Iseult Twamley

Open Dialogue (OD) is a radically inclusive, relational approach to mental health care. In 2011, our rural Irish adult community mental health service won a charitable grant with the purpose of developing 'a "whole family" recovery and Open Dialogue approach to care'. What happened next, and how it changed us ('us', in this instance, being our staff and those we serve) is the story of this chapter.

My aim here to share the experiences of changing from within: challenging ourselves, our practices and our service structure. In the spirit of OD, I hope to bring transparency, reflectivity and context, to share the story not the symptoms – and to open the way for more dialogue. As in OD practice, I will share my reflections on this story as we proceed.

> **Reflection:**
> I am struck as I write this by the power of the narrator in creating and shaping the dominant and public 'story' of this change – which could be storied in many different ways. This is one professional's perspective and views – mine – and I can only share what I have learnt and taken away and some voices (also chosen by me) of those who I have been on this journey with.

## Why was it needed?

In its principles and practice, OD prioritises the voice of the service user and their community, and the importance of dialogue as a central and healing force in mental health recovery. As a method of supporting people in distress, it offers hope for a new vision of mental health service provision. A model of mental healthcare developed in Finland, it has been implemented in countries such as the USA, Germany, Scandinavia and the UK, with reported success (Alexander, 2016; Schütze, 2015; Tribe et al, 2019; Gordon et al, 2016; Buus et al, 2017).

## Our context

West Cork Mental Health Service is a small community mental health service, serving a rural Irish population of 55,000, across 2000 square kilometres on the edge of the Atlantic. A contradictory place: isolated, yet a diverse and 'arty' community. Lacking easy access to urban specialist services, it has behoved us to be flexible and to work closely with community and non-statutory services. We provide community-based services, inpatient care, outpatient clinics and residential hostel support. Routine care is provided by psychiatry-led outpatient clinics and decisions are made at professional multidisciplinary team (MDT) meetings, when clients and families are not present.

Our clinical director when this story begins was critical psychiatrist Pat Bracken and, as a team, we very much aligned ourselves with recovery values in mental health. Inspired by national policy (Department of Health, 2006) and our own values, our service vision document (West Cork Mental Health Service, 2010: 1) stated our aim for a service 'guided by a commitment to service-user involvement, a recovery philosophy, community-orientation and the importance of integrated (partnership) working'. We were committed to ongoing initiatives to increase service user involvement, with co-produced community mental health events and significant service user representation at local management level, before this was national policy. Therapeutic initiatives with holistic and recovery focus were encouraged. We were actively engaged in improving our service and seeking feedback. Within this ethos, we held a number of community trialogues (Amering, Hofer & Rath, 2002) – open meetings for service users/the community and mental health staff to discuss our service. We heard some very clear messages: that family and networks wished to be more involved in supporting their loved one, and that service users wished to have more say in their care and more consistency in the team around them. Such feedback is not, of course, unique to our service (Cohen, 2008; Horsfall, Paton & Carrington, 2018; Brown, 2019). However, it set us a mandate. Our partnership with Advancing Recovery Ireland[1] gave us a further structure and focus for changing our day-to-day mental health practice and addressing inclusion.

---

1. Advancing Recovery Ireland is an Irish national Mental Health Division initiative that brings together people who provide services, those who use them and their families and community supports, to work on making mental health services more recovery-focused.

Open Dialogue was on the radar for us; as the sole psychologist offering psychological interventions for psychosis, I was very conscious of the need for a more integrated approach with both the family/network and the mental health system. Under a co-operative leadership project, Adrienne Adams (family therapist) and local service-user/family members made an initial unsuccessful bid for OD to be incorporated into our ward. When I won a grant for OD training, the management team and staff were very supportive and the training was oversubscribed.

> **Reflection:**
> In OD we talk a lot about the first question that we ask: 'The history
> of the idea of the meeting' – i.e. why and how we came to be here,
> together, today. This question sets our foundation moving forward. It is
> this question I am trying to answer to you here.
>     And I notice that, when we began this project, we did not formally
> meet or dialogue all together about what we hoped or wanted to change
> (and what we hoped or wanted to stay the same…). We started as it
> were on another question: 'Now what?'

In focus groups held before the OD training, staff expressed hopes for change, specifically in relation to more family/network involvement supporting service user recovery. Staff also spoke of families needing information and education, and of problematic family dynamics. There was acknowledgement, too, that working in teams and with families would be a challenge. One staff member noted: 'I suppose we'd all be afraid of what meets us when we go out into a family, what history we're dealing with and what's going to come at us…' We hoped, I think, that the training would upskill us to know 'what to do with' (and how to change) the families we wished to invite.

> **Reflection:**
> This is my closest understanding to what I think we thought we needed.
> Writing this in 2018, I now think that what we thought we were asking
> for and what we ended up 'needing' were very different. Perhaps writing
> this chapter will help me understand that better.

A truism about dominant practices is that we don't see them as practices but as 'the ways things are'. When we commenced our training with the Finnish OD trainers, Mia Kurtti and Birgitta Alakare, we encountered a mirror that reflected back to us certain things we didn't know about ourselves and hadn't particularly questioned. We hadn't noticed that we had never had the opportunity to discuss together our values and practices until the training gave us that opportunity.

Some of us with lived experience of mental health issues (ourselves or in our families) spoke about this with our colleagues for the first time – a breaking of an 'us and them' taboo previously unarticulated. We became aware that our take on the clinical responsibility legally adhering to psychiatry (that a psychiatrist is clinical lead on all cases) was not shared by the Western Lapland team. The hierarchy within professions started to shift as every voice in the room was treated as equal by our trainers. Our concerns about risk ('What would you do in Finland when..?') contrasted with the calm response to every apocalyptic scenario put to the Finnish trainers: 'Well, we would talk about it…' One aspect of OD practice, that of not making decisions about the service user without that person being present, really challenged our notion of ourselves as a recovery-oriented service and highlighted many non-transparent areas of our practice (from professional-only meetings to lack of access to case notes). Six months on, staff were to articulate a shift to a more OD way of working as both a 'no-brainer' and a 'drastic change'. A taste of things to come…

## What is it/what does it involve?

OD presents a unique challenge to any implementing team: it requires a fundamental shift in routine mental health practice (how we meet, understand and work with clients) and also a fundamental shift in the organisational system and structures. It is fair to say that we (certainly I) did not appreciate the full magnitude of these changes as we began our implementation.

In terms of its development, the OD approach originated in the 1980s in a small Western Lapland mental health service (very similar in geography and population to our Irish service). OD emerged through asking and answering the question: How can we do this better?

The Finnish team came to understand that care seemed more helpful when they involved those people important to the person ('networks'). This involved a shift in perspective from seeing the 'problem' as located inside the client to 'seeing all the problems as problems in the actual social situation of the patient' (Seikkula, Arnkil & Eriksson, 2003: 190) Fundamental to the approach is a shift away from an immediate emphasis on trying to eradicate symptoms.

Specifically, the approach emphasises the importance of the network as a source of support and a means to enrich the 'dialogue'. Dialogical approaches to mental health emphasise that crisis (psychological/psychiatric) occurs because of a need for dialogue; that words have not yet been found for the person's experience to be shared and, through the sharing, for new constructive perspectives to be found. This social constructionist viewpoint is evident in the writings of Seikkula and Olson about psychosis (2003: 409), in which they conceptualise psychosis as a 'temporary, radical and terrifying alienation from shared, communicative practices… a "no man's land" where unbearable experience has no words, and thus the patient has no voice and no genuine agency'.

Through continued clinical innovation, team reflection and ongoing research, the approach evolved into what we know today: a value-based 'way of thinking and working' (Haarakangas et al, 2007). The practice of not talking about service users outside of their presence is an example of an innovation developed to address the challenge of staff speaking either negatively or expertly about the network when they are not present (Andersen, 1995). This was understood to be an impediment to being fully present and responsive to the network when they were there.

> **Reflection:**
> A topic of curiosity to me now… the paradigm shift quietly taking place. In hearing about this time of OD development in Finland, what is very alive is a willingness to not have the answers, to value unique human experience, to emphasise connection over expertise – and, by implication and in practice, moving away from the hierarchies and certainties of the biomedical model of 'mental illness'.

At the core of OD are the 'treatment meetings': meeting with the person at the centre of concern and their personal and professional networks. Treatment meetings became the forum for understanding, for therapeutic dialogue, and for making decisions about future support.

The seven systemic and organisational principles that the team developed in Western Lapland were as follows:

1. Immediate help – any person in mental health crisis (self-defined) can phone a direct line to the mental health service to request help, which can be provided in 24 hours if needed. In Finland, any concerned person can make this call.

2. Social network perspective – working with the family/network is core. The network is defined by the people themselves, so can include family members, friends and even pets. On the initial phone call and at every subsequent meeting, we ask: 'Who needs to be there when we meet again?'

3. Flexibility and mobility – the team offers flexibility and mobility about the time, location and duration of meetings. Similarly, treatment options (eg. individual psychotherapy) are integrated as needed.

4.  Responsibility – all team members hold responsibility for the treatment process.

5.  Psychological continuity – teams are consistent over the mental health journey, including through inpatient admission, supporting the establishment of trusting relationships, shared stories and understanding over time.

6.  Tolerance of uncertainty – fundamental to the approach is a shift away from an immediate emphasis on trying to eradicate symptoms and instead taking the time for a therapeutic process that mobilises the psychological resources in the person and network. Practically speaking, this can mean deferring the prescription of sedating neuroleptic medication until at least two or three meetings have been held (Seikulla & Arnkil, 2006).

7.  Dialogism – dialogue is the therapeutic engine of OD; dialogue can create new meanings for the person's experience and new possibilities for the future. In particular, OD aims to foster the co-existence of multiple, separate and equally valid 'voices,' or points of view, within the treatment meeting – what Bakhtin calls 'polyphony' (Olson, Seikkula & Zeidonis, 2014). Based on systemic and dialogical theory, this practice emphasises deep listening, reflective responses, open reflections, transparency and shared decision-making. Clinicians 'reflect' openly on their ideas and feelings in the meeting, including ideas about treatment planning, for network members to comment on and agree or disagree (Olson, Seikkula & Zeidonis, 2014).

## Open Dialogue in our context

In our implementation of OD, we were immediately confronted with the challenge of our current system. Despite our recovery-oriented focus and efforts at stakeholder participation, our existing structures and procedures were, like those of many Western psychiatric systems, built around the needs of staff: that is, MDT meetings for professional-led discussions and decisions; a system of outpatient clinics for assessment and care-planning, staffed by psychiatric registrars on short-term placements; a clear hierarchy of professional input; communication in professional language and addressing professional concerns; emphasis on relationships with the mental health team rather than within the person's network and community, and therapy/ therapeutic conversation as a privileged addendum for the few, rather than inherent to our day-to-day practice. Implementing OD was going to challenge these practices and many more.

# The change process

> Lord, grant me the serenity to accept the things I cannot change,
> the courage to change the things I can and the wisdom to know the
> difference. (Irish Serenity Prayer)

### Phase I: piloting dialogical practice

Our first conversations asked, 'Is it feasible (or desirable) to transport a Finnish model and system to our Irish organisation?' As just one example, our system requires referral by GP to our MDT; there is no possibility for self-referral. Some people argued that there was a need for and value in the MDT space for professional discussions. As Seikkula and Arnkil (2006: 9) point out: 'Good practices simply cannot be duplicated. The difference of contexts and actors should always be taken into account.' To begin, we decided to work with a subgroup of our clients, as faithfully to the principles of OD as we could, to explore the practice and how we and our clients experienced it.

Practical challenges arose immediately: how to bring multidisciplinary teams together to offer flexible home-based care when they were already juggling separate caseloads and work schedules? Also, we decided that we, as a service, were not ready to cede clinical responsibility to a team without a psychiatrist, so service users attending the pilot programme would also attend routine outpatient clinic appointments for mental health treatment planning and decision making. This was not a 'perfect' start, as it meant our pilot meetings could offer a therapeutic space but not the inclusion and decision-making capacity of a full OD implementation. However, we were backed by lots of enthusiasm and goodwill from the staff who had trained with us.

> **Reflection:**
> I recall the fear that some of us had (I certainly) about the assimilation and dilution of the radical nature of the principles that asked us to be present, transparent, and bring what dialogical equality we could to our meetings with people. My fear was perhaps a mirror of those of my colleagues who were reluctant to change.

Our biggest and most immediate challenge was one we had not foreseen. We introduced an open referral policy: if the team or any person thought they might benefit from our pilot, we would accept them. However, we got no referrals – or, to be accurate, we got very few referrals, very far apart. Somehow, team discussions in the MDT could not agree on 'appropriate referrals'. Clients were either too troubled or not troubled enough, not ready yet or past the point of crisis.

**Reflection:**
This is a painful memory. We were so excited to start, and so frustrated by the lack of referrals. It also speaks to hierarchies in the team – as the grant-holder of the project, I had a privileged consultant voice within the team, but not a leading one. My perspective had influence but no power.

The project struggled on, with referrals coming from allied health professionals and, gradually, MDT and psychiatry. Staff and network feedback was very positive on the whole.

We struggled with the dual pathway we had created, which meant that decisions reached with networks in the OD meetings could be contradicted or ignored when the service user attended their outpatient clinic meetings. Care-planning decisions continued to happen in outpatient appointments with psychiatry, where the network and OD team were not present. Another challenge was that teams were drawn from across our catchment area and staff struggled to attend supervision.

However, we were offering home-based dialogical meetings to clients and their families. Feedback from service users and families was very positive. The funders were pleased, and so was senior management. In fact, senior management's main issue was the slowness of referrals (we worked with 23 families over the first 2.5 years), which was frustrating, given the external and internal investment in the training. Thus, our second implementation stage was thrust upon us.

### Phase II: creation of an Open Dialogue care pathway

We were told by senior management that the solution to the slow referral process was to have an opt-out policy: from September 2015, all new referrals to the local catchment area (Bantry) were to be automatically referred to an OD pathway for all their mental health needs (with the exception of out-of-hours crisis presentations). This pathway was named the OD 'clinic' – a term very deliberately chosen to explain our role within the existing system. Like the other outpatient clinics, we would assess, plan care and support the person's mental health journey – but we would do this in multidisciplinary teams, with the person's network, and using transparent dialogical practice.

In a very short time, my colleague Adrienne Adams and I were charged with recruiting a team from existing staff who would be seconded to the OD clinic as part of their usual work.

This phase involved making different compromises. In creating a virtual 'clinic', we became tied to a day and venue – a Tuesday, in a community location – thus losing flexibility and mobility in responding to crises. Our clinical experience was that conversations at the family home seemed more comfortable and deeper – but the size of our catchment area made this impossible for a team that only worked together one day a week.

However, we now had a regular team, with psychiatry support for the decisions reached in treatment meetings. We arranged a system of available psychiatry 'consult' for the teams, which could be an in-meeting phone call or invited attendance at the meeting. As I write, we have supported more than 300 service users in this 'clinic' over the past three years.

### What changed?

For part of our service and some of our clients, we (almost overnight) changed our service delivery model. Treatment-as-usual involves assessment, care-planning and ongoing monitoring in traditional psychiatry-led and run outpatient clinics, with some discussion in MDT professional-only meetings.

For the OD clinic, new entrants to the service meet with a team of two or three mental health professionals (usually not a psychiatrist). They are invited to attend with relatives and family members, as they choose. Sessions are approximately 1.5 hours long and dialogical in nature. The team and person/network use the sessions to come to a shared understanding of the person's challenges and agree a plan, which can include referral to any professional in the MDT, medication, community resources etc. These sessions are where decisions are made about the person, in their presence and with their involvement. Notes are shared, as are letters.

The new form of service delivery had immediate practical implications. We needed to create OD-friendly 'assessment structures', as required by the system. We had to train staff in writing transparent and therapeutic letters.

### Training

Initial and ongoing training has been essential. The idea that this way of working is an easy transition is usually dispelled early in dialogic training, because of the fundamental shift in power and perspective that a dialogical stance takes. Changing the conversation to follow what the client or network needs and wants to talk about and engaging in truly collaborative decision-making is a huge shift in practice.

Adrienne Adams and I trained as OD trainers. We instituted a programme of in-house training to develop skills for regular staff and facilitate clinical placements. Training is largely experiential, using videoed role-play. Time and again, our learning is that people can only hold and stay present with what they are trained and supported to hold.

### Multidisciplinary working

OD requires a level and depth of multidisciplinary working that was unprecedented for us. Practically, we devoted much time to creating a paperwork system so we could co-ordinate the multiple teams working simultaneously and track referrals and discharges etc. We had no admin support (our Operations Lead, AnnMarie Hohmann, was a great help with this).

Most of us were used to working alone with clients. Now there was always a colleague present to observe our practice (when we were all also learning a new practice). This could feel exposing. Clinical styles had to be adjusted. In my usual role as a psychologist, I enjoyed the challenge of developing the therapeutic alliance with my individual clients. The dynamic was very different in OD, and occasionally I found I slipped into 'working independently', much to my own frustration and that of my colleagues! Power differentials came into play also, as we had to learn what it meant in practice for every voice to be as equal as possible in the room – unacknowledged power dynamics were challenged; some of us had to step up with our voices and opinions – and some of us had to step down. Our experience over time has been that staff really appreciate having a colleague present with them in clinical sessions:

> You're not on your own. That's a *huge* shift, you know 'cos sometimes...
> you could leave a session being quite, you know, burdened by
> something ... but this way of working is *so* supportive. (Staff member)

An unanticipated complication is that now I find it very unusual to practise, train or supervise without a colleague present to reflect with.

### Willingness for hearts to be broken

Working in a dialogical way makes very different demands on staff. Mental health professionals are trained to work within the current mental health paradigm, with its emphasis on assessment, diagnosis and treatment plans. These can function as distancing practices that protect the mental health professional from the lived reality of the person's distress. In OD we can hear people's stories at a depth and intimacy that is unusual in routine mental health care.

The dialogical approach asks us to believe that listening to the person, meeting them in their unique reality, is not just a nicer way of doing business but is both necessary and therapeutic. It requires us to accept that our ideas and models are possibly helpful but not as important as the knowledge and understanding of the person and network. Therefore, in session, our words are not as important as theirs either, and we are required to respond to them and to their emotions.

Taking a relational and dialogical stance in mental health work means opening yourself to the possibility of connecting to others' distress. As Taiwo Afuape (2011: 120) writes: 'Therapy in this way involves an opening of hearts with a willingness on the part of the therapist to have theirs broken.' As a mixed staff group, most of us did not have therapy training, so we needed to resource ourselves better to allow us to 'tolerate the uncertainty'. We grew to understand the importance of slowing down in response to difficult emotion in the room – as opposed to our (trained and instinctual) reflex to rush to a solution or happier state. We were reinforced in this by Seikkula's (2002) paper demonstrating the importance of sitting with difficult emotions in successful OD cases.

Letting go of the pressure to 'fix' appears to be both the most challenging change and one of the most rewarding, allowing staff to be more present and attuned to the needs of those in the room. It is humbling, but also more congruent, because the reality of mental health is that we often don't have the answers – we have educated hopes.

> It's a challenge for us to… stop advising people… because that's what we *do* you know and that's what we're *trained* to do… it's very hard sometimes to *shut that off* in your head, you know, because you want to… people are desperate… in pain and suffering and you want to… help them. (Staff member)

Initially we noted an increase in referrals to psychology and counselling from our clinic. Over time, this has decreased, we surmise because teams have built up confidence in their ability to 'hold' those difficult experiences within OD.

### Clinical responsibility and risk assessment

For us, psychiatry as consult rather than psychiatry as routine meant a change in nursing and allied health professionals' clinical responsibility. It was new for some professionals to act as (in effect) keyworkers, holding responsibility for the assessment and care-planning. For some of us, it meant stepping up in terms of bringing our voice and opinion into the negotiation of care. In Western Lapland, this shift in voice and responsibility was one of the main reasons that training was given to all staff (Haarakangas et al, 2007). We found that staff members had different levels of tolerance of uncertainty – for example, when they felt psychiatric assessment for hospitalisation might be needed. In practical terms, training in risk assessment and working with suicidal people within a dialogical frame became important. We came to understand that the strong and trusting relationships we were building with people and with their network were an essential part of 'managing risk'.

### Cultural shift/attitude change

Changing the culture of an organisation is the holy grail of organisational development (Davidson, 2005). As one of our staff said after the initial training:

> Amongst teams… it's got to be OD as well, we've got to practise what we preach, as a culture… and that's going to be a massive change.

Two years after our first training, another staff member talked about our implementation as a 'quantum leap… [from] tablets and now we are offering our reflections'. The changes we see can be tracked in the in-house focus groups, where staff emphases could be seen to change over the course of the initial pilot from (for example) fixing a problematic family system to acknowledging the privilege of working with a family; from the importance of identifying symptoms and causes to adopting a non-expert position and asking service users what they want:

> I find myself stopping interpreting and diagnosing, when I'm listening. I *have* to just go with what the person's saying, so for me that's been a complete … change… from a medical model of… 'everything's a medical issue' to 'this is all normal human experience.' So it's been a very big shift in my practice. (Staff member)

One of the main findings of Colm Hayes' master's study of the clinic staff (2017) was that the clinic was 'a veritable hotbed of experiential learning and professional growth'.

### Inclusion: families, other professionals

Few of our staff members had experience in therapeutic work with families. The shift to including families and networks has proved a challenge. Many of our clients are isolated from their familial or other social networks, and others prefer not to include family. The majority of our sessions still may not include network members. However, a network approach (eg. using genograms and systemic questions) is still core to how we work. One positive development has been the frequent referral to us of family or community members by satisfied discharged clients.

A new subgroup within an existing team can easily become an 'in-group' and be experienced as exclusionary by staff who are not involved. We made a point of training the allied professionals in the team and ward staff members worked at our clinic on rotation. It can be a challenge for professionals who have not been trained in OD to be invited into a dialogical reflective network meeting. We noted that it was easy for these meetings to take a more 'monological' turn, with professionals talking at the client, rather than listening to each other. We realised how important it is that invited professionals know what to expect and feel comfortable. OD staff members needed to be able to gently challenge and reflect, and invite the dialogical back in. Some of us struggled to do this with invited professionals from higher up the traditional hierarchy. Old habits die hard.

> **Reflection:**
> I am aware, writing this, that work still needs to be done to foster more inclusivity within the wider team. It is easy to be perceived as the easier, more exciting path. We have started more conversations at our clinic recently about how we can offer support to team members working with clients who are not accessing OD.

Another in-group/out-group issue for which we didn't sufficiently prepare was the challenge of working within a completely different paradigm for only part of the week. On the one hand, staff reported that the dialogical model enhanced their other working practices, which became more transparent and inclusive. This excited us in terms of possibilities for supporting healthcare professionals who are not implementing the whole OD system. On the other hand, staff struggled with routine aspects of the traditional non-OD system, such as MDT meetings where clients are discussed and decisions made about their care in their absence.

## Evidence that it helps

> Look into the successes and mistakes of (your) activity in order to detect the more successful paths, avoid the more unsuccessful ones and notice potentials (you have) left unused. (Seikkula & Arnkil 2014: 182)

Ongoing service evaluation and research is a core element of the OD initiative. This section details some findings to date on both service user and staff experiences.

Service evaluation and research, critical for the assessment and evaluation of any innovation, still has to happen in the context of clinical realities. Particularly in a 'real-world' implementation, research and evaluation are competing for time and resources with service deliverables. Our compromise was to work with postgraduate students to help us answer our questions.

### Service user experience: research

*Phase one: service user and network experiences of the initial pilot*

Our first question was how service users and families experienced this new way of working. Psychology master's student Nicola Keane (2017) did a qualitative study of family/network experiences of our initial pilot. Eleven networks (45% of the total pilot sample) were interviewed. Results were very encouraging, highlighting in particular the very positive relationship with staff, which they differentiated in terms of trust, equality and transparency from their experiences with mental health professionals in other services. Participants spoke about enhanced communication within the family and reduced stigma around mental health. They said the dialogical sessions supported a greater sense of agency and involvement in the mental health journey. Participants reported enjoying and benefiting from our reflections, in particular (to our surprise) when we disagreed. These initial results were of great interest as, within recovery, a challenge is how mental health services support not just the service user's inclusion in care, but their autonomy and connections as well. Perhaps with this way of working, we were some way towards that.

*Phase two: service user and network experiences of the Open Dialogue care pathway*

We were curious as to how this new way of working affected service users' understanding of their mental health, which Niamh Doyle explored in her DClinPsy thesis (Doyle, 2019). She interviewed six people on our OD pathway, and collected evocative accounts comparing their experience with non-dialogical services. Their narratives supported OD as a humanising approach that facilitates, rather than imposes, meaning, and can reduce self-blame.

Responses to our routine session rating scale indicate that service users and network members experienced the sessions as positive in terms of relationship, goals and overall approach. The average score for service users is 9.5/10, and for network members it's 9/10.

Mental Health Area Management has recently agreed to fund a comprehensive audit of clinical activity, service deliverables and client and family experiences of our clinic compared with treatment as usual, with a view to informing future developments.

### Staff experience: research

Staff and network relationships are the core of a dialogical approach. Our exploration of staff experiences also took two stages.

*Phase one: staff experiences of the initial pilot*

We conducted focus groups with trained staff pre-OD training ($n = 20$); six months post-training (n = 11); at two-year follow-up ($n = 13$), and at three-year follow-up ($n = 10$). We asked them about OD and their experiences of the clinical practice, recovery and OD, and opportunities and challenges of implementation. Their responses initially revealed practical concerns about implementation, in terms of logistics (organising teams) and dynamics (working so closely in teams). Over time, the focus shifted to the value of reflections, the benefits of team working and the privilege of being able to work in this way.

*Phase two: staff experiences of the Open Dialogue care pathway*

Colm Hayes (2017) conducted this research for his psychology master's degree. He interviewed 10 staff on their experiences of the OD pathway. Practitioners described how OD allowed them to meet service users as people, rather than as problems. He found a 'spirit of collegiality' and an inclusive working environment among practitioners at the clinic, which was seen to encourage both service user autonomy and practitioner growth. He concluded that OD represented 'a cultural shift in practice that requires practitioners to abandon traditional roles and ingrained attitudes'.

## Challenges in researching Open Dialogue

State bodies reflect the neoliberal priorities and political values of the time. Time- and cost-efficient, evidence-based treatments are the buzz words. An approach that prioritises human relationships, individual choice and tolerance of uncertainty is not an easy sell, and then only to the extent that it does not threaten or seek to replace existing practices. What is wanted or demanded of us is to legitimise the approach within the parameters of the dominant paradigm – that is, to demonstrate that it will save money and that it will provide positive, measurable outcomes under the best standards of experimental design.

The level of investment and effort required to run such randomised control trials is way out of reach for small local implementation, as in our case. Luckily the NHS ODESSA trial (Razzaque & Stockmann, 2016) is taking this research forward in a large-scale trial of Open Dialogue for crisis care.

In another respect, such research requirements impose their own agendas on our clinical work – for example, administering questionnaires is in clear conflict with establishing a dialogical space. Of more concern is the emphasis on technical equivalence that experimental trials use, which is inherently in contradiction with the individualised flexibility in a values-based approach to care. As Seikkula & Arnkil (2014: 176) remind us: 'If one wishes to transfer network dialogue practices from one context to others, there are no shortcuts. In the new contexts, local negotiations, local networking and local learning processes are required.' More naturalistic and contextual designs can inform our local practices and answer to local priorities – are we meeting the needs of our service users and community? Is this approach working for our context and system? The prioritisation of the voices and perspectives of service users and their networks is not always emphasised in the more experimental model, and yet is the most important and valuable perspective we can get.

> **Reflection:**
> Sometimes there is a sense of conflict of paradigms and values between the research that the mainstream requires for adoption and the values of the approach itself. At its worst, the research process can become a route for co-option and assimilation. The idea of co-produced research, working in equal partnership with our stakeholders, is an exciting possibility for the future. We have not been able to finance this yet but, in terms of inclusion, dialogism and transparency, it feels the best fit to me.

## Future directions

Having weathered an almost complete change in senior staff and management, the project currently continues. (Whew! Pause for a breath…) In terms of further expansion, the implementation of the whole model requires team and management sign-up and significant investment in training. At the time of writing, this is not yet decided, and is likely to be dependent on ongoing research and policy developments.

Our project initially partnered with Advancing Recovery Ireland, and I still feel that dialogic practices have much to offer in this broader arena of recovery. Arising from this and the interest expressed by staff and service users in our region, we are offering a series of dialogical skills workshops. These aim to support mental health practitioners to use OD skills and values, regardless of their work setting. We also teach on the nursing, social work, OT and clinical psychology training courses and regularly offer specialist placements. In this sense, at this time, we are focusing on changes to mental health practice rather than changes to structure.

Locally, we would like to have more capacity to respond to crises and more involvement on the local mental health ward. Whatever happens needs to happen collaboratively, with all voices present.

Reflection:

The longer I do this work, the more cautious I am about creating my
own master plan for OD world dominance. It becomes more important
to me to work alongside teams that wish to learn these practices and
values and develop their own ways of moving forward. I don't think OD
is something you can impose on a team or system, but the idea of the
invitation, the support to explore… that excites me.

## How to counter co-option, assimilation and dilution

### *Reluctant revolutionaries*

No project occurs in a vacuum. Any innovation can be taken as a criticism of
what went before – or what is still happening. Part of what the project (staff)
had to deal with was the image of OD itself. Variously positioned as an agent
for overthrow of the medical model, a miracle cure, or a Finnish aberration
for which there is no evidence, OD has attracted increasing attention in
recent years. As the only Irish implementation project, we attracted extremes
of responses: some people said they wanted to move to West Cork to access
our service; some questioned why we were allowed to practise at all. Both
extremes were exacerbated when one family was featured on a national
documentary speaking favourably about their experiences of our service
(Radio Telifis Eireann, 2017). It is hard to quantify the impact of trying to
implement change in the eye of such a storm. Not good, and not easy.

Reflection:

What, you might legitimately ask, did we expect? We were in retrospect
very naïve not to anticipate resistance to implementing a non-hierarchical
therapeutic system and practices in mental health care. Perhaps natural
revolutionaries do not apply to work in large state bodies. Most of us aim
to do our jobs well enough to support our clients, please our bosses and get
an adequate pension. Politics occur at the micro-level (team dynamics) but
the macro questions (What are we doing? Why?) have occurred mostly at
the fringes of the mental health community. In recent years, these debates
have moved to the mainstream, and critical and reflective positions are
taking centre stage (Johnstone & Boyle, 2018). My experiences in that
respect no doubt mirror those of many others who, by questioning from
within, feel the full force of the system's resistance to change.

### *Working with ourselves as we work with others*

Beginnings are hard but keeping going seems to be harder. It seems that systems can tolerate pilot projects, temporary changes, much more easily than long-term change. And history is littered with innovative, promising mental health change projects that don't attract repeat funding or dissipate over time.

Leading change initiatives can feel risky (in a risk-averse system). There is an obvious pressure to succeed, and also a high bar for success: the investment in time and money must prove worth it. This pressure can be felt by everyone at all levels of the system. Staff on the ground need to feel that what they are doing has management support. I think now that sustainable projects need to build in strategies to support those delivering them – supervision from an experienced change agent at the very least. I would also recommend introductory training in the approach for the people who manage the clinical workers, so they understand what the staff are undertaking and the underpinning theory and rationale. Senior managers who have the courage to commit funding and approval to innovative projects will also benefit from regular acknowledgement and reassurance. Training and feedback events should include dialogue with service users and network members and their testimonies. Such trialogues need to happen regularly throughout the project.

### Reflective practice

Tom Andersen reminds us that 'We each take who we are… with us in the therapy room' (Andersen, 2005). We often forget to consider that this applies to the mental health professionals as well as our clients and service users. Studies consistently reflect high levels of stress, emotional exhaustion and burnout in mental health professionals (Lasalvia et al, 2009; Morse et al, 2012). The saying 'Be careful when a naked person offers you a shirt' comes to mind. Supporting the emotional resilience of staff has become a primary focus in my training and supervision. Weekly reflective practice meetings are essential for the sustainability of the project and the practice. As a colleague noted, without it things could become 'quite dangerous' given that 'this work demands so much more of you as a person'.

### Pushing open doors

Every innovation needs allies within and outside the organisation. In the early days, we didn't have access to any English-speaking OD implementation projects. When you are the only such project in your country, you spend a lot of time explaining and defending it. These are useful and important conversations. However, the networks that we have since developed within the OD 'movement' are critical for our morale, reinforcing shared values and facilitating critical reflection from a dialogical perspective. Equally, allies from other mental health change movements, such as the Annual Critical Perspectives Conference at

University College Cork (see Lydia Sapouna's chapter 1 in this book), provide connection and cross-fertilisation that enrich our theory and practice. Rai Waddingham (2018) has spoken of the dialogical space that can exist in peer support networks, such as the Hearing Voices Network, and there is much to be learnt from this skill base, in my experience. Similarly, trauma-informed research and practices have much to offer our work.

> **Reflection:**
> As I think of this, I realise that we did not resource ourselves properly with allies when we began this work. Part of the old mentality of the mental health professional is that we are there to help, and perhaps that mindset is partly responsible for our not knowing how to ask for help when it is needed.

I have found it important to be able to speak the language of our colleagues, to be able to present some of our experience and that of our clients in terms that others will understand and appreciate. Acquaintance with relevant national and organisational policies is critical, to link the changes we are making to the stated direction and aspirations of the organisation itself and to allay concerns about the threat of radical dialogical revolution (!).

### Keeping our doors and ears open

There can be a terrible temptation to fall into sales talk. When people are hesitant or critical, there is an understandable urge to report the good news and the exciting research, in order to reassure concerns.

And yet.

In organisational change, as in any network, listening is much more important than speeches (however impressive). If I could change one thing about our implementation, I would have had a lot more dialogue, with everyone. To be fair to us, as an implementation team on the ground, we were excluded from some conversations at senior management level in the organisation. And some invitations by us to senior or influential figures to conversations, or conferences, were not taken up, due to competing priorities.

> **Reflection:**
> And that context matters, because at some level, perhaps, I didn't trust the power of my voice in this system. Speaking for myself then, I think that my enthusiasm, my passion, my fear that the chance would pass meant I was more willing to seize opportunities and move with management directives than I would be now.

Equally, a rigid and technical approach to OD adherence (as required for research) has its advantages in initial set up; we *have had to* make certain changes to our practice and system or we would not have been 'doing Open Dialogue'. When other professionals asked us to continue to talk about our OD clients in the professionals-only MDT meetings, we said it would not be possible if we were 'doing Open Dialogue'. However, the needs for sustainability may require a more flexible approach. In the longer term, it might have been better for the project if we had taken time to dialogue and deliberate on the issue and values informing it. We could have come up with a solution that was not OD exactly, but was owned and agreed by all concerned. Tom Andersen (1987: 2) warns us to find the 'appreciable difference' (not too much to be rejected; not too little to make no difference) needed to stimulate change.

Now I realise the need for ownership of the project within the system (at all levels) and from our stakeholders, the community we serve. These conversations, had I paid attention, were a hallmark of the OD implementation originally (Haarakangas et al, 2007). I have come to think that slow, collaborative change, at a pace that everyone can tolerate, may be better than leaving some of us behind.

It is worth mentioning the elephant in the room here. Biomedical psychiatry is called to make the biggest shift in practice and worldview in order to participate in OD interventions. Psychiatry is the leading profession in mental health and, as such, the support and buy-in from psychiatrists can make or break a change initiative. Often positioned as carrying the ultimate clinical responsibility for large numbers of clients, psychiatrists use evidence-based guidelines to support their clinical decisions. They are asked to take the biggest risk in changing their practice, and the change may feel exposing and disempowering. As one psychiatrist, reflecting on their experience in our implementation, put it:

> There is a challenge as… a psychiatrist… our whole professional ethos
> and expectation of us is to be in there with a diagnosis, you know,
> and to determine the treatment and to guide the treatment and to say
> what the treatment should be ultimately. And for us to stop that… is
> hard, you know. You're going against your peers in some ways… that's
> difficult professionally… 'cos if something goes wrong, you have to
> defend what you're doing, and the easiest way to defend what you're
> doing is to say, 'Well this is the standard way of doing… psychology or
> psychiatry or whatever'.

Reflection:

In supporting this, I wonder whether I was somewhat silenced by my position as psychologist. It was very easy and comfortable (indeed desirable) for me to contemplate working in a more psychotherapeutically informed service; this was my language and practice; I had less (power, status, challenge to my model) to lose than my medically trained colleagues.

## Not the answer to everything

Early on I decided that every presentation would include a slide that said 'Open Dialogue is Not The Answer To Everything'. I didn't need the reminder myself. But it is helpful to acknowledge it and critical for the sustainability of the implementation. Nothing endangers us more than setting ourselves up as having the answer (particularly in an approach that underlines the importance of multiple truths). I believe (and our research has borne this out) that this approach has much to offer in terms of a more humane, accessible, equal way of doing mental health care. That in itself can be enough. I have lost count of the number of times we have been surprised at clients' progress 'when all we have been doing is talking'. I have also known clients who didn't want to participate in network meetings, clients for whom a biomedical frame has been more congruent and helpful. Dialogue must stay open and how we provide care must continue to evolve.

## At the same time, it's not what you are already doing

Many of us working in mental health services hope that we listen, that we are inclusive, maybe even transparent. We may also meet families and networks in their own homes. People often comment to me that they are doing OD already. This opinion is usually dispelled early in dialogic training, because of the fundamental shift in power and perspective that a dialogical stance takes. The requirement to 'drop the clinical gaze' is very challenging. We have been trained and reinforced in that gaze and position for so long that we are unaware how fundamentally it changes the possibilities for dialogue. We are used to setting the agenda, and to drawing on our models and theories (diagnostic, psychological etc) to explain and guide; formally or informally, that is what we do. Without the training, reflective practice and supervision that we have put in place, our clinical practice would drift back. It is not easy to stay open, to tolerate uncertainty, to risk admitting not knowing. Then again, this practice has also been a gift, a way to experience working with those we serve in a different, more human and relational way. As one of our service users put it:

I just felt when I'd go in to the doctors, I felt like, I dunno, I used to just close up, I had something really bottled up but I couldn't get it out... whereas [the OD team] were in my living room and it was like talking to someone I knew all my life.

## References

Afuape T (2011). *Power, Resistance and Liberation in Therapy with Survivors of Trauma: to have our hearts broken*. New York, NY: Routledge.

Alexander MJ (2016). *Parachute NYC Participants' Outcomes*. NAMI National Convention, Denver; 6–9 July.

Amering A, Hofer H, Rath I (2002). The 'First Vienna Trialogue': experiences with a new form of communication between users, relatives and mental health professionals. In: Lefley HP, Johnson DL (eds). *Family Interventions in Mental Illness: international perspectives*. Westport, CT: Praeger Publishers (pp105–124).

Andersen T (2005). The network concept of network therapy: a story from the European Nordic North. In: Lightburn A, Sessions P (eds). *Handbook of Community-Based Clinical Practice*. New York, NY: Oxford University Press (pp177–189).

Andersen T (1995). Reflecting processes; Acts of informing and forming: You can borrow my eyes, but you must not take them away from me! In Friedman S (ed). *The Reflecting Team in Action: collaborative practice in family therapy*. New York, NY: The Guilford Press (pp11–37).

Andersen T (1987). The Reflecting Team: dialogue and meta-dialogue in clinical work. *Family Process Journal 26*: 415–428.

Brown B (2019). Responsibilization and recovery: shifting responsibilities on the journey through mental health care to social engagement. *Social Theory & Health*: 1–18.

Buus N, Bikic A, Jacobsen EK, Müller-Nielsen K, Aagaard J, Rossen CB (2017). Adapting and implementing Open Dialogue in the Scandinavian countries: a scoping review. *Mental Health Nursing 38*(5): 391–401.

Cohen BMZ (2008). *Mental Health User Narratives: new perspectives on illness and recovery*. Basingstoke; New York, NY: Palgrave MacMillan.

Davidson L (2005). Recovery, self management and the expert patient – changing the culture of mental health from a UK perspective. *Journal of Mental Health 14*(1): 25–35.

Department of Health (2006). *A Vision for Change: report of the Expert Group on Mental Health Policy*. Department of Health, Ireland.

Doyle N (2019). *Treated as a person, not a case: exploring meaning-making in an Open Dialogue informed mental health service*. Unpublished DClinPsy thesis. Cork: University College Cork.

Gordon C, Gidugu V, Rogers S, DeRonck, J, Ziedonis D (2016). Adapting open dialogue for early-onset psychosis into the US healthcare environment: a feasibility study. *Psychiatric Services 67*: 11.

Haarakangas K, Seikkula J, Alakare B, Aaltonen J (2007). Open Dialogue: an approach to psychotherapeutic treatment of psychosis in Northern Finland. In: Anderson H, Gehart D (eds). *Collaborative Therapy: relationships and conversations that make a difference*. New York, NY: Routledge (pp221–235).

Hayes C (2017). *Between Two Worlds: exploring practitioner experiences of delivering the Open Dialogue approach in an Irish mental health setting.* (Unpublished master's thesis.) Cork: University College Cork.

Horsfall D, Paton J, Carrington A (2018). Experiencing recovery: findings from a qualitative study into mental illness, self and place. *Journal of Mental Health 27*(4): 307–313.

Johnstone L, Boyle M, with Cromby J, Dillon J, Harper D, Kinderman P, Longden E, Pilgrim D, Read J (2018). *The Power Threat Meaning Framework: towards the identification of patterns in emotional distress, unusual experiences and troubled or troubling behaviour, as an alternative to functional psychiatric diagnosis.* Leicester: British Psychological Society.

Keane N (2017). *An Open Dialogue-informed approach to mental health service delivery: a pilot study of the experiences of service users and support networks.* (Unpublished master's thesis.) Cork: University College Cork.

Lasalvia A, Bonetto C, Bertani M, Bissoli S, Cristofalo D, Marrella G et al (2009). Influence of perceived organisational factors on job burnout: survey of community mental health staff. *British Journal of Psychiatry 195*(6): 537–544.

Morse G, Salyers MP, Rollins AL, Monroe-DeVita M, Pfahler C (2012). Burnout in mental health services: a review of the problem and Its remediation. *Administration and Policy in Mental Health and Mental Health Services Research 39*(5): 341–352.

Olson M, Seikkula J, Ziedonis D (2014). *The Key Elements of Dialogic Practice in OD: fidelity criteria.* Massachusetts, USA: Massachusetts Medical School.

Radio Telifís Eireann (2017). *Schizophrenia: the voices in my head.* [Audio broadcast.] RTE 1; 19 September.

Razzaque R, Stockmann T (2016). An introduction to peer-supported Open Dialogue in mental healthcare. *BJPsych Advances 22*: 348–356.

Schutze W (2015). Open Dialogue as a contribution to a healthy society: possibilities and limitations. *Advances in Psychiatry and Neurology 24*(2): 86–90.

Seikkula J (2002). Open Dialogue with good and poor outcomes for psychotic crisis: examples from families with violence. *Journal of Martial and Family Therapy 28*(3): 263–274.

Seikkula J, Arnkil T (2014). *Open Dialogues and Anticipations: respecting the otherness in the present moment.* Helsinki: THL publications.

Seikkula J, Arnkil T (2006). *Dialogical Meetings in Social Networks.* London: Karnac.

Seikkula J, Arnkil T, Eriksson E (2003). Postmodern society and social networks: open and anticipation dialogues in network meetings. *Family Process 42*: 185–203.

Seikkula J, Olson ME (2003). The Open Dialogue approach to acute psychosis: its poetics and micropolitics. *Family Process 42*(3): 403–418.

Tribe R, Freeman A, Livingstone S, Stott J, Pilling S (2019). Open Dialogue in the UK: qualitative study. *BJPsych Open 5*(4). E49. doi: 10.1192/bjo.2019.38.

Waddingham R (2018). *Living Beyond the Labels: life lessons from lived experience.* International Meeting on the Treatment of Psychosis. 30 August. Tornio, Finland.

West Cork Mental Health Service (2010). *Moving West Cork Mental Health Service in a Recovery Direction.* Cork.

# Chapter 6

# Pause before prescribing: rethinking antidepressant use in general practice

## Bryan McElroy

Antidepressant prescribing, in the context of people presenting in distress to their general practitioner (GP), is on the rise. From my experience in practice, it appears that most GPs fail to give comprehensive information when prescribing antidepressants that would allow for fully informed decision-making. This is not only poor practice, it also has many long-term repercussions for doctors, patients and society at large.

In May 2015, I undertook a Quality in Practice (QIP) initiative titled 'Antidepressant prescribing: a structured approach'. This was subsequently published in the Irish GP journal *Forum* in September 2015 (McElroy & Holmes, 2015). Between 2017 and 2018, I used this QIP initiative to audit antidepressant prescribing in a 3,000-patient, eight-GP, rural Irish practice. In this chapter I will discuss the QIP initiative in detail, summarise the audit, and offer some personal and critical reflections on the process, and on the wider context of prescribing antidepressant medication.

### Why change how GPs prescribe antidepressants?

To set what I write in context, I should explain that I am a GP with a diploma in clinical psychiatry. I have a special interest in providing effective care for mental and emotional wellbeing. Over the past 10 years I have read extensively around this topic, attended numerous conferences, been actively involved in mental health advocacy groups and met many people, personally and professionally, who have been affected by the use of antidepressants. My aim here is to help promote more dialogue, critical thinking and change and shed light on an area of practice that has profound implications for individuals and society as a whole.

Prescriptions for antidepressant drugs have increased substantially worldwide in recent years. A study examining prescribing trends for mental disorders in England from 1998 to 2010 found that antidepressant prescriptions increased by 10% per year on average (Ilyas & Moncrieff, 2012). In Ireland, between 2009 and 2017, prescriptions for eight antidepressants available from the Health Service Executive (HSE) increased by 64% (McDermott, 2018). GPs are typically the first professional a person consults when they experience symptoms of depression for the first time.

In everyday practice, a structured approach is necessary to ensure that GPs are prescribing safely and effectively, in accordance with current, evidence-based best practice, and to ensure that patients are told about the pros and cons of starting antidepressant therapy. Indeed, clinicians have an ethical duty to educate patients, so they are able to make a fully informed choice about this important therapeutic intervention. Current guidelines from the Irish College of General Practitioners/Health Service Executive (ICGP, 2006) and the UK's National Institute for Clinical Excellence (NICE, 2009) recommend that GPs provide patients with the following information about antidepressants:

1. the gradual development of the full antidepressant effect
2. the importance of taking the medication as prescribed and the need to continue treatment after remission of symptoms
3. potential side effects
4. the risk and nature of discontinuation symptoms with cessation of the antidepressant.

However, in clinical practice, I have encountered many cases where patients have been started on antidepressant medications without being given any such information. Journalist Niamh Drohan highlighted discrepancies between the guidelines described above and current practice, in an article in the *Irish Examiner* (Drohan, 2013). She visited seven GP practices across Ireland and posed as a student suffering from stress and anxiety. She was prescribed antidepressant medications in each case, and stated:

> In all cases, adequate information regarding possible side effects associated with taking antidepressants was not provided to me. I was also not informed that if I stopped the medication abruptly, I could face a withdrawal-like reaction.

In a recent survey of 1,829 people taking antidepressants, 55% of those who attempted to stop their medication experienced withdrawal effects, and

27% became addicted to the medication. Only one per cent of participants recalled being told about withdrawal effects when prescribed the drugs (Read, Cartwright & Gibson, 2018).

Further complexities arise when you consider the uncertainty surrounding how antidepressant therapy actually produces beneficial effects. Meta-analyses of published and unpublished data show no statistically significant difference for the most commonly prescribed type of antidepressant, selective serotonin re-uptake inhibitors (SSRIs), over placebo for mild to moderate depression, and only slight differences for severe depression (Moncrieff & Cohen, 2013). This suggests that a large proportion of antidepressants' mechanism of action is due to the placebo effect rather than the correction of a specific 'chemical imbalance', as was initially hypothesised (Bracken et al, 2012). There is now significant evidence to show that adverse childhood events (ACEs) are associated with depression in later life (Chapman et al, 2004), raising the possibility that the root of some cases of depression may be unresolved psychological trauma. A study of 2,047 men and women conducted in Mitchelstown, County Cork, found that ACEs are common among older adults in Ireland and are associated with higher odds of later-life depressive symptoms, particularly among those with poor perceived social support (Cheong et al, 2017). Furthermore, recent research has emerged suggesting inflammation may play an important role in the aetiology and treatment of depression (Dantzer et al, 2011). This reveals that inaccurate, or at least unproven, scientific assumptions have become the basis for much of what GPs currently communicate to patients and how we practise.

As clinicians, GPs have an ethical duty to respect their patients' autonomy in making their own decisions. In the section 'Information for patients', current medical ethics guidance from Ireland's Medical Council states (2016: 15-16):

> You must give patients enough information, in a way that they can understand, to enable them to exercise their right to make informed decisions about their care. Consent is not valid if the patient has not been given enough information to make a decision. The amount of information patients need before making a decision will vary according to a number of factors, including: the nature of the condition, the type of investigation, the complexity of treatment, the risks associated with the treatment or procedure (and the risks of non-treatment) and the patient's own wishes. You must not keep back any information that the patient needs to make a decision unless disclosure would cause the patient serious harm. In this context 'serious harm' does not mean the patient would become upset or decide to refuse treatment.

When it comes to antidepressant prescribing, there seems to be an ingrained habit not to fully inform patients by not explaining honestly and comprehensively about the nature of depression and the pros and cons of drug therapy. This is clearly an area that needs more attention in primary care.

## Complexities and obstacles to change

The issue of antidepressant prescribing is topical, complex and highly relevant in general practice. When reflecting on a predominant medical intervention, such as antidepressant use, I find it useful to keep in mind the triad of evidence-informed practice, which explains clinical decision-making. The triad includes practitioner resources, best research and population values (Research in Practice for Adults, undated).

Opinions about antidepressant therapy vary widely within each of these areas. GPs often have very different preconceptions, knowledge and confidence in supporting patients out of a depressive episode, whether through drug-based treatment or through alternative approaches. Some doctors readily prescribe antidepressants, informed by guidelines that advocate such practices. However, the formation of the Critical Psychiatry Network (CPN)[1] in the UK and the Council for Evidence-Based Psychiatry (CEPUK),[2] which comprise psychiatrists and academics who critique many of the current predominant practices, including the use of antidepressants, exemplifies the diversity of viewpoints in this area. The CPN and CEPUK aim to shed light on the limitations of antidepressants, the long-term negative outcomes, misconceptions about how they work and the role of pharmaceutical industry interest groups in policy-making and educational arenas.

Responses to a large meta-analysis of antidepressant efficacy (Cipriani et al, 2018) also illustrate the diversity of perspectives. The Royal College of Psychiatrists welcomed the research, saying it would 'finally put to bed the controversy about antidepressants, as it clearly showed that these drugs work in lifting mood and helping most people with depression' (Rimmer, 2018).

The CEPUK countered with the following statement:

This statement is irresponsible and unsubstantiated, as the study
actually supports what has been known for a long time, that various
drugs can, unsurprisingly, have an impact on our mood, thoughts and
motivation, but also differences between placebo and antidepressants
are so minor that they are clinically insignificant, hardly registering

1. www.criticalpsychiatry.co.uk (accessed 27 March 2019)

2. www.cepuk.org (accessed 19 August 2019).

at all in a person's actual experience. But even these differences can be accounted for. Most people on antidepressants experience some noticeable physical or mental alterations, and as a consequence realise they are on the active drug. This boosts the placebo effect of the antidepressant, helping explain these tiny differences away. Furthermore, the trials only covered short-term antidepressant usage (8 weeks) in people with severe or moderate depression. Around 50% of patients have been taking antidepressants for more than two years, and the study tells us nothing about their effects over the long term. In fact, there is no evidence that long-term use has any benefits, and in real-world trials (STAR-D study) outcomes are very poor. (CEPUK, 2018)

These contrasting perspectives on the same study and data show that evidence garnered from large studies is open to very different interpretations and requires critical evaluation – as do any guidelines that may result.

Patients' ideas and expectations about antidepressant use also range widely (Anderson et al, 2015). Personally, I have heard perspectives ranging from 'I don't believe in taking drugs for emotional problems' to 'I need a pill – something now, doctor. I have tried everything else and it doesn't work'.

I have encountered many factors in general practice that contribute to poor-quality antidepressant prescribing. When presenting my QIP and audit in educational settings to more than 40 GPs/GP registrars and discussing these issues with many colleagues, I have observed myriad complexities and obstacles to change.

Views on what causes depression, what antidepressants are, how they work and how safe they are vary widely within the medical community. In my experience, the information doctors have about antidepressant medications largely depends on their education and training in medicine and psychiatry, the books or journals they read and the frequency of contact they have with pharmaceutical representatives and advertisements. Most Irish GPs (I would estimate 90%) meet pharmaceutical company representatives and advertising on a very regular basis. Pharmaceutical company information tends to downplay risks and exaggerate the beneficial effects of antidepressant drugs, giving the drugs a positive appeal to GPs. It is also clear that exposure to pharmaceutical advertising affects GPs' prescribing decisions (King & Bearman, 2017; King et al, 2013). Perhaps more importantly, the theory that a 'chemical imbalance' is the root cause of depression still predominates in medical culture, and if GPs believe this theory (which, in my opinion, most GPs do), this influences their prescribing habits and the information patients receive from them.

GPs often have apprehensions about fully informing patients about potential side effects, withdrawal effects or admitting the uncertainty around the mechanism of action, as they believe these would deter patients from taking antidepressants or reduce the efficacy of the intervention. The latter is referred to as the nocebo response (Colloca & Miller, 2011), where a patient's negative expectations would cause the treatment to have a less beneficial effect than it would otherwise.

GPs often perceive there are few options other than prescribing medication when someone presents with depression (Hyde et al, 2005). There is a sense of obligation to do something meaningful to help the person who is in obvious distress and GPs may have little or no education, experience or interest in alternative options for guiding someone out of a depressive episode. Indeed, qualitative research exploring GPs' attitudes towards antidepressant prescribing indicate that their ethical and professional imperative is to 'do the right thing' for individuals by striving to achieve the 'right care fit' (Johnson et al, 2017). Irish GPs have welcomed the relatively recent introduction of Counselling in Primary Care (CIPC), a service introduced by the HSE in 2013, which provides counselling for those experiencing mild-to-moderate depression. GPs unanimously agreed that CIPC has been of benefit in treating mild-to-moderate mental health disorders (Rafferty & Bradley, 2019). However, CIPC is limited to six to eight sessions and to medical card- holders only. Otherwise, counselling must be sought privately – which can be costly and therefore a deterrent to patients. These limitations of counselling, as well as the fact that many patients are reluctant to try it, often leave GPs feeling they have no alternative but to prescribe an antidepressant.

In addition, mental health issues typically require longer and more complex consultations than, say, a sore throat. As taking a thorough history and engaging in active listening takes up most of the time of these consultations, fully informing patients about antidepressant therapy creates a time management challenge. With 10–15 minutes for consultations being standard in most GP practices in Ireland, fully informing patients about antidepressant drug therapy is often put on the back burner and eventually forgotten about.

Patients often have pre-existing beliefs either for or against antidepressant medication. Exploring these beliefs and coming to a consensus decision poses yet another time pressure and clinical challenge.

Therefore, coming to a consensus on whether to prescribe and how to prescribe an antidepressant and then how to describe antidepressant drug effects is quite a complex issue.

## Quality in Practice (QIP) tool

Improving quality in antidepressant prescribing by devising protocols and providing adequate patient information leaflets can help GPs deliver safer, more effective healthcare. This leads to greater consistency among doctors in a practice and across services. Patients are better informed and have more choice in the decision-making process.

I perceived an obvious need to develop a QIP tool for doctors initiating antidepressant prescription, in order to:

- facilitate patient autonomy by informing patients fully of all the relevant details about antidepressant therapy
- improve communication between doctor and patient about important issues in relation to antidepressant therapy
- ensure appropriate risk and side effect communication and documentation.

Quality in Practice initiatives are projects GPs undertake to provide solutions to common problems encountered in general practice. They are designed to improve the quality and safety of patient care. Ideally, they are simple in their design, easy to implement and can be applied by other GP practices nationally.

As part of my QIP, I designed a checklist template for GPs that guides them through a step-by-step process to ensure they are covering the areas described in the NICE (2009) and ICGP/HSE (2006) guidelines for the management of anxiety and depression. I used a GP software programme to create an 'aide memoire' that would serve to remind GPs to discuss important issues before prescribing an antidepressant. When a doctor sees a patient and is considering initiating antidepressant therapy, he or she can open up the Antidepressant Prescribing Protocol (ADPP) in the patient's file. The ADPP guides the doctor through a list of key areas to cover in a discussion with the patient (see the checklist at the end of this chapter). This checklist could also be printed off to generate a patient information leaflet or consent form. I also designed it so it could be used for auditing antidepressant prescribing practices in the future.

## Audit of antidepressant prescribing

Clinical audit is a way to find out if healthcare is being provided in line with best standards and allows care providers and patients to know where their service is doing well and where there could be improvements. An audit cycle involves quantifying a marker of practice relative to best standards, implementing a change, and then reviewing this at a later date to investigate if the change has made a difference in improving quality in practice.

Between 2017 and 2018, I undertook an audit of antidepressant prescribing in a rural GP practice in Ireland. The practice consisted of eight GPs with a combined practice list of more than 3,000 patients. For the first phase of the audit, in September 2017, I reviewed the notes of 30 patients who had been prescribed an antidepressant for the first time in the previous three years. These 30 patients were randomly selected using GP software and the search-term 'antidepressant drugs'. I sought documentation indicating disclosure of side effects, withdrawal effects, and discussion of the duration and mechanism of action prior to initiating antidepressant therapy. The results were as follows.

### Phase 1: Review of current practice

Preceding first prescription of an antidepressant:

- 0 of 30 patients had discussion of side effects documented in notes (0%)
- 0 of 30 patients had discussion of withdrawal effects documented in notes (0%)
- 1 of 30 patients had discussion of duration of action documented in notes (3%)
- 0 of 30 patients had discussion of mechanism of action documented in notes (0%).

### Phase 2: Intervention

I presented my QIP and phase 1 audit findings at a meeting with all the GPs who worked in the practice. I discussed the purpose of the audit, current guidelines and how to use the ADPP. I reviewed the relevant literature and explained the results from phase 1 of the audit. The practice GPs discussed possible improvements to their current practices and I guided each doctor through how to use the ADPP on their GP software. The doctors were instructed to document if they discussed side effects, withdrawal effects, duration and mechanism of action with all patients before prescribing an antidepressant. I also gave them a supplementary patient information leaflet to help ensure they had obtained fully informed consent from the patient before prescribing an antidepressant. The doctors appeared interested in the project and willing to try their best to improve on their practice.

### Phase 3: Review of practice post-intervention

The audit cycle was completed between October 2017 and April 2018. I reviewed the notes of all patients who were newly prescribed an antidepressant medication in the six-month period of time. I identified 24 patients, of whom:

- 11 had discussion of side effects documented in notes (46%)
- 9 had discussion of withdrawal effects documented in notes (37.5%)
- 7 had discussion of duration of action documented in notes (29%)
- 7 had discussion of mechanism of action documented in notes (29%).

The results of the audit indicated there was improvement in all four areas measured, but, disappointingly, not as much as I had hoped for. The largest area of improvement was documentation of side effects, which rose from 0% to 46%. I observed that the ADPP was being used by some of the doctors, and not by others.

## How to bring about change?

In my view, antidepressant use is not a straightforward area of general practice. It is influenced by a range of socio-economic and cultural factors, as well as prevailing belief systems. I do not believe GPs intentionally mislead patients; they aim to guide patients towards what is best for their physical, emotional and psychological wellbeing. However, GPs act on what they know, or think they know, and are trained to diagnose and treat based on a predominantly biomedical model of responding to human beings presenting in distress. The fact that GPs are the first port of call for people in distress is something I think we as a society need to question. Why do we encourage people in very low mood and typically with complicated mental and emotional struggles to seek help from a professional who has 10 to 15 minutes to try to alleviate their distress?

GPs are encouraged and trained as doctors to give proactive medical responses to states of distress within this 10–15-minute consultation framework. They do this by putting people into diagnostic boxes. Each of these diagnostic boxes (for example, depression) is associated with specific drugs that the doctor will immediately call to mind – and in the case of depression, these will be antidepressants. Many GPs I speak with are frustrated because they understand the limitations of psychopharmacology, they recognise the need for a range of responses to human distress and they are mindful of the social and personal determinants of mental health – they deal daily with ordinary people trying their best to manage the ups and downs of life. This whole system needs rethinking and remodelling in order to avoid more and more people being inappropriately prescribed antidepressant medications for lack of alternatives – drugs that may be doing them more harm than good.

What GPs can do is communicate the facts about what we know about depression and antidepressant therapy. We can have open, clear, transparent discussions with patients about the potential benefits, risks and limitations of the psychotropic drugs we prescribe. But one of my main concerns is that many GPs are themselves not fully aware of the facts when it comes to depression. When I presented my QIP and audit to GP audiences, many had never questioned the theory they were taught in medical school – one that is reiterated by pharmaceutical marketing – that depression is due to a biochemical imbalance in the brain. Many also had little or no knowledge of the existence of withdrawal effects from antidepressant drugs and still believed these drugs have no addictive qualities. This begs the question, how can patients be fully informed about antidepressants, and how can GPs fulfil their ethical duty to inform them fully, if GPs themselves are not fully informed?

In my view these are the areas that most need to change in general practice, in medical schools and even in psychiatry. In order for GPs to change how they practise, they need to be educated in a more thorough, holistic and realistic way about the pros and cons of the psychotropic drugs they prescribe. And for this to happen, we need to be relieved of the pharmaceutical influence that prevails in Western medical education settings.

I had never questioned much of what I learned about mental health in my medical training until I attended the Annual Critical Perspectives Conferences at University College Cork. These conferences opened up for me an ability to think critically and creatively when it comes to mental health issues. This is another area that is completely absent from conventional medical school and GP training settings. One of the simple and key switches in my thinking has come through reading the work of Joanna Moncrieff, a psychiatrist and senior lecturer in psychiatry at University College London. Moncrieff (2009, 2008) advocates that we need to stop looking at antidepressants from a disease-centred perspective (that these drugs will treat this disease called 'depression') and move to what she calls a drug-centred approach (these drugs achieve these effects, which may provide some relief but do not 'treat' the depression). We could then speak sensibly and realistically to people about the fact that these drugs are chemicals that we put into our bodies, much like alcohol or cocaine, and that they have psychological and physical effects as well as withdrawal effects. This approach would help doctors to communicate information about what the drugs actually do rather than create a context of disease (depression) and cure (antidepressant), which is not factual and ultimately misleads both doctor and patient.

I had hoped that having my QIP paper in *Forum* magazine (McElroy & Holmes, 2015) would generate some interest in this topic among GPs in Ireland. I was disappointed not to receive any feedback on the initiative following its publication. The results of my audit in the rural GP practice showed how challenging it is to create meaningful change in this area. In spite of my best efforts, improvements were small and were likely to be of little significance in the long-term in terms of changing practice. Looking forward, I realise that I need more support from equally motivated colleagues and more technical expertise to bring about more sustainable and significant change and expand on the work that I have done thus far.

The QIP and audit were intended to be used as a day-to-day 'aide memoire', leading to safer prescribing and enhanced patient autonomy. It was my aim that they would serve to facilitate further education, discussion and reflection among GPs. I think the projects achieved these goals to some degree, although the results of the audit indicate how challenging it is to bring about substantial change in the context of general practice in Ireland.

## Change by example

Perhaps one obstacle is that GPs feel helpless to try anything else, not knowing what else to do. GPs are trained to treat – to refer or to prescribe. My experience is that there is a lot the GP can do in their consulting room without reaching for a prescription pad.

I have had an interest in mental health since I was a fourth-year medical student, more than 10 years ago. Shortly after completing my first year in practice, I heard a lady by the name of Mary Maddock speak at a wellbeing seminar about her negative experiences of being forced to take psychiatric drugs for many years. I spoke with Mary after her presentation, and it was she who recommended that I attend the Annual Critical Perspectives Conference at University College Cork. The perspectives and stories shared by professionals and people with lived experience of severe distress challenged much of what I had learnt in medical school and the practices that predominate in psychiatry and general practice in Ireland. Since then, I have attended a number of these conferences, read many books from a critical psychiatry perspective, and gone on to train as a GP and undertake a diploma in clinical psychiatry. I have also trained as a hearing voices group facilitator[3] and a Three Principles facilitator,[4] and in Eye Movement Desensitisation and Reprocessing (EMDR) and the Alexander technique.

3. www.hearing-voices.org (accessed 19 August 2019).

4. https://3pgc.org (accessed 19 August 2019).

When a person presents to me, I therefore see them through quite a different conceptual lens than a GP who has had only the conventional mental health training that they would have received in a medical university or a GP training scheme.

When a doctor is educated in the conventional setting, we are trained to look for symptoms and make a diagnosis. With depression, this essentially means that, if a person presents and we elicit in their history that they have been feeling predominantly low for more than two weeks, and have in addition between four and five other symptoms (eg. poor sleep, poor appetite, poor concentration and low energy or libido) and 'objectively' they come across as sad, low or depressed, then we can make a diagnosis. The diagnosis then dictates the management plan and the therapeutic options we are trained to offer – lifestyle advice, a referral for counselling, or antidepressant medication. I personally find this a very limiting and often misleading approach.

I view humans as creative, social beings, and depression is, in a sense, a manifestation of this creativity. People who present with and fit the criteria for depression have almost all experienced significant trauma and usually are coming to their GP overwhelmed with negative thoughts about themselves, the world and the future. My initial approach is to listen as deeply and respectfully as I can to the person in front of me. After listening, I may ask some more questions to clarify my own understanding of where the person is coming from. I then typically ask for permission to offer my own perspective or reframe their experiences in a way that is meaningful and that recognises the role of the underlying thought and perception patterns that I believe are causing them to feel this way. Most people value this perspective and feel understood.

I often then share my understanding of what appears to me to be a universal principle – that our thoughts create our feelings from moment to moment and shape our experience of life from the inside out. Typically, I recommend books, podcasts and videos for the person to read, listen to or watch over a two-to-three-week period, after which we review the situation. I may also give some lifestyle advice, local counselling or options. I sometimes offer a leaflet I have written called the BRAIN document (Benefits, Risks, Alternatives, Information and Nothing), if they are interested in reading up on the pros and cons of antidepressant therapy.

**B: Benefits** – what are the benefits of taking antidepressant medication?

Evidence suggests antidepressant medication can improve mood over time, especially for moderate or severe depression. However, there is an element of uncertainty about how these medicines actually bring about reported benefits. In studies comparing antidepressant medication with placebo pills, many people who took the placebos also benefited. There are also studies that suggest antidepressants may help mitigate other conditions such as menopausal or fibromyalgia symptoms.

**R: Risks** – what are the risks involved?

Some important factors to consider include possible side effects, withdrawal effects, dependency and risk to the foetus during pregnancy. These factors may be more or less important depending on the antidepressant and the individual taking the medication. (Here the leaflet refers the patient to www.medicines.ie for specific information on a particular drug, and rxisk.org, a free, independent drug safety website that helps a patient weigh the benefits of any medication against its potential dangers.)

Psychological and/or physical dependencies with regard to antidepressant therapies are controversial issues. It was commonly believed that antidepressants are not addictive. However, it is now well established that withdrawal effects do occur. Withdrawal reactions can be severe and occasionally debilitating and/or long lasting. See the websites listed above for further information.

**A: Alternatives** – are there any alternatives to antidepressant therapy?

- Lifestyle: improvements in levels of physical activity, diet, sleep hygiene and limiting alcohol or other substances are proven, sensible and often very effective ways to address low mood.
- Exercise: 30 to 60 minutes of vigorous exercise per day have been consistently proven in many studies to improve mood. If you are very physically unfit or have physical conditions that limit your ability to exercise, discuss these issues with your doctor or appropriately trained fitness instructor. It is often wise to increase physical activity levels gradually.
- Psychotherapy and counselling: speaking with a trusted professional is another intervention with proven efficacy. Confiding in trusted friends or family members is often also helpful.
- Bibliotherapy (books): there are many books available by reputable authors on the topic of mental wellness. (I specifically recommend *Loving What Is* by Byron Katie (2002) and suggest

they consult the self-help/mental health section of their local library or bookstore.)

- Problem-solving: tackling problems or making changes in relationships or at work or home life may mitigate symptoms of depression. It may be worth taking some time and energy to address these issues.

- Renew interests/ find creative outlets: there are many simple, but effective ways of helping to shift low mood. Make a list of activities you enjoy and try to spend more time and energy engaging in some of them. For animal lovers, consider adopting a pet or volunteering at a local animal rescue.

There are myriad reasons why people find themselves in low moods and likewise myriad ways that people recover. Seek out multiple perspectives and keep an open mind.

**I: Information** – ask yourself 'Do I need more information?' or 'Where can I find more information?' if you are unsure about what decision to make. It may be helpful to discuss your options with a therapist, a psychiatrist, a friend or a support group. There are many resources available online. (Here I recommend www.patient.co.uk; www.mentalhealthireland.ie; rxisk.org and www.medicines.ie.)

**N: Nothing** – what would happen if I did nothing or waited a while?

Many cases of depression have a lifespan of six to eight months and spontaneous recovery is common, especially in those who have a diagnosis of mild-to-moderate depression. Some experts argue that moderate to severe depression should be treated promptly with antidepressant medications. However, others argue that treating depression inappropriately with medications can do more harm than good in the long term.

While this approach does not work with everyone, I am continually surprised by the number of people who, at our review, report a significant shift in their mental and emotional wellbeing. I am much more interested in working with people at a psychological level, so I prescribe far fewer antidepressants than many of my GP colleagues. I would, of course, love to have more time with my patients and I hope to develop my practice to accommodate this.

## References

Anderson C, Kirkpatrick S, Ridge D, Kokanovic R, Tanner C (2015). Starting antidepressant use: a qualitative synthesis of UK and Australian data. [Online.] *BMJ Open* 5(12): e008636 (accessed 19 August 2019).

Bracken P, Thomas P, Timimi S, Asen E, Behr G, Beuster C (2012). Psychiatry beyond the current paradigm. *British Journal of Psychiatry* 201(6): 430–434.

Chapman DP, Whitfield CL, Felitti VJ, Dube SR, Edwards VJ, Anda RF (2004). Adverse childhood experiences and the risk of depressive disorders in adulthood. *Journal of Affective Disorders* 82(2): 217–225

Cheong EV, Sinnott C, Dahly D, Kearney PM (2017). Adverse childhood experiences (ACEs) and later-life depression: perceived social support as a potential protective factor. [Online.] *BMJ Open* 7(9): e013228 (accessed 19 August 2019).

Cipriani A, Furukawa TA, Salanti G, Chaimani A, Atkinson LZ, Ogawa, Y (2018). Comparative efficacy and acceptability of 21 antidepressant drugs for the acute treatment of adults with major depressive disorder: a systematic review and network meta-analysis. *Lancet* 391(10128): 1357–1366.

Colloca L, Miller FG (2011). The nocebo effect and its relevance for clinical practice. *Psychosomatic Medicine* 73(7): 598–603.

Council for Evidence-based Psychiatry (CEPUK) (2018). Do antidepressants work? The new research proves nothing new. [Online.] *CEPUK;* 22 February. http://cepuk.org/2018/02/22/antidepressants-work-new-research-proves-nothing-new/ (accessed 5th August 2019).

Dantzer R, O'Connor JC, Lawson MA, Kelley KW (2011). Inflammation-associated depression: from serotonin to kynurenine. *Psychoneuroendocrinology* 36(3): 426–436.

Drohan N (2013). Depressing truth about treating depression in the young. [Online.] *The Irish Examiner;* 3 April. https://www.irishexaminer.com/ireland/depressing-truth-about-treating-depression-in-the-young-227126.html (accessed 19 August 2019).

Hyde J, Calnan M, Prior L, Lewis G, Kessler D, Sharp D. A qualitative study exploring how GPs decide to prescribe antidepressants. *British Journal of General Practice* 55(519): 755–762.

Irish College of General Practitioners/Health Service Executive (2006). *Guidelines for the Management of Depression and Anxiety Disorders in Primary Care.* Dublin: ICGP/HSE.

Ilyas S, Moncrieff J (2012). Trends in prescriptions and costs of drugs for mental disorders in England, 1998-2010. *British Journal of Psychiatry* 200(5): 393–398.

Johnson, CF, Williams, B, MacGillivray, SA, Dougall NJ, Maxwell M (2017). 'Doing the right thing': factors influencing GP prescribing of antidepressants and prescribed doses. *BMC Family Practice* 18(1): 72.

Katie B (2002). *Loving What Is: four questions that can change your life.* London: Ebury Publishing.

King M, Bearman P (2017). Gifts and influence: conflict of interest policies and prescribing of psychotropic medications in the United States. *Social Science & Medicine* 172: 156–162.

King M, Essick C, Bearman P, Ross J.S (2013). Medical school gift restriction policies and physician prescribing of newly marketed psychotropic medications: difference-in-differences analysis. *BMJ* 346. https://doi.org/10.1136/bmj.f264 (accessed 19 August 2019).

McDermott, S (2018). HSE prescriptions for antidepressants and anxiety medications up by two thirds since 2009. [Online.] *The Journal.ie;* 1 August. www.thejournal.ie/ireland-antidepressant-anxiety-medicine-prescriptions-4157452-Aug2018/ (accessed 19 August 2019).

McElroy B, Holmes K (2015). Antidepressant prescribing: a structured approach. *Forum* September: 33–34. http://owenduignan.com/wp-content/uploads/2016/09/Antidepressants.pdf (accessed 26 August 2019).

Medical Council (2009). *Guide to Professional Conduct & Ethics: responsibilities to patients.* Dublin: Medical Council.

Moncrieff J (2009). *A Straight Talking Introduction to Psychiatric Drugs.* Ross-on-Wye: PCCS Books.

Moncrieff J (2008). *The Myth of the Chemical Cure: a critique of psychiatric drug treatment.* Basingstoke: Palgrave Macmillan.

Moncrieff J, Cohen D (2013). How do psychiatric drugs work? *British Medical Journal 338*(7710): 1535–1537.

NICE (2009). *Depression in Adults: the treatment and management of depression in adults.* London: National Institute for Health and Clinical Excellence.

Rafferty M, Bradley C (2019). Counselling in primary care: a general practitioner's perspective. *Irish Medical Journal 112*(2): 869.

Read J, Cartwright K, Gibson K (2018). How many of 1829 antidepressant users report withdrawal effects or addiction? *International Journal of Mental Health Nursing 27*(6): 1805–1815.

Research in Practice for Adults (undated). *What is Evidence-Informed Practice (EIP)?* [Online.] www.ripfa.org.uk/about-us/about-evidence-informed-practice/ (accessed 27 March 2019)

Rimmer A (2018). Large meta-analysis ends doubts about efficacy of antidepressants. [Online.] *British Medical Journal 360*: 22 February. https://doi.org/10.1136/bmj.k847 (accessed 19 August 2019).

## Antidepressant prescribing protocol checklist

☐ Side effects of therapy – short term

☐ Withdrawal/missed dose effects eg. emotional lability, sleep disturbance, irritability

☐ Expected duration of treatment

☐ Adjuncts/alternatives to treatment discussed eg. exercise/counselling/ bibliotherapy/self-help/mindfulness

☐ If female, considered need for contraception

☐ Need for ECG considered eg. pre-existing heart disease + citalopram derivatives

☐ Interactions with other medication eg. NSAIDs increase gastro-intestinal bleeding risk – need for gastroprotection?

☐ Organic cause considered/outruled eg. hypothyroid/low B12 or folate status

☐ Course of prescription/overdose risk considered

☐ Patient information leaflet given on medication

☐ Side effects of treatment – medium term

☐ Side effects of treatment – long term

☐ Best practice of tapering off drug with guidance of doctor if/when appropriate

*Side effects – short term*

Increased agitation, insomnia, occasional suicidal ideation

Gastro-intestinal disturbance eg. nausea, vomiting, diarrhoea

Venlafaxine/mirtazapine – headache

*Side effects – medium term*

Emotional numbing (may be experienced as positive or negative effect)

Increased risk of gastro-intestinal/urogenital bleed

Sexual side effects (may be experienced as positive or negative effect)

Delayed ejaculation/anorgasmia

Increased weight eg. mirtazapine

*Side effects – long term*

Increased risk of osteoporosis

Escitalopram/citalopram can increase QT interval/risk of sudden cardiac death

Psychological/physiological dependence – may have difficulty stopping the medication

Hyponatraemia – especially in elderly people

If taken when pregnant, risk to foetus eg. IUD/autism.

### Consent addendum:

I (name) _____ , of

(address) _____ ,

consent to the use of _____ (drug name)

having discussed the potential benefits/risks and counselling with

Dr _____

I have received a patient information leaflet that includes alternatives to medications as well as details of local counselling services, and I have decided to proceed with a course of treatment.

Signed (doctor) _____ Date: _____

Signed (patient) _____ Date: _____

# Chapter 7

# Women and power: Drayton Park Women's Crisis House

## Anne Cooke, Shirley McNicholas and Andie Rose

One morning three of us had a conversation about a house. Tears were shed: good ones.

Shirley McNicholas is Women's Lead for Camden & Islington NHS Trust in London, and Founder/Manager of Drayton Park Women's Crisis House. Andie Rose is a member of the Camden & Islington Women's Strategy Group, and someone who has stayed in the house. Anne Cooke is a clinical psychologist and academic. The house we were talking about, 32 Drayton Park, is a large Victorian villa that looks much like its neighbours, in a typical north London street. Part of the UK's National Health Service (NHS), for more than 20 years it has offered an alternative to hospital for women experiencing mental health crises. It is run on trauma-informed, feminist and systemic principles, and furnished in a homely, inexpensive style, with an airy living and dining space at the back overlooking the garden. Each resident has her own en-suite room and there are cosy rooms for individual conversations and even massage.

In line with our brief for this chapter, our conversation covered why Drayton Park was needed, how it got off the ground, what it's like, obstacles the team have overcome, Andie's and other women's experiences of the project, evidence that it helps, what the 'active ingredients' are likely to be, thoughts about the future and critical reflections. We titled the chapter in homage to Professor Mary Beard, whose book of that name Shirley had just read on the train and brandished animatedly throughout our conversation.

*Anne*: What's Drayton Park like?

*Andie*: It's for women only, with women-only staff. The first time I went I wasn't sure they'd take me, given my 10 years of hospital admissions, mostly under section. But I needed to be in a women-only environment and to feel safe. The house had a homely feel, not remotely 'psychiatric'. My first thought was, 'Will they be able to cope with me here?' My second was, 'How will *I* cope being here? Will I just end up back in hospital with the same old medical model approach, the same old medication and the same old restriction of freedom?'

After what seemed like a lengthy assessment (I couldn't understand why they wanted to know so much about *me* rather than just my 'symptoms'), I was accepted. I didn't realise at the time just how life-changing my contact with this place would be. Drayton Park is one of just two places that have helped me move forwards towards getting the therapy I needed.

At first, I was a bit overwhelmed by how much staff wanted to check in with me. I remember my first night. A member of staff called Michelle asked me to leave my door open so she could check on me regularly. Because I was used to hospital, I automatically assumed I was on 'close observations' and left the door propped open with a chair. I was expecting staff to sit there and watch me, like they do in hospital. I'd always felt this was really intrusive, especially with male staff. When Michelle came to check on me, she looked surprised that I'd left the door wide open and asked why, was I afraid? I explained, and she told me that she'd just meant leave it unlocked. It was my first night and they wanted to be able to check I was OK. She emphasised that I could make my room as safe as I wanted to and make it my own. It was *my* room, my private space and I had the key. I couldn't quite get my head around that.

That was back in 2004. I've had other admissions over the years. Each time I feel bad coming back to the 'steps of shame' – my name for the front steps – because here I am having a crisis again. But once over the threshold, the warm welcome from staff makes things OK.

The house is comfortable and you can tell every effort has been made to make it homely – so different to the hospital environment. There's an aromatherapy room where you can get a massage. The garden is big, with quiet corners where you can sit and relax. A member of staff once helped me ground myself by walking barefoot on the pebbly path. That was a different take to the usual hospital one of giving me meds when I get anxious or dissociate. There's a cook who caters for most dietary needs – the weekly roast dinners seem to be the most popular!

On your first day, you agree a plan – it's actually called an 'agreement plan' – with the names of your workers and your timetable for the week, including reviews of your stay. That feels empowering. Sometimes I've had no idea what I really wanted or expected, but that was OK too. The staff offer one-to-one sessions twice a day, and they also always make time for you if you need it. They spend time around the house and so can see if someone perhaps isn't doing too well and check in with her.

There's richness of diversity among the women who work there. They each have their own way of working, but the most important thing for me is always the therapeutic relationship you have. Each time, you build another layer of trust. It's such a huge relief to talk about my issues as a woman, to a woman, in a women-only safe space.

The staff listen to me without fear or judgement. I've been given confidence to find my voice. I'd previously tried for years to access the right therapy but kept getting turned down because of my 'psychiatric history'. But Rachel [one of the deputy managers] and the local day hospital manager took on the challenge and encouraged and supported me to try again. With their help, I was finally accepted for psychotherapy. That has been the most effective treatment for me – I call it my 'dialysis'.

Another staff member, Julie, helped me with my housing problems. She understood where I was coming from and gave me the confidence to stand my ground and assert my rights.

Each staff member has different skills, but they share the same values. They work in what I call the 'Drayton Park compassionate way'. They meet you where you're at. They understand and respect that things can be different each time, but keep the consistent, compassionate care going. They want to know what's happened to you, who you really are, despite the 'symptoms' playing havoc in your mind. The focus is on the person, the soul. They respect all aspects of you, whoever you are. No judgement, no shame, no expectations, just the opportunity for you to work out what's going on for you and find ways forward. It's not rocket science – it's humanity.

*Anne:* It sounds as if staff attitudes – and the ideas that guide their work – are central. Shirley, how do you recruit and keep people?

*Shirley:* What we're most interested in at interview is people's values and motivations. We need to hear a convincing account of why the person wants to work with women, why they care. Many have their own or family experience of psychological distress. Once someone's appointed, they become part of a very supportive framework. As you'd expect, each team member has individual supervision, but in a sense the team also has constant supervision because we all work from the same office, including managers and senior staff. It isn't for everyone. We talk to each other all the time, checking in with plans for each individual woman. We take referrals in the office as well, so again we're listening and coaching new staff until they're confident about the process.

On top of this, and the usual mandatory training, the team also takes part in training on domestic and sexual abuse. Once a year we also have a team day on trauma-informed working. The team days are an important chance to stop and remind ourselves of what we're trying to do and why. The things we do make a real difference to women's lives, and our job is to keep doing them well, even if we've done them a hundred times. Staff have to be able and willing to work with the same women on multiple occasions while keeping an open heart. People sometimes ask what enables us to do that. Having that annual space to refresh ourselves and our motivation is vital. Also, I think the staff feel 'free' to use their particular skills. That's empowering and protective, as the staff are valued and get a lot of positive feedback from the women staying here. The shared office helps too, and we are all encouraged to use our annual leave to take regular breaks to refresh.

*Andie*: Drayton Park is a special place, and I'd love to see other places set up and follow this model. I found my feminist voice here and became a member of the Women's Strategy Group – a group of eight women who have used the local mental health services and who work with Shirley to help improve them.

*Anne*: I know you've talked to many other women who use Drayton Park, Andie. What do they say?

*Andie*: The thing you hear most often is 'We're so lucky to have this place'. People say what a difference it makes having their stories and experiences heard and validated. They talk about the one-to-one sessions and say they feel listened to. They mention the team and the support they offer, even after you leave. They talk about the quiet, calming space that gives you an opportunity to focus on the important issues and hopefully start a fresh journey of healing.

*Anne*: Going back to when Drayton Park first opened, why was a crisis house needed?

*Andie*: I needed somewhere that felt safe and didn't retraumatise me. The unwanted attention from men you often get in hospital often made me worse. I also didn't feel it was right to have male staff watching me at night, or to have medication forced on me by groups of male and female staff. Those things just raised my anxiety and exacerbated my crises. The different approach taken at Drayton Park showed me that the hospital restrain-and-inject procedures were unnecessary.

*Shirley*: In the early 1990s there was a lot of dissatisfaction with mental health services, and particularly services for women. There were many reports of women being assaulted. More than 500 sexual attacks are reported every year in UK hospitals, and many more go unreported (Williams, 2014). Women were avoiding services out of fear. There was no provision for women with children. Pressure groups, including the Women's Mental Health Network here in London – were pushing for women-only services. National Mind was running a campaign called 'Stress on Women' (Darton, Gorman & Sayce, 1994).

At the same time, evidence was accumulating that it is possible to offer safe crisis care within a less restrictive environment (Perkins et al, 1996; Copperman & Knowles, 2006). Hospital services were stretched and people were looking for innovative ways to create capacity.

Locally, several things came together. First, the two local authorities in this area, Camden and Islington, both had a history of social justice politics and one had a dedicated Women's Equality Unit. Second, Rabbi Julia Neuberger was the Chair of the NHS trust at the time. She had a keen interest in women's issues and was very supportive of the project. So was Claire Murdoch, a senior manager in Camden & Islington NHS Trust, who has since gone on to be National Mental Health Director at NHS England. Both were keen for the trust to be a pioneer and to develop a women's crisis house. They put in a successful funding application to the London Implementation Group – the body responsible for developing London's NHS services. Both local authorities agreed to contribute funds.

I was appointed Project Development Worker, and what made a huge difference was being in post for a year before the service actually opened. It meant I could research things properly, visit other services, gather feedback from service users and make recommendations. One of the most important things I did early on was to set up a working group made up of women who used services, people from the voluntary sector and a few key professionals who had a vision and passion for change. The group argued strongly against employing a traditional multidisciplinary team; they wanted us to employ women from a variety of backgrounds who could provide a range of emotional and practical responses. They also argued for the service to be able to accommodate children with their mothers. The advance thinking we were able to do meant that, from the word go, there were very clear processes in place that provided consistency and containment (Bion, 1970), both for the staff and for the women using the service. The policies also provided reassurance to senior management that the advisory group was taking the issue of risk very seriously and that we knew what we were doing. We agreed the referral and assessment processes with senior clinicians, who were then able to see from feedback and from the minimal number of incidents that we were providing a safe service.

*Anne*: That was more than 20 years ago and Drayton Park still seems to be thriving. Andie has described her experience of it. Shirley, can you briefly describe it from your point of view?

*Shirley*: We are a residential crisis service and take telephone referrals 24 hours a day. The fundamental criterion is that the woman is otherwise likely to be admitted to hospital. This is important in enabling the trust to continue to offer this alternative – it reduces pressure on inpatient beds. It is also economical – a stay in a crisis house is more cost-effective than a stay on a ward (Howard et al, 2010).

We offer an assessment at the house as soon as possible. There are two assessment slots every day. If a woman is offered a place, it's usually for one week in the first instance. During that time, she has intense support from a team with skills in containing and managing risk, working with crises and with disclosures of trauma and abuse, and safeguarding. The team includes body therapists – shiatsu and aromatherapy massage – and we can accommodate children with their mothers. We work hard with each woman, her supporters and other services to make sure that a robust support plan is in place for when she goes home. The average length of stay is 21 days and the majority of women return safely home. Occasionally women are transferred to hospital if the risk is so severe that it can't be contained in a voluntary community setting. I'd say that happens about once a month.

Sometimes we don't offer a stay in the house. This might be due to a sense from the assessment that the woman might pose a threat to others or that her risk to herself at this time is too high and she would require a level of observation that only hospital can provide. If this is the case, we may ask the hospital to refer the woman back to us as soon as she is able to safely spend periods of time without observation. Sometimes we have to ask women to leave if they break their agreement. This is usually to do with threatening behaviour towards other women and staff or using drugs and alcohol.

*Anne*: What are the guiding ideas that underpin the service?

*Shirley*: Drayton Park offers an alternative to hospital for women in acute crisis. It operates on the principles of a 'trauma-informed environment' (Elliot et al, 2005). Trauma-informed approaches have evolved over the last 20 years and Drayton Park has been part of that development. The team is trained in the approach and works to embed its principles in day-to-day practice (Sweeney & Taggart, 2018; Sweeney et al, 2016).

A core component is 'routine inquiry'. At every initial assessment, we ask whether the woman has experienced or is experiencing any form of trauma. If the answer is yes, we provide an opportunity to speak about it and be heard. National data about the high incidence of trauma and abuse in the lives of women coming to mental health services (Read et al, 2018) are borne out in the disclosures made daily at Drayton Park. Our model of care is threaded through all aspects of the service, from its philosophy to how we open a bedroom door.

*Anne*: Tell me more about that. How is the trauma-informed approach reflected in your policies?

*Shirley*: There are lots of components to it. I'll go through them in turn. First, we are a women-only staff team. Staff are appointed on the basis of their skills, attitudes, knowledge and experience, rather than professional qualifications. The majority have either come from the voluntary sector or are looking to be psychologists or therapists in the future. Others are nurses who want to practise in a collaborative and therapeutic way and want to have a voice. When I worked as a nurse, a long time ago, I noticed that many nurses did not feel empowered as therapeutic practitioners. At first, very few nurses applied to work with us. I assume this was partly because the positions were not designated as nursing posts. This has changed as the service has become established. However, it's important that the team continues to be made up of staff from a variety of backgrounds.

Second, as I explained earlier, women who use services have been involved from the beginning. They contributed in a major way to the design of the service and are involved in its ongoing management. Over time, the advisory group has morphed into the trust-wide Women's Strategy Group. We're trying to extend some of the same principles to other services – for example the new women's psychiatric intensive care unit (PICU).

*Andie*: I've been involved in the Women's Strategy Group ever since my first encounter with Drayton Park. As a service user, I've seen a lot of change in services and experienced first-hand the slow disintegration of our priceless NHS. Despite this, when I attend the meetings – which are usually held at Drayton Park – it's so reassuring to see the familiar faces of the women who are the backbone of the service there. They have inspired so many with the feminist model of working with women in crisis. Drayton Park isn't just a women's crisis house, it's about women and power.

*Shirley*: Getting back to how the trauma-informed approach is reflected in our policies, the third element is that staff are trained and supervised in the approach, including the impact of domestic and sexual abuse on mental health.

Fourth, we accept self-referrals as well as referrals from workers. Women refer themselves by phone and the process is the same as for professionals. Fifth, as I mentioned, our initial assessment includes routine inquiry about past and current trauma.

*Anne*: Say more about that? I always wonder why *all* mental health assessments don't include that. On the other hand, a criticism I hear of the trauma-informed approach is that it can become a bit one-size-fits-all: seeing everything in terms of trauma. Someone said to me, 'But what about those of us who have severe problems but haven't experienced trauma? We're sick of being told that our problems must be due to some kind of trauma we've forgotten. I hear voices but I haven't been abused or traumatised.' How does Drayton Park approach that issue?

*Shirley*: Just because we ask the question that doesn't mean we expect the answer always to be yes. As with all mental health services, we ask a range of routine questions, such as whether people are feeling suicidal. Of course, they aren't relevant for everyone, but we know they often are. It's the same with asking about abuse and trauma. Our experience bears out what we know from research (eg. Khalifeh et al, 2015) and from many personal accounts (eg. Filson, 2016) – namely, that these are relevant questions for many women. We understand that for some the answer will be no, and that others will choose not to say. In those cases, we'd never tell someone that the issues she's facing are due to trauma. We're just opening the door and saying to people, this is a place where you *can* tell. If (and *only* if) someone does, we help her to explore possible connections between what's happened to her and how she's feeling.

Going back to my list, number six is that we don't use 'care plans'. Instead, as Andie said, we have 'agreement plans'. Each plan starts with 10 standard, typed statements: for example, 'You will have access to staff 24 hours a day.' The next part of the plan is an individual one drawn up by the woman with her worker, together. It includes the issues she wants to address, the names of her workers, how she wants to arrange the one-to-one sessions, a safety plan if she feels at risk, agreements about medication and other substances, and contact with children. It's an agreement plan rather than a care plan because we do things *with* rather than *for* or *to* the woman. This is the foundation of the Drayton Park model. We're part of the trust IT systems and we upload the agreement plan in the care plan section of the person's electronic notes.

This ensures it's available to other colleagues and can be used as a reference in other services.

Seven, as Andie mentioned, twice a day we offer an opportunity to talk one-to-one. This isn't therapy but includes everything from filling out benefits forms to sharing heart-rending stories of childhood abuse. The team helps women to develop and try out coping strategies, grounding techniques and ways of managing dissociation, flashbacks, voices, terror and urges to self-harm. We recognise that different things help different people, so it's vital to support each woman as she tries things out and develops strategies that work for her.

Eight, we've developed our own self-harm policy, on the basis of feedback. Women are often skilled in using alternatives to self-harm. In the early days we agreed a policy that includes staff keeping clean blades that women can use when nothing else is working. Although this seems dramatic and risky, it had a paradoxical effect, as the women knew it would: the knowledge that they could come for a blade meant that self-harm reduced. Our non-judgemental approach enabled many women to show their wounds or scars to someone else for the first time. Again, although it felt counter-intuitive to staff who'd worked in settings that intervene by force if necessary, we found a way of working that didn't involve taking control away from the woman. We trust each woman's judgement, but we're also aware of our limits and are honest about them. It's been rare that working with someone in this way has not been possible.

*Andie:* My self-harm reduced over the years. The staff encouraged me to approach them if I had urges to harm myself. It did take a while – I had to feel safe with them before I could talk. But then I was slowly able to understand what had led me to that point. Gradually I was able to open up more – trust was being built. It helped that the staff were open to discussing self-harm and not anxious about it. I never felt punished like I had in hospital, where staff set off alarms once they discovered you'd self-harmed, and sometimes cancelled your leave or threatened to move you to a more restrictive ward. That always made me feel worse.

*Shirley:* I'm so glad you've found Drayton Park helpful, Andie!

*Anne:* I think you'd got to number eight in your list, Shirley?

*Shirley:* Yes. Number nine is that we manage risk by psychological means rather than physical containment (Bion, 1970). Instead of 'observations', we have nine 'contacts' – we verbally check in with the woman and try to have at least a brief conversation, human contact. The team contains risk, and in turn we contain each other's anxieties – the principle of psychological containment applies to the staff too. It's a household of women – there's talking all the time! We're constantly updating each other, debriefing, keeping things focused and held.

Our tight working structure is also very containing. We all use the same format to guide referral-taking and assessment conversations. Our risk management framework includes completing a 'contact form' each day. It has the names of all the women currently using the service, and next to each a list of time slots for the contacts, starting at 7am and going on throughout the day until midnight. It doesn't mean that the whole team runs to find every woman at exactly 7am, but we do make contact within 60 minutes of that time. Staff sign to say they've had contact and that the woman is safe. If they don't have contact, it's flagged in the team to decide what to do next – for example, if a woman is not in the house and we can't reach her on her mobile, do we wait and call her again or do we contact the police for a welfare check immediately. I swear that my tombstone will say, 'Is the contact form up to date?'! Each contact is an intervention in itself, part of our containment structure both for the women and for the team. Women know that, whatever else happens, someone will regularly come and find them. For the staff, reporting back after contacts to the rest of the team in the house gives us an opportunity to share anxieties and decisions and to support each other.

We make most decisions as a team, so staff members are never solely responsible for something. For example, we always take a break in an assessment process to talk to other team members without the woman present, to help decide if we should offer her a place. There's always someone to share ideas and worries with. That's what makes our work possible. It also means we can make decisions straight away – no waiting for a weekly review meeting, for example. The shift team are empowered to make decisions and to be the therapeutic agents. The institution respects people's skill and life experience. That gives us job satisfaction. That mixture of tight structures and team working is what makes the job possible.

Number 10 is that we positively promote diversity both in the team and the building. We try to ensure that our artwork, posters and leaflets speak to women from all walks of life. We want women who are staying to find images that they can relate to and that make them feel welcome. We have noticeboards focused on issues affecting particular women – for example, a Black women's one and an LGBTQI one.

Number 11 is home-cooked food. Women often tell us what a difference it makes having our chef cooking their meals. They like to know who the chef is and talk to her so it's personal. Food is so important and cooking for someone is a nurturing thing to do. The chef is a very important person in the team.

Number 12 is our 'knock three times' policy. One thing women often find difficult in hospital is that, even if you have a single room, it's often not really treated like yours. People barge in, including when you're getting dressed. Like Andie said, that feels disrespectful and can make you feel unsafe. Here we knock and wait five to 10 seconds for an answer. If there's no reply, we knock again, saying the woman's name, and wait. If there's still no reply we knock again, say our name, the woman's name and that we're going to use our key to open the door. This procedure allows the person to get dressed or off the toilet, and means we don't retraumatise someone who, for example, has been abused in their bedroom and had no power to say no. The Women's Strategy Group is currently working to get this policy adopted throughout the trust, and it's being piloted in the new women's PICU.

Number 13 is that we welcome children. This can be a challenge, of course, but many mothers have the main or sole responsibility for their children, and, even if they're in acute distress, many will wait until they are sectioned and taken into hospital because they don't want to leave their children. Fathers and other men in women's lives are also welcome to visit and be part of their plans if the woman wishes.

Finally (14th!), the service is provided in a homely, domestic setting. We try hard to achieve this, despite needing to stick to NHS policies about infection control, fire and ligature risks. Women often comment that it's like a 'home from home'. The fabrics are warm and soft, and there's carpet on the floor that muffles noise. Both of those are important when working with traumatised women in crisis. The environment itself plays a huge role in enabling people's recovery.

Drayton Park has continued to thrive despite experiencing many challenges over its 23 years. The extensive development phase before opening established strong foundations. We've lost some funding over the years due to NHS cuts, and have had to limit some of our provision – for example, we offer fewer groups now. But we've survived because the service has proved an effective alternative to hospital. The trust is committed to the service and has always supported us in reorganising our resources so we can continue what we are doing. In turn, Drayton Park contributes to the trust's positive reputation.

*Anne*: That must have been a challenge, especially as the service is so counter-cultural in the NHS. Recently things seem to have become even more stretched, medicalised and focused on managing immediate risk. Can you maybe say something about how you've overcome resistance and obstacles over the years?

*Shirley*: Well there have been a lot! In the beginning it was senior men not seeing the need for a women's service and laughing at us in meetings, saying things like 'Is massage going to cure schizophrenia then?' People stereotyped us as 'a bunch of lesbians' and spread rumours that men weren't allowed in the building. There's been a lot of misogyny and many challenges to the service's power base. For example, before the service started, we secured agreement for it to run without a consultant psychiatrist. The advisory group had fought hard to ensure that it was a real alternative to hospital, including in its guiding ideas and the type of staff who would deliver it. I think some in the trust found that idea threatening, and when the service opened a consultant psychiatrist was assigned to us anyway. When that person moved on, we successfully argued for the funding to be used for sessions from a female GP instead. That worked brilliantly and helped us look after women's physical health as well as their mental health – something there's been a lot of emphasis on recently. Sadly, we lost the money for that a while ago. Even now, every new senior manager in the trust asks why we don't have a psychiatrist, and we have to explain and argue our case. It isn't that a psychiatrist couldn't be helpful; it's the impact that their power and influence would have on the dynamics of the team, perhaps on the culture (which famously 'eats strategy for breakfast'), on the guiding ideas, and on service users' confidence that the service offers a genuine alternative.

I also have to keep arguing the case for employing staff on the basis of experience, skills and attitudes rather than profession. The national nursing establishment exerts pressure for certain roles to be reserved for qualified nurses. That would limit who we could employ. Even if only the senior posts were reserved for nurses, that would affect not only the culture but the possible career pathways (and therefore the attractiveness of the job) for non-nurses. The key to overcoming all these challenges has been designing and articulating a robust and safe alternative. Job descriptions, person specifications, the recruitment process and staff contracts all provide assurance and protection.

We do employ specialist staff on a sessional basis. Massage, for example, is an extremely popular part of the service. Often people ask to continue after they leave and are referred on to low-cost centres in the community as part of onward planning. We can also refer women to a counsellor who is with us one day a week. She is very experienced and can contain a high level of distress and trauma. She can offer up to 16 sessions, continuing after the woman goes home if needed. This allows a significant piece of work to be done, perhaps working through trauma from historical abuse, and sometimes helps women prepare to engage in longer-term therapy. We try to promote this possibility to Black, Asian and minority ethnic (BAME) women in particular because we know that, statistically, they are less likely to have been offered talking therapy or counselling (Jeraj, 2015). For women who have disclosed abuse for the first time, this can be an opportunity to speak more about what happened to them while they are still in the safe place where they first disclosed. Others include those considered high risk who have not been offered counselling in other settings for fear that the emotional work of therapy might increase the risk beyond what the service can contain. Throughout the year we also host poetry workshops run by Leah Thorn.[1] All of this adds to the richness of the trauma-informed environment we can offer.

*Anne*: Talking of people leaving, apart from perhaps continuing with counselling, what support do you offer women after they go home? I know it can be a really hard time. The first two weeks after leaving hospital are a peak risk time for suicide attempts (Wise, 2014).

*Shirley*: Every Wednesday we run a support group for women who've stayed here. They say it makes a huge difference not having to go 'cold turkey' from the support. Most come just for a few weeks but there's no time limit, and some come for years. The group is facilitated by staff, and numbers vary from four to about 18. The trust and community benefit too, as it's often enough to support someone and so reduces demand on other services.

*Anne*: That all sounds brilliant but nowadays we're often asked for formal evidence of effectiveness for any service. Is there any for Drayton Park?

*Shirley*: Yes, a number of formal evaluations have been published (Killaspy et al, 2000; Johnson et al, 2004; Howard et al, 2010). The results suggest that women who come here are similar to those admitted to hospital in terms of demographics and the severity of their problems, or 'symptoms'. Most prefer it and choose it if they have the option. A stay here seems to be as effective as hospital in reducing 'symptoms'. It's also more cost-effective, as I mentioned earlier.

We're also continuously developing the service in the light of experience and feedback. It's important to be honest and to acknowledge that, like any service, we sometimes make mistakes. Sometimes we fail to offer someone a place and, on reflection, we think we probably should have. This kind of work is never an exact science, and it's important to acknowledge when you've got something wrong. Women also tell us when they feel we haven't met their expectations, and we've had some formal complaints. I feel strongly that it's important to listen carefully to the feedback and act on it. For example, at one point there were comments about the model not being followed at night. The

---

1. www.leahthorn.com (accessed 10 August 2019).

policy is that women can make their own decisions about when to sleep, but some staff were telling women in the communal areas to go back to bed. We took the feedback seriously and wrote a new night guide for staff and residents.

*Anne*: I guess we need to stop soon, but there are a couple of things I really wanted to ask. Shirley, you've been at Drayton Park for more than 20 years. What motivates and sustains you to keep going?

*Shirley*: I was given a once-in-a-lifetime opportunity to develop a service from scratch with a group of amazing women. I was then privileged to be asked to manage it. Every day is different, and every day I'm inspired by something one of the team does, or one of the women staying. I'm indebted to the members of the Women's Strategy Group, who are a supportive network for me. I was never interested in working in 'management' as such, but my role gives me the power I need to protect the service and the creative freedom to keep developing it. Many of my Drayton Park colleagues over the years could easily have got more senior positions elsewhere, but they've stayed here because of the job satisfaction and their commitment to our goals.

I've also been active in helping the trust improve its service to women more broadly, and a few years ago I was designated Women's Lead. That role has allowed me to spread my wings, to get involved in related projects and in providing training. Really, what more could I want? I believe completely in what we are doing and every day I see the difference it makes to women's lives.

*Anne*: How do you see the service developing in future?

*Shirley*: There are four things I'd like to see. First, I'd like us to build on the trauma-informed approach and keep revisiting its principles. Second, I'd like to develop a clearer and more comprehensive training programme for staff. Ideally it would be accredited so women could have something tangible to take with them when they leave that validates their learning and experience. One possibility would be a certificate in trauma-informed women's mental health practice, in collaboration with a university. Third, I'd like to involve more volunteers. Fourth, I'd like to encourage more research. I'm really glad that Hannah, a clinical psychology trainee at Canterbury Christ Church University, recently interviewed women about their experiences of Drayton Park and of hospital (Prytherch, 2018).

*Anne*: OK, the last thing we need to address is critical reflection. What do the two of you think? Is there anything you would have done differently if you could go back, or something you'd like to change?

*Shirley*: We should have bought the house next door years ago and turned it into a women's resource centre. The team is sure that, if we had a day service as well, we could increase the number of women we divert from hospital and have a stronger base for women to flourish.

*Andie*: I'd like to have access to a day service and a crisis line staffed by the women I've worked with and with whom I've built a trusting relationship.

*Anne*: What do you think has kept Drayton Park going and enabled it to thrive where other crisis houses have come and gone? Why do you think there aren't more crisis houses?

*Andie*: I hope more will open. But, for Drayton Park, I think it's been Shirley's compassion and her unwavering commitment and determination, together with other longstanding and dedicated staff and the ever-strong army of kick-ass women from the Women's Strategy Group. We're always on hand to ensure Drayton Park won't be going anywhere. The women who've used Drayton Park also hold the thread firmly together. Its strength comes from us all – forever and always ready to fight the good fight!

*Shirley*: Time for lunch, I think!

## Acknowledgements

*Andie would like to add:*

Reading the chapter through, I realise that I mention only three staff members: Michelle, Rachel and Julie from years back. It wouldn't be right and fair not to mention others like Gracia (I recently had probably my most productive admission and the stuff I learnt from her was phenomenal); Fiona – for always tolerating my craziness and just being a true rock; Georgia – quietly compassionate, a woman of few words but huge heart; Dee – the mother of Drayton Park and Christmas fairy! Rose – kindness and understanding; Flo – empathetic, gets it so well. The fantastic Diane Frazer, who is a warrior of a woman. Natalie, Jan and Amira, the massage therapists. I could also go on about women who have now left, like Zoe and Isobel. I'd also like to acknowledge all the women, past and present, from the Women's Strategy Group, whom I absolutely adore and with whom I feel such a sisterly solidarity. All these women have been the warriors who have shared the same spirit and made a difference in my life, and I'm sure other women's lives too.

## References

Bion W (1970). *Attention and Interpretation*. London: Tavistock.

Copperman J, Knowles K (2006). Developing women-only and gender sensitive practices in inpatient wards — current issues and challenges. *Journal of Adult Protection* 8(2): 15–30.

Darton K, Gorman J, Sayce L (1994). *Eve Fights Back: the successes of MIND's stress on women campaign*. London: Mind Publications.

Elliott D, Bjelajac P, Fallot RD, Markoff LS, Reed BG (2005). Trauma-informed or trauma-denied: principles and implementation of trauma-informed services for women. *Journal of Community Psychology* 33(4): 461–477.

Filson B (2016). The haunting can end: trauma-informed approaches in healing from abuse and adversity. In: Russo J, Sweeney A. *Searching for a Rose Garden: challenging psychiatry, fostering mad studies*. Ross-on-Wye: PCCS Books (pp20–24).

Howard L, Flach C, Leese M, Byford S, Killaspy H, Cole L, Lawlor C, Betts J, Sharac J, Cutting P, McNicholas S, Johnson S (2010). Effectiveness and cost-effectiveness of admissions to women's crisis houses compared with traditional psychiatric wards: a pilot patient-preference randomised controlled trial. *British Journal of Psychiatry* 197(S53): 32–40.

Jeraj S (2015). Black and minority ethnic people are short-changed by mental health services. *The Guardian*; 25 June. www.theguardian.com/healthcare-network/2015/jun/25/black-minority-ethnic-people-shortchanged-mental-health-services (accessed 14 August 2019).

Johnson S, Bingham C, Billings J, Pilling S, Morant N, Bebbington P, McNicholas S (2004). Women's experiences of admission to a crisis house and to acute hospital wards: a qualitative study. *Journal of Mental Health* 13(3): 247–262.

Khalifeh H, Moran P, Borschmann R, Dean K, Hart C, Hogg J, Osborn D, Johnson S, Howard L (2015). Domestic and sexual violence against patients with severe mental illness. *Psychological Medicine* 45(4): 875–886.

Killaspy H, Dalton J, McNicholas S, Johnson S (2000). Drayton Park, an alternative to hospital admission for women in acute mental health crisis. *Psychiatric Bulletin* 24(3): 101–104.

Perkins R, Nadirshaw Z, Copperman J, Andrews C (1996). *Women in Context: good practices in mental health services for women*. London: Good Practices in Mental Health.

Prytherch H (2018). *Residential Suicide Crisis Care: stopping people from dying or supporting people to live*. Unpublished Doctoral Thesis: Canterbury Christ Church University.

Read J, Harper D, Tucker I, Kennedy A (2018). How do mental health services respond when child abuse or neglect become known? A literature review. *International Journal of Mental Health Nursing* 27(6): 1606–1617.

Sweeney A, Clement S, Filson B, Kennedy A (2016). Trauma-informed mental healthcare in the UK: what is it and how can we further its development? *Mental Health Review Journal* 2(3): 174–192. doi.org/10.1108/MHRJ-01-2015-0006 https://www.emeraldinsight.com/doi/full/10.1108/MHRJ-01-2015-0006 (accessed 14 August 2019).

Sweeney A, Taggart D (2018). (Mis)understanding trauma-informed approaches in mental health. *Journal of Mental Health* 27(5): 383–387.

Williams M (2014). Sexual violence soars in UK hospitals. *The Guardian*; 31 December. www.theguardian.com/society/2014/dec/31/sexual-violence-soars-uk-hospitals (accessed 14 August 2019).

Wise J (2014). Mental health patients pose high suicide risk in first two weeks after discharge, inquiry finds. [Online]. *British Medical Journal* 349: g4659. https://doi.org/10.1136/bmj.g4659 (accessed 14 August 2019).

# PART 2

Outside in

# Chapter 8

## Slí Eile: finding another way home

### Joan Hamilton

The experience of psychiatric breakdown disturbs the person on many levels. Most of all they feel very vulnerable and cut off from normal relations with family, friends and the wider world of their community. Their immediate need is to regain a sense of emotional security, preferably within a supportive relationship with others. Regrettably, traditional psychiatric hospital care often adds to the sense of isolation and alienation felt by the person.[1]

My vision for 'another way' (*slí eile* in Irish) came about through the harrowing experiences that I and my family went through when my daughter, Geraldine,[2] became caught in the revolving door of the traditional biomedically oriented psychiatric (since then euphemistically renamed 'mental health') services in Ireland in the early 1980s. In this chapter, I describe my own journey in attempting to develop another way to support people in distress, away from the traditional psychiatric system. The journey starts in 1995 and ends in 2017, with my retirement as the CEO of a residential community farm for people in recovery from their distress. I will outline why another way was needed, what it involved, the challenges, obstacles along the way, and the successes we celebrated. The chapter aims to provide hope and inspiration to those who are considering setting up 'other ways'.

1. Professor Phil Barker, speaking at 'Community as Method', the first meeting of the Slí Eile Board, held at Cork Airport, 8 November 2002.

2. Geraldine gave permission for her name to be used in this chapter.

## Some background

My Irish husband, Gerry, and I, together with two sons and two daughters, located from Jersey to County Cork, Ireland in 1967, where two more sons were born, completing our family. It was the experience of our youngest daughter that eventually led to the setting up of Slí Eile.

Geraldine had her first breakdown and admission to hospital in 1980 when she was 16, the start of that slippery slope. It was a living nightmare for us, and I cannot even begin to imagine what it was like for her. She would be admitted to hospital, receive drug treatment, then be discharged back home, where she continued to struggle. Without having addressed the reasons for her breakdown, it was just a matter of time before she would once again be in crisis and re-admitted, and with each admission it seemed to us that she lost a little more of herself. Over a 14-year period, her stays at home got shorter, her stays in hospital longer, until she ended up in long-stay 'care', totally withdrawn, looking wretched, spending her days just sitting, hunched over, watching the clock until it was time for her next cigarette. My feelings of hopelessness and helplessness are best summed up by the definition of insanity attributed to Einstein – you keep doing the same thing over and over and expecting there to be different results. There had to be another way.

The seeds for setting up a residential farm were sown in 1995 after I attended the World Congress on Mental Health at Trinity College, Dublin. For the first time I heard of 'service users' and 'user movements'. What stayed with me were the words of a keynote speaker from Denmark: 'Buildings, buildings, we must change attitudes, not buildings.'

Up until then I had been afraid to go public about our experiences – afraid of how it might impact on Geraldine. But now, with her so wretched and withdrawn, conditions so dire, I felt there was nothing to lose. I rang the local RTE Radio (the Irish national public broadcaster) in Cork and arranged to meet their reporter for an interview. After my 20-minute interview was broadcast, I was contacted by five families, each with a son or daughter in psychiatric care, all leading wretched lives. I had been told by Geraldine's psychiatrist that she was a unique case and that it was not possible to provide a service tailor-made to meet her needs. When I met with these other families I learned, sadly, that she was not so unique after all.

We (the families) continued to meet, talk and gather information on a regular basis. Then, in May 1997, I was diagnosed with cancer (non-Hodgkin's) and needed time out from meetings for surgery and six months of chemotherapy. This was a good time for reflection. If we were to succeed in our quest for change, we needed more facts, more statistics, more information. It was only when I read the reports of the Inspector of Mental Hospitals that I first became aware of the rates of re-admissions – more than 74% of inpatient admissions in 1999 (Department of Health, 2000) – and how many patients were in long-stay inpatient care – almost 55% at the end of 2003 (Department of Health, 2004).

Between 1999 and 2007, endeavouring to understand what had led to my daughter's breakdown, I completed courses in interpersonal communication, counselling, disability studies and choice theory/reality therapy. All these equipped me well for the challenges and obstacles that followed in the years to come.

Meanwhile, while recovering from cancer, I had kept in touch with three of the families and, in 2000, had re-started the group meetings in Cork. By September we had 10–15 families at the monthly meeting. I proposed that we hold a public stakeholders' meeting, to include service users, service providers and families, where we could all put forward our concerns. We came up with a name for our group, the Cork Advocacy Network (CAN), and a title for the public meeting: 'Together – *can* we make a difference?' This was followed the year after by another public meeting, in January 2001, entitled 'Together we *can* make a difference!'

The then Minister for Health, Micheál Martin, had accepted our invitation to attend this second public meeting. The well-known journalist and national broadcaster Vincent Browne had agreed to chair the day's proceedings. I was in a panic that no one would turn up but, having told my story on *Liveline* (a popular daily radio programme on RTE National Radio, where members of the public can ring in), a flood of calls followed and then my own phone started to ring… and it just kept ringing. More than 700 people came – so many that Vincent Browne changed the agenda and the roving mike was passed around for people to tell their stories. You could hear a pin drop as we heard one harrowing story after another. For weeks after, my phone continued to ring. I had known there was a problem, but I was overwhelmed by the enormity of it.

Next, in early 2002, I was approached by RTE to participate in the *Would You Believe* television documentary series to raise awareness of the distress carried by families with a family member caught up in the psychiatric system. After I had told my story on television, including my ambition to set up a residential farm offering housing and support for people discharged from hospital, I was contacted by Mike Watts of GROW,[3] who told me about a 17-acre GROW residential farm in Australia. I was then put in touch with Diane Maxwell, who had worked at the farm and had gone on to set up a second residential facility in America. When Diane visited Ireland the following year, she stayed with me for a couple of days and our group, CAN, had the first of

---

3. https://grow.ie (accessed 10 August 2019).

many brainstorming sessions in my kitchen about setting up and running such a residential farm in Ireland. Slowly, a vision and plan for 'another way' started to emerge.

## Developing a Slí Eile approach

So, what exactly is this 'other way'? Over quite a few meetings of brainstorming, drawing on different ideas from both theory, practice and policy, a vision and approach slowly emerged, informed by principles, values and practices around community living (Mosher, 1999), recovery (Department of Health & Children, 2006), therapeutic communities (Campling & Haigh, 1999), choice theory (Glasser, 1999) and other examples of what have been variously called therapeutic farms (Loue, 2016), social care farms and community living farms.

The Slí Eile approach developed as one that:

- fosters a safe environment in which everyone is respected and listened to
- acknowledges the simplicity and complexity of the experience of daily life on the journey to recovery
- recognises that everyone is the expert in their own recovery journey
- offers an environment of hope and empowerment, where meaningful life activities support the process of recovery
- creates an environment that instils the belief that change is possible
- provides opportunities for individuals to participate actively in choices and decisions about their lives
- employs a non-labelling and non-judgemental approach.

To put these principles and beliefs into practice, it is necessary to explore meaning and purpose for each individual and foster personal control by supporting the individual in taking responsibility for their recovery. Self-determination and self-management are crucial elements in achieving personal control. It is also necessary to adopt a holistic and inclusive approach to living that recognises that health and wellbeing are influenced by a range of social, environmental and individual factors, as well as requiring a safe environment and the encouragement of creative risk-taking.

## From idea to a residential facility

It became clear early on that setting up such a supportive environment would need huge finances – the capital to set up the venture and the revenue to run it. With the help and advice from the Irish Council for Social Housing (ICSH), CAN set up a registered housing association (CANHA Ltd). Seven volunteers made up the Board of Directors, and I was elected as the Chair. This qualified us to apply for 95% funding from the government to purchase or build social housing. The next stage was to find a suitable property. It took us three attempts over the next several years before we struck lucky.

Our first attempt was a 12-acre property in North Cork. It looked ideal, with the main house able to offer residential support for up to eight tenants, stone outbuildings that could be renovated into accommodation for those requiring less support, and maybe a bungalow in the grounds for the more independent tenants who were settling into their chosen route to the wider community – either adult education, training, voluntary or paid employment. We agreed a purchase price and paid the deposit. At that point it became obvious that not all CANHA Board members shared a common vision. Some now wanted to open a drop-in centre or maybe a support group for families, instead of a residential project. This disagreement led eventually to the formation of Slí Eile as a separate housing association, with a new board.

We continued with our attempted purchase of the property but, after going through all the procedures, hiring architects, obtaining planning permission, getting the local community on board and incurring costs of more than €100,000, delays in getting the actual funds from the local authority meant we lost our deposit and the premises. We lodged a complaint with the Ombudsman, seeking reimbursement of the funds we had spent (and were told it could take two years), and started over.

This time we looked in Charleville, a small town in North County Cork. We decided to look for a house with a maximum of six bedrooms, which would not require the lengthy planning consent for change of use. If we used it as a pilot project, it could be up and running within six months and, once the complaint was processed and the debt cleared, we would try again with our proposal for a residential farm. We'd retain the pilot property as a move-on, independent and secure social housing accommodation.

An auctioneer in Charleville had a six-bedroom bungalow on his books, within walking distance of the centre of Charleville. It was one of 11 bungalows on a small housing estate. I went to my local TD (MP), updated him and told him we hoped to buy the bungalow. The following week I was pleasantly surprised to learn that the local authority would approve this new proposal. Not long after, the TD rang me to say he had confirmation from the Minister for Housing that funding was approved. Just like that.

Except that the helpful TD had also contacted the local newspaper with the news about the funding approval. The headline the following morning, squeezed onto the front page, read: €413,698 FUNDING FOR SLÍ EILE HOUSING PROJECT. That evening I received the first phone call from one of our new neighbours on the estate, informing me, 'There will be no mentally ill people moving in here.' The main concern she expressed regarded the safety of the young children living on the estate. The following morning, I received another phone call, this time looking for a meeting at the house of the chairman of the newly formed Residents Association. We asked for a neutral meeting venue but got no response. From then on we were subjected to a persistent campaign of harassment. Any time we visited the property, the neighbours would line up outside with placards, with texts such as 'RESIDENTS WILL NEVER ACCEPT SLÍ EILE', 'NO CONFIDENCE IN SLÍ EILE', and 'GET OUT STAY OUT.'

All attempts on our part to engage with residents were met with hostility. An anonymous letter was sent to me at my home:

> … I totally object to it. These people have a mental disorder and should not be in any estate. These people need 24-hour care… you got the money, take these people and put them in your own village.

The protesters even followed my car to my home and lined up across the road with placards. This continued for three months. They refused to take part in a televised discussion. We were at stalemate.

We decided that, to engage with the protesters and allay fears, we should prepare the house for a trial of six weekends. Margaret (not her real name), who I had known for many years and was at the time a patient in the local psychiatric hospital, said she was keen to give it a go, despite the protests. Maybe the protesters would meet her, talk to her? It was arranged that a volunteer would collect her from hospital on the Friday evening and she would stay at the bungalow with three or four of us for the weekend and we would then drive her back to hospital on Monday morning.

On the first Friday evening, we attempted to walk the short distance into Charleville and were surrounded by a group of residents holding placards right up to our faces, tapping them on the ground. It was so intimidating we returned to the house and went by car. On the two following Friday evenings I arrived to find that the keyhole had been blocked up with glue. We drove to the 11am Mass on Sunday and, when it came to make the sign of peace, Margaret turned around and shook hands with two of the protesters. I thought we might have a little breakthrough, but by the time we drove back to the house, there they were again, a double line of a picket!

I asked Margaret how the weekends were for her, with shopping, cooking, the support, the company, and the protesters always outside. 'Well, I'd rather they weren't there,' she said, 'but it's very good to be able to go shopping and to cook a meal. I have not been able to do that in very long time. I really enjoy that.' However, moving in had merely served to escalate the protest. On at least three occasions I had to call the police when we were blocked from driving out of the premises. We were between a rock and a hard place. To allow Slí Eile to be driven out of Charleville would surely send a signal to every group in the country that had a prejudiced attitude to persons experiencing mental health difficulties that they could drive projects like ours out of their back yard. How could we turn this around?

Then, by chance, a possible solution presented itself. I received a phone call from a friend with news of a property, Villa Maria, coming up for sale, on the other side of Charleville, well away from where we were now. This was another large, six-bedroomed, detached bungalow, with a reasonably sized garden and within easy walking distance to the town centre. A Board decision was taken to pursue this opportunity rather than prolong the ongoing struggle. Agreement was quickly reached between the owner, the Board, the Housing Authority and the Health Service Executive (HSE). The contentious property was transferred back to the County Council as social housing, and no further protests followed.

## The Villa Maria experience

With the 95% state funding to purchase Villa Maria and donations to cover the balance, we completed the purchase. Positive meetings with the local HSE resulted in a monthly grant of €16,000 to fund the employment of six part-time staff. One member of staff would be present at any one time, offering support to five tenants, 24 hours a day, seven days a week. The HSE required that staff had a third-level qualification in social care, or equivalent and, over time, also accepted lived experience as a job requirement.

I took on the role of CEO on a voluntary basis for 2006/2007. Fundraising, various other small grants, individual donations, and additional support from volunteers, meant we were able to scrape along financially.

Some renovations were needed before both staff and tenants could move into the house. While these were in process, we recruited the staff and introduced them, and the volunteers, to the work of William Glasser (1999) and the language of choice theory. This became the language of support in the house. All staff, as part of their contract, were required to attend at least the Basic Week and Basic Practicum at the William Glasser Institute Ireland.

Also, as part of the preparations, the Slí Eile Board members and I had meetings with the North Cork (our local) community mental health team. Most of the tenants would have been patients of this team. The main concern of the team was around administration of medication. It was explained that policy and practice on medication would be the same as when a patient was discharged from hospital, either to their home or living alone. The role of staff would be to support each tenant in taking their medication, but not to administer it. Slí Eile was offering housing and social support, not medical support – that would continue to come from the North Cork community mental health team. Each tenant would be responsible for ordering and collecting their medication and keeping it in a locked drawer in their bedroom.

## Life at Villa Maria

So, finally, in September 2006, six years after we first came up with the idea, Slí Eile Housing Association opened its doors to its first tenants in Villa Maria. Most came directly from long-stay care in either the local psychiatric hospital or one of the high-support hostels. The only requirement from Slí Eile was that the person themselves *wanted* to sign up to become a tenant.

At that time, my daughter, Geraldine, was living in an HSE-staffed hostel in Mallow, a small town 20 miles from Charleville. At first she was very nervous of moving but, after talking with the hostel staff, I suggested she try it for a couple of weeks but kept the hostel place open in case it didn't work. She came for two weeks and decided to stay. In future, all tenants were offered the same option: to come as a guest for two weeks before deciding whether to stay.

Most tenants had been living institutional lives for a long time. They had lost confidence in their abilities, including the ability to make the simplest of decisions. Working with the basic language of Glasser's choice theory, we started by putting up posters of Glasser's seven deadly habits (criticising, blaming, complaining, nagging, threatening, punishing, and bribing or rewarding in order to control), and his seven caring habits (supporting, encouraging, listening, accepting, trusting, respecting and negotiating differences). So simple, but oh so challenging! The role of the staff was to support tenants in making the choices involved, taking personal responsibility for their daily routine and showing self-respect and respect for staff and peers.

Gradually, a weekly rota for housework, cooking and shopping was established: whoever was on cooking rota would decide the day's menu and walk into Charleville the previous evening, with support from another tenant or the staff, to shop for ingredients. Most tenants were receiving welfare benefits, and as a result qualified for rent allowance. Each tenant paid rent and a contribution into the house 'kitty' to cover tenancy-related overheads, such as food, light, heating etc. In other words, the tenants were learning to live an ordinary life in a community setting. A wonderful volunteer came every Wednesday afternoon to discuss menus and ingredients. She supported each tenant in learning new skills, encouraging each one to be ambitious in planning their menus.

Another volunteer helped construct raised beds for growing vegetables, and we invested in a few hens (I became very good at applying for small grants). Every Saturday evening a volunteer came to the house and introduced the tenants to patchwork. With five people who had, until recently, led institutionalised lives, life was not always plain sailing. Tenants and staff discussed how best to resolve disputes in the house (whether among tenants, or between tenants and staff). They came up with self-awareness meetings (SAMs), which meant that anyone experiencing, or witnessing, a lack of respect, could call a SAM, and everyone present in the house at the time would have to attend. The staff would facilitate, but not attempt to resolve the dispute. Depending on the situation, staff would often role-play whatever issues had prompted someone to call a SAM, which often helped to bring clarity. Usually, a SAM cleared the air, although at times it could take two or three.

The staff handover was another important element in sharing information. The 30-minute handover, between 2.30 pm and 3.00 pm, became known as 'Community Feedback'. Staff and tenants would sit around the kitchen table and talk about the past 24 hours. I asked one tenant, who was shortly to move back to Cork city, what she found most difficult when coming to Slí Eile, and she said: 'Community Feedback.' Asked what was the best, she again replied: 'Community Feedback!' Community Feedback was more than tenants telling staff how they were: it was about taking back personal responsibility, recognising what made a day a good day or a bad day, what would help, what could be done differently, by the tenant but also by members of staff. It was a space for self-respect, respecting others and having a voice – something that was quite difficult after many years of institutionalisation. Some tenants found it challenging to say how they were, so we introduced 'scoring the day'; a low score indicated that their day had not gone well.

In June 2008, I visited Hopewell Community Farm near Cleveland, Ohio, in the US, as a volunteer for three weeks. On my return, drawing on the Hopewell model and their Four Stages of Recovery,[4] we introduced the framework for a 4-Step approach for tenants to progress through the project, based on respect and responsibility:

Step 1: new tenants settling in, taking part in activities in the house

Step 2: tenants taking more responsibility, setting short-term goals, less support

Steps 3 & 4: identifying long-term goals – involvement in either further education or voluntary or paid work.

---

4. www.hopewellcommunity.org/our-program/overview (accessed 20 September 2019).

Progress along the steps would be a process of self-evaluation. There was no time limit; it was up to each tenant to voice when they were ready to progress along their way.

As the CEO of Slí Eile but working as a volunteer, with the overall responsibility to report to the Board and the HSE and of employing and managing a team of staff and a growing number of volunteers, I found the early months hugely challenging. I contacted Social Entrepreneurs Ireland and they put me in touch with a business mentor, John Hickey, who was a lifeline and remained my mentor until my retirement in 2017.

## Building bridges and connecting with the local community

To build bridges, it was important that the tenants integrated well in the local community. Over the years, this was done in a variety of ways, of which the following are some examples.

Shortly after moving in, a volunteer offered to organise a fundraiser that would help counteract the negative publicity generated by the protest at the previous site and, at the same time, raise much-needed funds. A Christmas concert at the local church received great support from the wider community and ensured a memorable night.

The following year, four gap-year students from the local secondary school took on a project in the house to help with the garden and paint the windows. Their weekly visits included having lunch with tenants and staff, which was a really good shared experience, prompting one of them to ask, in relation to the protest, 'What was all the fuss about?'

As the months passed and the tenants' confidence grew, it became obvious that housekeeping, cooking and a little gardening were no longer sufficiently meaningful activities for them – not enough reason to get out of bed. But signing up too soon for outside activities, such as swimming at the local hotel pool, personal development courses and badminton, only added to a sense of failure when a tenant dropped out after one or two weeks. An in-house course on basic computer skills, funded through the Literacy Programme, was welcomed but there was also a need for supported interaction with the wider community beyond daily shopping.

Inspired by my own background in the food business, I suggested a feasibility study for setting up a small home baking enterprise, making brown bread and scones, with an emphasis on quality. Initially, there was a great response from the tenants, but a couple of days later they wanted another meeting before investing in an oven or other equipment. They said they didn't want to go ahead with the feasibility study, as they didn't have time. One tenant had talked to her family who did not agree with the idea: 'It won't work, who will buy the bread anyway?' Hmmm. There was visible relief all round when I explained that the house next door was vacant, the owner had agreed I could rent it for the time being, if anyone wanted to help, that would be great, but taking part in the bakery project was optional. A University College Cork graduate with a master's degree in social work agreed to act as project leader. I asked the tenants if they were OK if he joined us for coffee breaks and mid-day meals.

Two pubs, one small shop and the local Credit Union agreed to act as 'customers' for four weeks. Four out of the five tenants joined in the experiment and had fun carrying out market research: buying, tasting, and comparing prices and quality of products on the market. The tenants and the project leader would bake the bread and scones, walk into town and deliver them, then come back to prepare the dry ingredients for the following morning.

After the four weeks all were unanimously in favour of continuing; one tenant said how good it felt to have something normal to talk about with her family. The customers were all delighted with the products and said, 'Why stop?'

Renting the house next door to use its kitchen had served a purpose, but it would not qualify for a Food Production Licence. With a 75% grant and a bank loan, the garage at Villa Maria was converted into a commercial kitchen and we were granted a licence to sell to the public. Cuisine Slí Eile was born! If it was to gain support from the wider community, the consistency and quality of the products would be critical. Up until then, all staff were part time, but if we were to be a social enterprise, we would have to up our game. I explained to tenants and staff that to produce consistent quality products would require a full-time staff member to oversee the bakery. Our first full-time support staff member was appointed, two tenants also attended a food-handling course, and we set about establishing Cuisine Slí Eile. Deliveries around town were done on foot until, with a generous donation and fundraising, we bought an eight-seater van.

In 2011 we featured in the *Behind The Walls* documentary on RTE television,[5] and were approached by the proprietor of the SuperValu supermarket in Charleville, who had seen the programme. He expressed an interest in supporting Slí Eile and stocking our bakery products. This was a huge confidence boost to all involved, offering yet more opportunities for tenants to interact with the wider community. Over time, as sales increased, teamwork strengthened and tenants gained confidence and took more responsibility. The range of products also grew, to include apple tarts, gingerbread, rocky roads, cheesecakes and carrot cakes.

---

5. See under Video tab at www.slieile.ie (accessed 10 August 2019).

I asked tenants and staff what they thought about discontinuing having a member of staff sleeping in overnight. The staff phone could be left on the kitchen counter and if anyone felt the need for support, they could ring me, as I lived only 10 minutes away. After discussion, the tenants agreed to try it for two nights and talk again. Two nights became a week, and a week later all the tenants said it was a good move – good for self-confidence. Staff sleepovers were discontinued.

## Evidence that it works

There have been two formal studies of the Slí Eile Villa Maria project: in 2007 and 2013. In 2007, Lydia Sapouna was recruited to undertake an exploratory study of the experiences of both tenants and staff of the project since the opening of Villa Maria in September 2006. Her study found that the tenants were experiencing a very different lifestyle (Sapouna, 2007):

> ... tenants clearly articulated a new sense of possibility and prospects, particularly when comparing Villa Maria with other residential and hospital settings they had experienced in the past. Freedom of choice, a sense of responsibility and ownership as well as the opportunity to do 'normal life things' were viewed as new and welcome experiences. This was illustrated by tenants who observed that 'In a hostel they make your schedule but here I have to make my own' and 'In the hostel there was not much pressure to get out of bed, I felt there wasn't anything for me to do there… it's different here'.

The study also found that the tenants experienced a sense of community:

> All tenants talked about the importance of having a sense of responsibility and collaboration in the running of the house, with one tenant observing that 'We have a rota for all the work that goes on in the house and we sit down and chat, and we chat about what we are doing, all the courses we're doing, you know, the daily chores, if anyone wants to swap, and everyone's hobbies and what people want to do by themselves… it's very good'.

A few years later, Aoife Farrell (2013) undertook a participatory action research study, which found that Slí Eile was successfully implementing a social model of mental health care. She ascribed its success to a number of interrelated factors, such as the capability of its staff, its non-hierarchical management structure, open and honest communication, conceptual clarity, an organisational structure of the house that facilitated tenants in taking responsibility and control over their day-to-day lives, and positive relations with the local community. She concluded that:

> A social approach to working with people who experience mental distress in a supportive non-medical environment is effective, with, counter to the current provision of mental health services, the Slí Eile approach incorporating elements of the new social paradigm in mental health, representing changing attitudes and values in terms of how understandings of and responses to mental distress are conceptualised. (Farrell, 2013: 25).

She also pointed out that the Slí Eile approach represented excellent value for money and, although her study did not include a cost-benefit analysis, the cost per head per annum was strikingly lower than that of traditional psychiatric services.

## The Slí Eile community farm

However, setting up a community farm remained the overall ambition and goal. My visit to the Hopewell Farm had inspired and re-energised me to pursue something similar, but it presented such a huge challenge: where to find funding for such a project and, given the outcome of the first attempt, how to 'sell' the concept to potential funders, service users and families.

Nevertheless, the search began for a suitable location. At last, in July 2012, almost six years after the opening of Villa Maria, I heard, by accident, of a lovely vacant period property, Burton Park, at Churchtown, only 10 miles away from Charleville. It had six bedrooms, a cottage, and two self-contained apartments in the courtyard that could provide separate accommodation for additional tenants. This meant there was no need to apply for planning permission for change of use. After many discussions with the owners, we agreed a six-year lease on the house and 50 acres of organic farmland. We also agreed to buy the existing herd of 17 pedigree Aberdeen Angus cattle. Although a six-year lease was not ideal, it would hopefully provide enough time to demonstrate the value of a community farm model.

Before signing the lease, tenants and staff were invited for afternoon tea at the farm, after which the five Villa Maria tenants were offered the option to move to the farm, together with the staff, or remain at Villa Maria with no staff support. All five opted to relocate to the farm. A couple of weeks before the move, staff and tenants again went over to the farm. The tenants explored the house and the apartments and selected their bedrooms. Then, with the help of a merry band of volunteers, we relocated on the morning of

18 December 2012, a week before Christmas. The following May, the Slí Eile community farm at Burton Park was officially opened by the then Minister of State with responsibility for Mental Health, Kathleen Lynch TD, and Jeremy Irons, the actor, who had become Slí Eile's patron a few years earlier.

## Life at the farm

The mission statement for the farm, created over several community meetings by the tenants and staff, became:

> The Slí Eile Farm offers a place where people experiencing distress can find safety, acceptance and support to recover.

Life at the farm developed far better and quicker than any of us could have hoped. The welcome and support from the local Churchtown community was wonderful. A new routine was gradually established, which included driving to the Villa Maria bakery at 7.30am and returning to the farm around 11am. Tenants would walk to the local shop for daily commodities, such as milk and bread, and we would now do a single main shop once a week in Charleville. Given the responsibility that went with a large property and livestock, staff sleepovers were re-introduced.

The lease (€10,000 per annum), higher insurance to cover the farm, Villa Maria and the bakery, extra overheads, increased salary costs and general house maintenance now created an annual shortfall of some €70,000 just to survive. Nevertheless, somehow, over the first four years, with generous individual donations, enthusiastic fundraising and various grants, and the income from the increasing social enterprises, we thrived and were able to employ a part-time farm manager. In addition, with the support and guidance of a well-known organic farmer, Jim Cronin from County Clare, the farm's organic status was maintained, and we established a second organic social enterprise, selling quality organic produce to the local community and SuperValu supermarket in Charleville. Tenants are fully involved in the various aspects of the farm's daily activities.

In 2015, Sana Loue, an American researcher and author, visited Slí Eile and helped put more substance and guidelines to the 4 Steps. Sana was keen to include Slí Eile's approach in her book on therapeutic farms (Loue, 2016). In it, she refers to Sapouna's (2007) evaluation, observing that recommendations for programme improvement had been implemented:

> Many of the report's recommendations for program improvement have been implemented since the time of that Report, suggesting that quality

improvement is a high priority for the organisation. These program modifications include increasing tenant participation in the evaluation of their own progress, creating opportunities for joint planning of activities between tenants and staff, involving tenants and staff in broader decision-making, providing increased opportunities for staff and tenants to discuss tenants' future goals. (Loue, 2016: 87)

Setting short-, medium- and long-term goals is an important part of the 4 Steps approach. However, apart from organising occasional workshops and meetings between the tenant and their key support worker, we have yet to find the resources to introduce structured training for staff and tenants to assist in setting and achieving goals.

Slí Eile, because of its unique approach to working with people in recovery, attracts interest from outside groups, including third-level students. We receive annual organised visits from, for example, social work and mental health nursing students from University College Cork. The annual Harvest Festival is another way of making links with the community at large, attracting between 500 and 700 visitors, serving to promote the Slí Eile Farm and raising much-needed funds. Other open days over the last few years have included demonstrations on methods for growing potatoes and visits from the pupils of the local National School and Youth Club.

The farm also receives welcome support through corporate volunteering – 10 to 20 employees from medium to large companies volunteer to work a day on the farm, painting farm buildings, preparing for open days, planting cabbages, potatoes, carrots and onions, weeding and so forth. With so many hands, these become fun days for all, with tenants, staff and volunteers working together.

Since moving into the farm, we have introduced additional meaningful and structured activities to tenants. In 2014, we were able to buy three dairy cows. In 2015, tenants and staff converted a small outbuilding in the courtyard to start a farm market, open to the public from 10am to 1pm each Saturday for the sale of organic farm produce, teas and coffees and Cuisine Slí Eile 'home baking'. A year later, we successfully applied for a licence to sell dairy products, and now supply one-litre bottles of organic pasteurised milk at the Saturday market and make twice-weekly deliveries to SuperValu in Charleville. Customers have learned to come early to the Saturday market before the milk runs out.

The activities required in the running of the farm and the daily tasks such as animal husbandry, horticulture, cooking and household chores all provide further opportunities in gaining additional skills and confidence. Tenants who have progressed to Steps 3 or 4 now provide peer support for new tenants who have just arrived.

## Developments, reflections and testimonials

When a new 30-year lease was agreed in 2016, the way was open to seek capital funding to further develop the farm. At the time of my retirement in May 2017, we were applying for planning permission for self-contained accommodation for six more tenants and to develop the courtyard to accommodate the bakery, build a small purpose-built dairy and provide a coffee shop for the Saturday market. Villa Maria remains available to tenants, with the option of volunteering in the bakery and/or the farm.

Over the years, Slí Eile has had more than 40 tenants, some staying for only short periods and others for much longer. Some have returned to adult education or paid employment. Some have found it helpful to start back in education while still at the farm; others have moved to Villa Maria, while others have moved on to independent accommodation or have returned to live with their families. It has been my experience that the fewer admissions to hospital a tenant has experienced prior to coming to Slí Eile, the sooner they are ready to move on.

On reflection, foremost among the challenges has always been the never-ending search for funds and achieving acceptance of 'another way', not only from the traditional psychiatric service but also from service users and their families. We have found that it is the tenants themselves who, once they have developed confidence and self-belief from having a voice within the safety of the Slí Eile community and are more able to engage with the wider community (family, friends, mental health teams), have brought about gradual acceptance and growing support for the Slí Eile social approach. The challenge remains how to promote Slí Eile as an early option to support someone in distress.

In addition to the formal evaluations referred to earlier, we have received many testimonials from tenants moving on from their Slí Eile experience or in newspaper interviews and television documentaries. Those below give some flavour of how the Slí Eile approach has been experienced, not only by tenants but also by tenants' significant others.

> Before Slí Eile, my life was a living nightmare, I grew up in a very disturbed home… my stay in Slí Eile actually repaired the damage that plagued me throughout my life. The psychiatric system only served to reinforce that there was something 'wrong' with me and just added new layers of damage by labelling me. (Past tenant at Slí Eile Farm)

> I heard of Slí Eile through default by being very annoyed with lack of structure in my son's day whilst in recovery in hospital. I asked his

nurse, 'Is there anything else out there?' and he told me about Slí Eile. It was so uplifting to see light at the end of the tunnel. This was a far more humanistic approach to recovery. I felt such relief and am so happy to see my son blossoming into a lovely caring, confident young man, thanks to Slí Eile. (Parent of past tenant)

It was a life-changing experience for my son. It put structure into his life, and I found Slí Eile to be a great place and very good people running it. (Parent of past tenant)

I had a breakdown… in hospital for 10 months, not getting well, in bed until noon. Fantastic here… get back on your feet… I've started college. (Past tenant)

---

## References

Campling P, Haigh R (eds) (1999). *Therapeutic Communities: past, present and future.* London: Jessica Kingsley.

Department of Health (2004). *Report of the Inspector of Mental Hospitals for the Year Ending 31st December, 2003.* Dublin: the Stationery Office.

Department of Health (2000). *Report of the Inspector of Mental Hospitals for the Year Ending 31st December, 1999.* Dublin: the Stationery Office.

Department of Health & Children (2006). *A Vision for Change: report of the Expert Group on Mental Health Policy.* Dublin: the Stationery Office.

Farrell A (2013). Supporting recovery in mental health through community living: a case study of Slí Eile. *Critical Social Thinking: Policy and Practice 5*: 1–28.

Glasser W (1999). *Choice Theory: a new psychology of personal freedom.* New York, NY: Harper Colllins.

Loue S (2016). *Therapeutic Farms: recovery from mental illness.* New York, NY: Springer.

Mosher LR (1999). Soteria and other alternatives to acute psychiatric hospitalization: a personal and professional review. *Journal of Nervous and Mental Disease 187*(3 ): 142–149.

Sapouna L (2007). *Progress Report on the Slí Eile Housing Project (Villa Maria).* School of Applied Social Studies, University College Cork, Ireland. www.slieile.ie/progress-report (accessed 10 August 2019).

# Chapter 9

## Alternative approaches to mental health crisis: the Leeds Survivor-Led Crisis Service

### Fiona Venner

This chapter describes the work of the Leeds Survivor-Led Crisis Service (LSLCS), an award-winning charity that is nationally and internationally recognised as a beacon of excellence and innovation in mental health crisis care. The peer-led service has five main components: Dial House, an out-of-hours place of sanctuary; Dial House @ Touchstone (DH@T), a crisis service specifically for Black, Asian and minority ethnic (BAME) visitors; the helplines Connect and Teen Connect; groupwork for a range of different groups of people with diverse needs, and other crisis support services with partner organisations. Our services are also all accessible to deaf people. This chapter will describe these services and our alternative, non-medical, non-diagnostic approach to distress, as a survivor-led, person-centred, third-sector organisation.

### Beginnings

LSLCS was founded in 1999 by a group of campaigning mental health service users. They were people who had endured years at the gritty end of psychiatric services – sectioned, forcibly medicated, subjected to electroconvulsive therapy and psychosurgery. They passionately believed that there could be an alternative way: services outside of the NHS and local authority, staffed by people with direct, lived experience of mental distress.

The model that most attracted our founding mothers and fathers was the Soteria houses (Mosher, 1999) that operated in California from the 1970s to the 1990s, offering an alternative to psychiatric hospitalisation for people experiencing 'psychosis'. The Soteria philosophy of being 'alongside' people in crisis – not 'treating' or 'doing to' – inspired our founders and remains an essential guiding principle of our practice today.

In the mid-1990s, the Mental Health Foundation, a national UK charity, offered start-up funding for survivor-led crisis services in the third sector. As the campaigning founders did not have the infrastructure to be an organisation, LSLCS began as a partnership with the social services department of Leeds City Council for the first two years. Since 2001, we have operated independently as a charity and company, with our founders becoming our first management committee.

The organisation continues to deliver services that provide sanctuary and an alternative to hospital admission, Accident & Emergency, police custody and other statutory services for people in acute mental health crisis. Our services remain governed, managed and staffed by people with personal experience of mental health problems. We have developed our services based on knowledge we have gained through our own experiences of crisis and we use our expertise to help others, informed by our non-diagnostic and non-medical philosophy (Venner 2009; James 2010). We also develop, adapt and change our practice in response to the needs articulated by our visitors and callers and their experiences of what is and is not effective in supporting people in acute mental health crisis.

LSLCS calls the people who visit Dial House and DH@T and those who are involved in group work 'visitors', and the people who call the Connect helpline and Teen Connect 'callers'. In keeping with our commitment to survivor leadership, these terms were chosen by visitors and callers themselves at the beginning of our journey and will be used throughout this chapter.

## Services of Leeds Survivor-Led Crisis Service

### Dial House

Dial House is a place of sanctuary, open overnight from 6pm to 2am Monday, Wednesday and Friday through to Sunday, for visitors to access when they are in crisis. They can telephone to request a visit or turn up at the door. We receive around 2,500 visits per year. Visitors can use the house to take time out from a difficult situation or from a home environment where they feel unsafe or that may be exacerbating their difficulties. They can relax in a homely environment and receive one-to-one support from a crisis support worker.

### Dial House @ Touchstone

DH@T is a crisis service specifically for visitors from BAME groups, which is open from 6pm to 12am on Tuesday and Thursday nights, in partnership with another Leeds mental health charity, Touchstone. Staffed entirely by workers from BAME communities, DH@T is a culturally specific service, based in the heart of the most diverse part of Leeds. DH@T is also a bridge to Dial House, through the BAME staff who work in both services and who have developed positive relationships with people who struggle to trust community mental health services.

### Connect and Teen Connect

Connect is a helpline open 6pm to 2am every night of the year. The service provides emotional support and information for people in distress, by telephone and online. We receive around 7,000 calls a year. People can ring who are in crisis, anxious, depressed or lonely and they will be offered non-judgemental and empathic support and information about other services where needed. Connect is a resource for people in crisis, as well as providing a preventative service by supporting people before they reach the point of crisis. Connect also receives funding to provide emotional support to carers. Since 2018, Connect has extended its service to 13–18-year olds via Teen Connect. Paid helpline staff work alongside volunteers who have had a comprehensive and rigorous training programme and receive ongoing supervision, training and support. Many of them have their own experiences of mental health problems.

### Group work

LSLCS hosts a number of weekly peer-led groups held at Dial House and DH@T. These include a lesbian, gay, bisexual and transgender mental health support group, a trans-specific support group, a deaf support group, a Black men's group, a Hearing Voices group and a Coping with Crisis group.

The group work of LSLCS grew organically from the peer support that happens in Dial House and DH@T. Group work enables visitors to share experiences, gain new perspectives and develop skills as facilitators. It also reduces shame by supporting people from marginalised groups (ie. trans people, voice hearers) to come together in a non-judgemental, compassionate environment.

### Deaf project

It is a source of great pride that these services are all accessible to deaf people in crisis. Connect is delivered one night per week by deaf staff via Skype. A weekly support group (LSLCS's best attended group) is delivered by deaf staff and visitors are supported in Dial House and DH@T by hearing staff qualified in British Sign Language to Level 3. Deaf people are an extraordinarily marginalised group as a linguistic minority in a hearing world. There are higher rates of mental distress in the deaf community than the hearing community, as well as high levels of chronic isolation. Even when in acute crisis, deaf people cannot access support, due the inability of hearing services, statutory and voluntary, to communicate with them. LSLCS is unusual, as a hearing organisation, in employing deaf staff and supporting deaf people.

### Wellbean Crisis Café

LSLCS delivers the Wellbean Crisis Café in partnership with Touchstone, which is the lead agency. Open Saturday to Wednesday nights and bank holidays 6pm–12am, the Wellbean Café provides crisis support, social interaction and a hot meal. Located near St James's Hospital, the café has a specific remit to reduce visits to A&E if there is not a medical need.

### Leeds Suicide Bereavement Service

Delivered by Leeds Mind, the lead provider, and LSLCS, the Leeds Suicide Bereavement Service (LSBS) supports people who are bereaved by suicide, through individual, group and family work. Survivors of bereavement by suicide are recognised in the national Suicide Prevention Strategy (2012) as a high-risk group for completed suicide. LSBS provides timely, compassionate support, led by a staff team with direct, personal experience of suicide bereavement.

Across all our services, LSLCS supports people at acute risk of suicide and/or self-injury. During 2018, 62% of visitors to Dial House were suicidal, and self-injury was a presenting issue in 44% of visits. This includes a small minority of people who self-injure in severe or life-threatening ways.

## The philosophy of Leeds Survivor-Led Crisis Service

### The person-centred approach

The therapeutic approach of LSLCS is person-centred (Rogers, 1951). Throughout our existence, we have found this non-diagnostic approach to be compatible with our proud survivor-led history and philosophy, and a highly effective way of supporting people who are survivors of trauma and in extreme distress.

Applied to our work at LSLCS, this means:

- we believe in the individual's capacity to actualise
- we support the visitor/caller's direction
- the worker and visitor/caller together create the conditions in which the actualising tendency can flourish.

We understand the tendency to actualise to mean that people will always do the best they can, in the circumstances they are in, with the resources they have, and are innately motivated towards growth. Carl Rogers used the metaphor of potato seedlings growing in a dark cellar to explain this:

> The actualizing tendency... cannot be destroyed without destroying the organism. I remember that in my boyhood, the bin in which we stored our winter's supply of potatoes was in the basement, several feet below a small window. The conditions were unfavourable, but the potatoes would begin to sprout – pale white sprouts, so unlike the healthy green shoots they sent up when planted in the soil in the spring... They would never become plants, never mature, never fulfil their real potential. But under the most adverse circumstances, they were striving to become. Life would not give up, even if it could not flourish. (Rogers, 1980: 118)

Even when working with behaviour that may appear self-destructive, such as self-injury, we understand that a caller or visitor is trying their best to cope in the circumstances they are in, with the resources they have. Even when somebody's self-injury is severe or even life-threatening, we view this as their attempt to find ways to survive and thrive within the life that they have.

Supporting the direction of our visitors and callers is often described as 'non-directivity'. However, the phrase 'non-directivity' can be interpreted as passive. We understand this as actively supporting the tendency of the individual towards growth. We see and respect the person's creative attempt to survive, even if we don't think the outcome is desirable. For example, if a visitor is repeatedly stealing cars, necessitating that we involve the police, we still perceive this as an attempt to survive trauma and unbearable, intolerable distress.

Carl Rogers defined the 'certain facilitative conditions' as empathy, congruence (being genuine and authentic in the therapeutic relationship) and unconditional positive regard. We interpret this as an aspiration to treat our visitors and callers and each other with warmth, kindness, respect and compassion.

We support visitors and callers with the issues they bring to our services and respect their context and cultural background. We recognise that trauma and early life history can cause 'symptoms' such as hearing voices, flashbacks and hallucinations, rather than seeing these as representing an illness or disordered personality. This is one of the fundamental ways in which our person-centred approach differs from a medical model of distress.

### Being trauma-informed

Most of the work of LSLCS is with people who are survivors of trauma, most commonly sexual abuse. During 2018, abuse in the past or present, rape or sexual violence was a presenting issue in 74% of visits to Dial House. This statistic only refers to the times that people discussed issues relating to abuse. Often survivors will visit Dial House and speak about other matters. We would estimate that 80% of our visitors are survivors of sexual abuse that has often happened in early life, at the hands of caregivers and alongside other forms of abuse, such as emotional deprivation and neglect.

Many of our visitors have been labelled as having a 'personality disorder', but we conceptualise their distress and the relational difficulties they experience as an understandable response to inhuman cruelty. Our visitors often find it helpful to reflect on their experiences within a framework of 'complex post-traumatic stress disorder (PTSD)', which describes what has happened to them, rather than locating the problem as a fundamental part of their personality.

Through many years of supporting people who are survivors of trauma, we have developed expertise and knowledge in working with dissociation, complex relational difficulties and the coping strategies that people use to survive (for example, suicide attempts and self-injury).

For survivors of complex PTSD, because their trauma has occurred within the context of a relationship, we believe this is also how recovery will occur. In supporting survivors of trauma, we find Rogers' concept of psychological contact (Rogers, 1951) extremely helpful in its emphasis on the relationship being front and centre in the therapeutic work. As Yalom states: 'It's the relationship that heals, the relationship that heals, the relationship that heals' (Yalom, 1989: 91).

We have found the Rogerian conditions of empathy, congruence and unconditional positive regard the most effective tools to work with when supporting survivors of trauma, as they enable us to create a validating environment around people whose life experiences have often been invalidating. Much of our work in this area is providing the therapeutic conditions that enable people to see their feelings as containable and supporting them to begin to develop ways of regulating their emotions, other than through self-injury.

We aim to be trauma-informed in all our work, not just our interactions with visitors and callers. An organisation aspiring to be trauma-informed needs to embed this philosophy in policies, staff recruitment, training and support. As a survivor-led organisation, we are often supporting visitors while holding our own experiences of traumatic life experience, including abuse. A comprehensive structure of staff support is essential and at LSLCS this includes monthly reflective practice meetings. We also expect staff to attend vicarious trauma training every three years.

## The therapeutic practice of Leeds Survivor-Led Crisis Service

As an established, 20-year-old, survivor-led, person-centred organisation in the third sector, we are on the margins of the mental health system, while also being part of service provision in Leeds. We exist outside mainstream psychiatry, although most of our visitors and callers are signposted to us by the statutory crisis team and we are seen as an essential and integral part of the Leeds crisis care pathway.

Our position as a non-statutory, radical alternative to the medical model of distress means that we often attract people who are not involved with statutory mental health provision, either because they have fallen through the net or they have been excluded from services, or services have failed to engage them. Some of our visitors have histories of violence or other forensic histories, and many have been labelled as having a 'personality disorder' – a label we do not recognise as valid or helpful.

Where we would see our practice as presenting the greatest challenge to psychiatric orthodoxy and demonstrating an alternative approach is in the areas of diagnosis and working with risk, power and control.

### Diagnosis

LSLCS was specifically established to provide a non-medical, non-diagnostic approach to supporting people in acute mental health crisis. As outlined above, our philosophy stems from the Soteria model of being alongside people in crisis, as opposed to medicating or treating them.

As previously explained, our trauma-informed approach places the therapeutic relationship at the front and centre of our work – we believe the relationship *is* the intervention. As our philosophy states: 'We believe that, to deal with a crisis, a person must feel safe, listened to, and connected to other people' (LSLCS, 2007).

Carl Rogers objected to the use of psychiatric diagnoses because they place the locus of evaluation outside the person and in the hands of professionals (Rogers, 1951). Rogers states:

> There is a degree of loss of personhood as the individual acquires
> the belief that only the expert can accurately evaluate him and that
> therefore the measure of his personal worth lies in the hands of another.
> (Rogers, 1951: 224)

Furthermore, a central tenet of the person-centred approach is its respect of the individual's subjective reality. In developing his 1951 theory of personality development, Rogers outlined 19 propositions, two of which are:

> The best vantage point for understanding behaviour is from the internal frame of reference of the individual.

> Behaviour is basically the goal-directed attempt of the organism to satisfy its needs as experienced in the field, as perceived.

In other words, we can only understand somebody if we can see the world as they see it. Behaviour makes sense when it is seen as an individual's attempts to meet their needs, as they perceive them from their unique frame of reference.

In the 1950s, this was a radical departure from the psychiatric model of mental 'illness' as an objective reality described within a diagnostic handbook. Even in the 21st century, mainstream psychiatry still holds to this approach, labelling people with medical definitions (decided largely by White men) such as 'schizophrenic' or 'personality disordered'.

LSLCS receives frequent feedback from visitors and callers about the validating impact of receiving support from within a non-medical, non-diagnostic, alternative framework. Quotes collected between 2006 and 2018 include:

> NHS is diagnosis-led, Connect is person-led.

> It's less judgemental, open when other services aren't. A friendlier team, who don't come from a medical background.

> Can talk about absolutely anything and be validated, heard, accepted!

### Managing risk

Most of the work of LSLCS is with people at high risk of suicide and/ or self-injury. A smaller percentage of our work is with people who are at risk of committing crimes or who present a risk to others. How we work with risk is one of the ways that most differentiate us from the risk-averse culture of statutory services. Our approach, developed and adapted over 20 years, is essentially about trust – in the actualising tendency and in the innate capabilities of visitors and callers to manage the risks they present to themselves and others. We also believe in giving visitors and callers as much control as possible in relation to how they engage with our support and services and how the risks they present are managed. We are skilled and experienced in supporting visitors and callers to fully explore risk, for example with regards to their thoughts and feelings and plans in relation to suicide. Experience has taught us that if people are allowed to explore these stigmatised and often shameful thoughts and feelings in depth, this reduces the risk of them acting on them.

This approach has been tried and tested over many years with visitors who have thoughts of harming others, or who carry knives to feel safe or find it hard to stay at Dial House without using substances on the premises. Our practice of in-depth exploration with visitors and callers to identify ways we can work collaboratively with them to reduce risk requires a high level of psychological contact and mutual trust. We do not use standard risk assessment tools – we experience them as reductive and unsubtle, as they do not allow scope for such in-depth risk analysis.

As a survivor-led service in the voluntary sector, the LSLCS is without statutory power. That people come to us entirely of their own volition is hugely significant when compulsion is a feature of many people's experience of mental health services. The fact that people self-refer to our services and choose to be here means the starting point for the relationship and negotiating issues around risk are entirely different than if our staff were working under the Mental Health Act and trying to engage patients who might well not want to be in our establishment. So, for issues like working with substance use, our starting point is that people want to be with us. We have a pragmatic policy that does not permit people to use substances on the premises, although visitors can come to Dial House under the influence, as long as they are able to engage and are not a risk to themselves or others. The fact that visitors want to be in Dial House and are treated with respect, kindness, warmth and compassion means that this policy is almost never abused. We have high expectations of our visitors – we expect even people addicted to substances will not abuse our hospitality and use on the premises. Our experience over 20 years is that people live up to our expectations.

In the early days of LSLCS, we experienced suspicion and mistrust from statutory services with regard to our alternative, non-medical approach, fuelled by a mistaken belief that third-sector services run by medically unqualified staff could not work effectively with people at very high risk. In 2005, we were required to include our Working with Suicide and Working with Self Harm policies as appendices in our Service Level Agreement with the NHS (our contract to supply services to NHS patients). This was to allay our funders' anxiety about our ability to work professionally and appropriately with visitors and callers at risk. However, this is no longer a requirement and we have built a high level of trust in our work within and outside statutory services. We are seen, locally and nationally, as a beacon of excellence in crisis provision and are often asked to train staff and speak at conferences on the specific subject of managing risk.

A key component of the trust we have earned is our proven track record. In 20 years, we have never had a single serious incident where visitors have been violent to each other or to staff. Nor have we experienced a death or serious injury at Dial House or DH@T. We doubt that there are many mental health services (particularly crisis and acute services) with such an impressive record. We firmly believe that this is entirely because of the way we treat our visitors and callers, the trust we place in them so they retain their autonomy while at Dial House and DH@T. As Maytree, a sanctuary in London for people who are suicidal, states on its website: 'We believe that the seemingly high-risk option of sticking with trust often, in the end, carries lesser risks' (Maytree, undated). Our visitors and callers are fantastic ambassadors for us, giving extensive feedback that our approach is effective and supports them to reduce the risks they present:

> I haven't taken an overdose since January. Last year I had 18 overdoses – 18 hospital admissions. Since using Dial House, I haven't taken one. I haven't been in hospital once.

> Been taking drugs before but now I have been clean for the last 18 months and I need to thank Dial House @ Touchstone for this. My voices are telling me to harm myself, but I managed to keep myself clean by coming here.

> I phone Connect most nights. The staff are great and patient and they have helped me to not need to go to A&E, even though I've been suicidal loads of times they still understand me and they never seem to get fed up of listening to me.

### Power and control

The survivor movement and other critics of mainstream psychiatry have documented the disempowerment and lack of control people often experience in statutory mental health services. The Power Threat Meaning Framework (Johnstone & Boyle, 2018) articulates the impact of abuse of power and puts forward an alternative model for mental health support. In our experience, disempowerment often compounds the trauma people have experienced in early life and the structural oppression of experiences such as poverty and racism. As outlined above, the founders of LSLCS had their own experiences of sectioning, enduring forced medication and other oppressive treatment regimes, and they aspired for LSLCS to provide an alternative to mainstream psychiatry – a service that people would choose to access.

As outlined above, that we are a voluntary (third) sector organisation, as opposed to being part of the statutory public sector, is as fundamental to our identity as being survivor-led. All our visitors and callers self-refer to Dial House, Connect and our group work. This is highly significant for mental health service users, who may have been subject to coercion and compulsory detention by the statutory services. The importance of self-referral was highlighted in the 2011 Mind report *Listening to Experience* – a scathing analysis of mental health crisis care in England and Wales. The report stated:

> We urgently need more direct access options. This means that people can self-refer, and there should be an explicit acknowledgement that individuals know what they need. (Mind, 2011)

Our visitors and callers also regularly feed back to us about the value of both the ability to self-refer and our empowering approach:

> You provide unconditional positive regard, respect, true compassion, acceptance and respect and kindness – this is seriously lacking in other mental health services – Thank you!

> When it's a choice between either A&E and them treating me like I'm nobody, or getting support from you, I call you and I feel accepted.

> Self-referral rather than going through a damaging NHS system.

## Evidence that it works

In order to ensure that we are providing respectful, consistent, compassionate and empathic crisis services, we undertake more monitoring and evaluation than our funders require. Although it is a requirement of an NHS contract that we provide evidence of efficacy, for us the primary reason for monitoring and evaluation is to ensure we constantly monitor what works and does not work in supporting people in acute mental health crisis.

Feedback is collected through visitor and caller feedback books, questionnaires, online and text feedback, reviews with regular visitors and callers and focus groups, where visitors and callers meet with trustees of LSLCS to critique our services.

Feedback from 2006 to 2018 can be grouped into five themes, from which we have identified what we refer to as 'the five elements of effective support':

- listening
- treating people with warmth, kindness and respect
- people do not feel judged or assessed
- being in a different and calm environment
- peer support.

As a survivor-led service, it feels right that visitors from across our 20-year history articulate our philosophy and therapeutic approach and how this supports the delivery of effective crisis support.

### Listening

It's ace here, you really listen, understand and respect me.

Sometimes it don't take a genius to work out that if you sit down and listen to someone and acknowledge the way they're feeling – that it's alright to feel shit – then they're gonna feel better.

You listen, you don't judge, you don't tell me what to do.

I felt so safe, comforted & listened to.

### Treating people with warmth, kindness and respect

Just a short note to say thanks to K for helping me to wash my hair. It seems like such a simple thing to help with, but it is the fact that Dial House are there to help with everything including simple things which makes Dial House such a unique and fantastic place. Thanks again.

As the visitor herself states, it is a small task to support someone to wash their hair, but the fact that our staff think it's an important thing to do says so much about our whole approach. Arguably, it is the love underlying this act that this visitor is referring to.

Because we have a well-established reputation, a plethora of national awards, frequent media coverage and international recognition, we have the confidence to publicly state that one of the ways our service is effective is that visitors and callers receive love from our staff and from each other. It is a sad indictment of both our society and mental health services that this remains a risky statement to make, but it is our passionately held view that healing and recovery from trauma and mental health crisis will only occur through the transformative impact of being truly in contact with another person. We believe strongly in the central place of love in crisis support as a necessary therapeutic condition and in the value of human touch, within carefully considered parameters.

Other feedback demonstrating the power of kindness, compassion, warmth and affection includes:

> The staff are without question some of the kindest, warmest, most caring, understanding, genuine, friendliest people I've ever had the pleasure of meeting. I consider myself very lucky to have been supported by such people and believe that on more than one occasion either a member of staff or the house has made a significant difference to me and my life.

> I feel like talking to you all is replenishing the hope in my soul.

### People do not feel judged or assessed

LSLCS receives extensive feedback about the value of not feeling judged. This includes our lack of reliance on paperwork and standardised care plans, risk assessment forms and so forth:

> People don't judge you, which helps when everybody else does.
> I feel accepted here and can be honest about how I really am. No one judges me; the workers are empathic and kind.

Our survivor-led, non-diagnostic approach is also highly valued by visitors and callers:

> It is different to other services – it is easier to talk to staff. Staff are nice. They don't judge you or put a label on you – saying 'that's what's wrong with you'.

> It's not just a job to youse, you know what it's like, you're living proof you can get through it.

### Being in a different and calm environment

> Thank you for getting me away from the funny farm for a couple of hours. The peace and quiet was a nice change from the noisy, hectic, crazy ward.

People can visit Dial House when they are inpatients, even if they are under section, providing they have permission to leave. The above quote powerfully illustrates that people in acute mental health crisis need a sanctuary or a place of asylum, in the proper sense of the word. The quote starkly highlights that this is often not how inpatient wards are experienced.

> It's like a sanctuary here, I calmed down as soon as I walked in – feel safe and more like me again.

> A welcome haven and a place of safety which has really helped me cope tonight, as I felt so isolated in my flat on my own tonight.

### Peer support

The group work programme of LSLCS grew organically from the peer support that happens naturally at Dial House and DH@T. In addition to the support they receive from staff, visitors receive kindness, warmth and companionship from each other. The mutual support visitors provide for each other reduces loneliness and isolation. For our deaf, trans and voice-hearing visitors, peer support also, crucially, reduces stigma and shame:

> It has given me comfort to know there are others with similar problems to me.

> It is helpful and inspiring to see other visitors with their own problems and ways of coping with them.

> We don't look different here and I felt that I belong somewhere.

## Cost-effectiveness and expansion

In addition to the positive impact we have on the lives of our visitors and callers, we generate savings to the health economy through reducing admission to psychiatric inpatient beds, visits to A&E, police and ambulance contact and use of other statutory services:

> The ambulance service was considering taking legal action against me because they said I called them too much. I didn't have anyone else and I felt like I was going to die or have a heart attack. They kept telling me it was just anxiety. Now I call Connect when I feel that bad. They do help me and I feel cared about for a while.

> The number of hospital admissions has been reduced because when I feel suicidal or I'm hearing voices I prefer to come here.

I don't use the Samaritans or the police as much because I come to groups.

In recognition of both the cost-effectiveness of our services and their therapeutic value for visitors and callers, we have received a significant increase in funding from NHS Leeds in the last six years, despite the current period of austerity. The turnover of LSLCS has more than doubled during this time. We have received funding to expand both Dial House and Connect and to open new services, including DH@T and Teen Connect. This is a great testimony to the efficacy of our non-medical approach in both improving people's lives and saving considerable costs to the health economy.

We have demonstrated our value further by having Social Return on Investment (SROI) analyses undertaken about our organisation in 2012 and 2018. SROI is a credible national tool that is used to demonstrate the impact of projects that are difficult to evaluate, such as regeneration schemes or community development work. Through a process involving consultation with all stakeholders, an SROI consultant undertakes a cost-benefit analysis. By comparing the costs of an organisation to its benefits, you can demonstrate cost savings to the community and the long-term value of investment. An organisation ends up with an SROI ratio. Our ratio is £1 to £7.50–£12.50 (2018 SROI ratio). This means that, for every pound invested in LSLCS, society gets £7.50–£12.50 back. This includes through the prevention of suicide and through people not accessing public sector crisis and emergency services.

The current environment of economic austerity and the Crisis Care Concordat[1] have highlighted the need for cost-effective mental health crisis provision. Every mental health trust and council in the country has had to both save money and meet the statutory requirements of the Crisis Care Concordat to provide parity of care for people in mental health crisis. The penny seems to have finally dropped that it is cheaper for people to have access to services like LSLCS rather than admit them to hospital. It is also infinitely preferable for people's quality of life. This recognition has resulted in the increased investment in LSLCS in Leeds. It has also led to the development of crisis services in the third sector across the UK, including the Sanctuary in Bradford[2] and the Sanctuary in Bristol,[3] which are both explicitly based on the LSLCS model.

---

1. The Mental Health Crisis Care Concordat is a national agreement between services and agencies involved in the care and support of people in crisis setting out how they will work together better to make sure that people get the help they need. It was launched in February 2014. Its signatories include health, policing, social care, housing and local government organisations and the third sector. www. crisiscareconcordat.org.uk/about (accessed 11 August 2019).

2. www.mindinbradford.org.uk/the-sanctuary (accessed 11 August 2019).

3. www.bristolmentalhealth.org/services/bristol-sanctuary (accessed 11 August 2019).

Providing consultancy to charities, councils and mental health trusts who want to develop alternative crisis provision has become a formal part of our work. This enables us to champion our philosophy and practice as a survivor-led, person-centred service in the third sector that remains passionately committed to providing non-medical, non-diagnostic services.

## Concluding comments

Over the last 20 years, LSLCS has supported nearly 3,000 people through what began as our flagship crisis service, Dial House. We have consistently delivered warm, kind, effective and compassionate crisis services as an alternative to the mainstream medical model approach to extreme distress. Through both the delivery of outstanding crisis services and effective monitoring, evaluation and sharing of information, we have gained the respect and trust of statutory and non-statutory services and workers and developed a national and international reputation as a beacon of hope, creativity and excellence.

We have adapted our practice to ensure our services are accessible to people from minority groups, including BAME, LGBT and deaf visitors, and have developed to become a trauma-informed organisation.

Our support for people in extreme distress and at high risk has consistently demonstrated that recovery from trauma and crisis is reliant on human connection, relationships and humanity. As stated in the Mind report, *Listening to Experience* (2011):

> What people overwhelmingly want is to be treated in a warm, caring, respectful way, irrespective of the circumstances in which they come into contact with services. In other words, all of us would like to be treated with humanity.

The point is further powerfully highlighted by a Dial House visitor:

> A safe, calming environment has been created, where the workers are exceptionally aware of the state people are in whilst they are in crisis and they are able to receive people in a personal yet non-invasive way and give time and space to people, recognising them as human beings in distress rather than a number to be dealt with or get seen to. If it were not for this service many people would return to the hell realm of a hospital environment and otherwise take their lives through utter desperation of having nowhere to turn which can provide the level of support Dial House can offer.

Our alternative, explicitly loving approach to mental distress has proven successful, cost-effective and highly valued by visitors and callers. Our experience and proven track record should inform the development of mental health services to ensure that people in extreme distress are treated with the love and humanity we all need for healing and recovery.

## References

James A (2010). A beacon of hope. *Mental Health Today* February: 18–19.

Johnstone L, Boyle M, with Cromby J, Dillon J, Harper D, Kinderman P, Longden E, Pilgrim D, Read J (2018). *The Power Threat Meaning Framework: towards the identification of patterns in emotional distress, unusual experiences and troubled or troubling behaviour, as an alternative to functional psychiatric diagnosis.* Leicester: British Psychological Society.

Leeds Survivor-Led Crisis Service (2007). *Philosophy.* [Online.] www.lslcs.org.uk (accessed 26 August 2019).

Mind (2011). *Listening to Experience: an independent inquiry into acute and crisis mental health care.* London: Mind.

Mosher L (1999). Soteria and other alternatives to acute psychiatric hospitalization: a personal and professional review. *Journal of Nervous and Mental Disease 187*: 142–149.

Rogers CR (1980). *A Way of Being.* New York, NY: Houghton Mifflin.

Rogers CR (1951). *Client-Centered Therapy.* London: Constable.

Venner F (2009). Risk management in a survivor-led crisis service. *Mental Health Practice 13* (4): 18–22.

Venner F, Noad M (2013). A beacon of hope. In: Coles S, Keenan S, Diamond B (eds). *Madness Contested: power and practice.* Ross-on-Wye: PCCS Books (pp332– 349).

Yalom I (1989). *Love's Executioner and Other Tales of Psychotherapy.* London: Penguin Books.

# Chapter 10

# Canerows peer support services

## Paul Brewer

> I feel tortured and torn from my family and life, my boyfriend and from
> working to create a better life for my community. I have been in the
> system, care homes and hostels all my life. I am not a sinner or a criminal.
> I just need love and to give love to the right causes. (Hospital patient)

Good mental health services are built on compassion, described as '[a] deep
awareness of the suffering of another coupled with the wish to relieve it'
(Cochinov, 2007). Warm and positive interactions with staff in psychiatric
hospital have – unsurprisingly – been associated with greater patient satisfaction
(Henry et al, 2012) and may also improve future engagement with mental health
services (Wykes et al, 2018). When employees step beyond the confines of their
professional roles, to go the extra mile and respond with their full humanity,
these moments are remembered by patients and applauded by colleagues.
The managerial challenge has always been to sustain a team of frontline staff
in hospital wards who can 'walk in the shoes' of the people in their care,
consistently taking on extreme, unusual and distressing feeling states.

In recent years the ability of psychiatric ward staff to respond with
compassion is being tested as never before as financial pressures mount.
Problems in recruiting and retaining good managers (Care Quality
Commission, 2017) undermine the creation of coherent teams and managerial
capacity to support staff effectively. Admissions are shorter, patients are more
distressed and the introduction of 12-hour shifts is widespread. Stress is on
the rise among staff, as is the risk to their mental health through burnout,
a concept that is hard to define (Schaufeli, Maslach & Marek, 1993) but is

characterised by compassion fatigue. In today's under-resourced NHS, the gold standard of compassionate care may only be maintained at a personal cost to the mental health of staff.

This chapter is about Canerows, an innovative peer support project for people from Black, Asian and minority ethnic (BAME) communities, based in the London Borough of Wandsworth, and how it is helping NHS psychiatric wards under these pressures to regain their humanity.

In her influential paper published almost 60 years ago, Menzies (1960) proposed that organisations unconsciously create 'social defences', the interpersonal equivalent of Freud's defence mechanisms in the individual. These are structural and cultural adjustments made in an attempt to protect individuals within organisations from being overwhelmed by the feelings and stresses generated by their key tasks. An obvious example is the way soldiers are trained to obey orders without question so they can cope with the prospect of death and killing.

Changes introduced into the NHS to 'drive efficiency' also serve social defensive functions at the caring interface. To maximise bed use in urban areas, hospital wards are no longer aligned with geographical areas and patients are admitted to wherever a bed happens to be empty. Ward teams, community teams and specialist teams operate independently, with patients passed between them. 'Continuity of care', once a service aspiration (Bachrach 1981), has been abandoned and patients face a bewildering succession of relationships. Patients of crisis and home treatment teams complain that they are expected to answer the same menu of questions from an ever-changing line-up of staff at each visit. The social defensive function for frontline staff is that the short-term nature of contacts reduces the danger that they may be overwhelmed by the intractable distress of those in their care.

Individual staff can no longer develop relationships with patients over time; instead the relationship is with the organisation as a whole, through the patient's records. The importance of record-keeping has been elevated, and staff are sanctioned to spend time in the safety of the office to update them (Gilburt, Rose & Slade, 2008; Thibealt, 2016).

In hospital wards, junior and agency staff are typically involved with the bulk of the day-to-day contact with patients, but they in turn are protected by rosters that move them from ward to ward, reducing prolonged exposure to patients and the risks that this may pose to their own mental health (Kings Fund, 2015). Time-strapped ward staff are reduced to conversations that are often task-driven; Csipke and colleagues (2014) found that 16% of patients in some London hospitals had had no meaningful one-to-one contact with staff within the previous week.

Some efforts have been made to drive staff back to the front line of compassion. A manual distributed by the charity Star Wards in 2009 – *Encouraging the Art of Conversation* – contains the tools staff need to initiate conversations with their patients – skills that apparently needed refreshing. Anyone emailing our local NHS trust on a Thursday now receives an automated response explaining that, on 'Talk Thursdays', staff do not respond to emails. Thursdays are proudly reserved for staff to engage in face-to-face contact with patients. While laudable, the initiative perversely appears to legitimise staff to withdraw from contact with patients on the other six days of the week.

Life on acute psychiatric wards has a tendency to become bound by unresponsive rules that are, at times, baffling to patients. These govern, for example, the times when the kitchen is open for drinks, and the times when staff will not respond to a knock on the office door. One of our peer support workers, who spends much of his week in the admission ward environment mediating between patients and NHS staff, has coined the term 'regimentality' to describe unnecessary demands for behavioural conformity. These rules are, ostensibly, to ensure the smooth running of a busy ward, but the power gained through their implementation also serves to protect staff by creating emotional distance between rule-makers and rule-takers.

As with the 'defence mechanisms' that Freud described within the individual, 'social defences' are adaptations rather than solutions. In protecting staff from the primary cause of anxiety, fresh stress is introduced into the system as staff and patients experience alienation and everyone's capacity to express and share their common humanity is reduced (Rose et al, 2015).

## What does the project involve?

Canerows was founded in 2007 by a group of concerned former inpatients from BAME backgrounds who wanted to restore some sanity to the mental health system through the reintroduction of 'compassion and ordinary human kindness' (Reynolds, 2010). The intention is to provide patients with support from people who have faced similar challenges (Campbell & Leaver, 2003), delivered by an independent, autonomous organisation with its own values.

Canerows arose from the Sound Minds charity,[1] a 'community within the community' (a term coined by founder member Devon Marston) that has evolved organically over the past 26 years. Sound Minds is located in a former community air-raid shelter beneath a church in Battersea, south west London. An often-heard criticism of building-based services in the early years of this century was that day centres were where people 'just got meaningless together'

---

1. www.soundminds.co.uk (accessed 19 August 2019).

– a view shared by our founding group. By contrast, Sound Minds has a strong ethos of being 'user-led' and is delivered by people who have lived experience of mental health problems, the majority from diverse backgrounds. The success of Sound Minds stands on the quality of our relationships and particularly the enabling and levelling effect brought about by sharing skills in music and the arts. It is a place where a degree of madness is accepted and understood. People are encouraged to be confident, creative and fully themselves. Sound Minds is valued because of the protection it affords from the stigma of wider society and because it helps people develop the resilience to overcome it (Huggett et al, 2018). There is no specific goal to serve people from BAME backgrounds but BAME groups are over-represented in hospitals generally and in the local community, and this is reflected in the Sound Minds membership.

Despite government initiatives such as Delivering Race Equality (Fountain & Hicks, 2010), on average people from BAME backgrounds are over-represented on psychiatric hospital wards, stay in hospital longer, are more likely to access mental health services via the police and are more likely to experience control and restraint, compared with the general population (Care Quality Commission, 2017). Data collected on the use of the Mental Health Act in Wandsworth show that Black people are five times more likely than white people to be assessed under the Mental Health Act and three times more likely to be detained.

## The Ward Visiting Service

Coral Hines, James Brathwaite and Devon Marston are long-term users of mental health services. They had already contributed to the development of Sound Minds, but were motivated to do more to improve the inpatient care they experienced and the patchy support available when they left hospital. To begin, they organised consultation meetings with NHS managers and clinical staff but soon realised that complaining from the sidelines had little impact, so instead they decided to try to make a positive practical difference by contributing within NHS structures. Canerow's Ward Visiting Service is one such initiative.

A team of around 18 people with lived experience of mental health problems visit six acute mental health wards at Queen Mary's and Springfield Hospitals, run by South West London and St Georges Mental Health NHS Trust. These 'ward visitors' have no agenda other than to talk to patients. More recently, after much negotiation, a small team of former inpatients from the local secure unit have also begun weekly visits to the forensic wards. Peer-led group activities are provided to the wards (including secure environments) and peer support staff assist with staff training. Canerows also runs a one-day-per-week drop-in and social support club called 'Mama Low's Kitchen' in Wandsworth and organises social and training events. One-to-one post-discharge peer support is available to Wandsworth residents leaving one local acute ward. All peer support workers are recruited, trained, managed and supervised by Canerows, enabling them to maintain a culture and approach that is distinct from the NHS.

For people joining the Canerows team, the starting point is to gain experience as a ward visitor. Applicants are interviewed before completing a three-day course, accredited at Level 2 by Sound Minds with the Open College Network London. The course is designed to help people anticipate some of the issues they will find when ward visiting. All recruits must have experienced mental health issues and almost all have also experienced inpatient care.

Sharing mental health experience and understanding of all aspects of recovery are essential to realising the potential of peer support. Peer support is about replacing 'us-and-them' interactions with 'us and us'. There is a mutual benefit to these interactions. The members of the current team speak seven languages between them. On the wards, the team will talk to anyone, regardless of whether or not they have a strong cultural connection.

> I just feel like a million dollars! On that ward, I look at how other people are, I think about myself when I was in that position, and I feel like I'm giving something back because I'm not in that position any more… It's a two-way thing, you know, because I get great satisfaction from doing the ward visits. (Ward visitor)

> When you have a laugh and a joke and everyone's involved, that's really nice and you can see that you've made a difference to somebody on that day. (Ward visitor)

Peer support is also about the instillation of hope that occurs when meeting someone who has shared a similar path and shows, by their example, that there is a way forward (NSUN, 2017):

> They took time to listen and helped me to be optimistic; they give encouragement and hope. (Hospital inpatient)

During their training, peer support workers are encouraged to identify their own boundaries in the role and those aspects of their lives and experiences that they are personally comfortable to share. In this way, peer support workers are arguably freer to be themselves, to offer more of themselves and to respond uniquely. They identify how sharing aspects of their own story might benefit another person currently going through similar experiences:

> I want to pass on my experience of being on the ward from a different perspective.... and also to support patients and help them... look towards being discharged... to give hope really. (Ward visitor)

The training also addresses confidentiality, safeguarding and data collection systems. There is a focus on how to work constructively with NHS staff, the key being to understand the pressures that they are under and the restrictions placed on them through the NHS culture and the responsibilities they hold.

After the completion of Disclosure & Barring Service (DBS) checks and NHS-led inductions, new trainees accompany experienced visitors for a month as volunteers before joining the main rota. Visitors then receive payment from Canerows for their visits.

To keep fresh, and to avoid both burnout and harassment from the Department for Work & Pensions over benefits entitlements, most visitors make no more than two visits per week. There is no agenda or structure to conversations; visitors are encouraged not to restrict themselves to a care-giving role. The benefits of peer support conversations need not be one-sided, but visitors are encouraged to remain positive, even-handed and open-minded.

> We have to make a stand on what matters. It is not really about ethnicity, it's about humanity and respect. It's about being a three-dimensional human being, and appreciating the people we meet in the same way. (Ward visitor)

Inevitably talk turns to shared experiences: being cared for on a ward; experiencing extreme and intense feeling states; medication; being looked after in the wider mental health system, and the particular stigma that goes with hospitalisation.

> When you see people who have been in the same situation as yourself and they're thinking along the same lines that you were thinking – that there's no hope... by talking, being friendly with one another, it can help you through that. (Ward visitor)

Advocates of peer support argue that experiences of hospitalisation and serious mental health crisis can prompt us to renegotiate our relationship with our irrational selves. We become more open and aware of our own vulnerabilities, more accepting of our own madness, and thereby better able to tolerate and be more compassionate towards the madness of others (Repper & Carter, 2010).

We have recently developed and introduced our own impact measures that are acceptable to acutely distressed people. These rate the service itself in terms of the expected specific benefits of peer support as identified in the existing literature (for example, Repper & Carter, 2010). Visitors are also given a simple survey tool for patients to express their concerns and make suggestions about the care they receive. Results and any comments and trends are presented in regular reports to our stakeholders, including the local NHS Clinical Commissioning Group (CCG) and Acute Care Forums. The Royal College of Psychiatrists (2010) recommends 'visits from the outside world' as a means to help reassure patients and reinforce their cultural identity.

Our own data show that the most common issue raised with visitors is insufficient information about the sectioning process. Other concerns that have been highlighted, and subsequently discussed with NHS managers, have included the importance of maintaining activities for inpatients, even when the ward is under pressure; the availability of skin creams for Black people prone to dry skin; the range of ethnically diverse foods available, and the quality of food offered. Ward visiting teams also record the number of people engaged by each team at each visit, the demographic profile of the people with whom they engage and any problems they encounter. Everything is brought to fortnightly group supervision sessions, which are also a social opportunity for the visiting team. Issues relating to NHS staff teams are as likely to be explored as those arising with patients.

Almost all the people joining the ward visiting team have been unemployed for some years. The roles offer valuable experience and a stepping stone into care work for some, and around one in five of all those trained in the past 10 years have gone on to more substantive, paid, care-related work elsewhere.

In 2017 we achieved funding from the CCG to expand our post-discharge support service. The current postholder works with just one acute ward. He spends time each week getting to know everyone who has been admitted and has self-defined a central part of his role as modelling humane interaction to prevent the culture of the ward sliding towards what he calls 'regimentality'. Where people indicate that they would appreciate his support after they leave hospital, he will arrange to meet up. Peer support post-discharge is wide-ranging and individual. It can be very practical, such as helping people to keep appointments or preparing for work; it can be involvement in music-making or gardening or simply a chance to meet up regularly and chat over coffee.

I met up with a guy who had recently been in hospital and a group of his friends. He introduced me first as a rapper and MC, an interest that we share. During the conversation I explained my role and they were really curious and were amazed to learn that I had been in hospital myself. A whole conversation about mental health followed on that helped us all. (Peer support worker)

## Evidence that it helps

It is not methodologically sound to compare the outcomes of peer support with those of clinical services (Penny, 2018). The finding that peer support may impact on admission rates and length of hospital stays (Johnson et al, 2018) is incidental to its aims, which can only be legitimately defined from within the service user movement itself. In 2008, we were approached by Patience Seebohm, who offered to evaluate our project as a doctorate project. The qualitative research (Reynolds & Seebohm, 2010) confirmed our confidence in our approach and helped us to expand and gain further funding. To conduct the research, three service users who were not directly connected to the work were trained in interview techniques. Interviews were conducted with all stakeholders: patients, ward staff, commissioners and peer support workers themselves. All were positive about the nascent service. The report concluded: 'There was no doubt that the visitors were making a positive impact', perhaps disproportionately so, given that most visits are for just an hour a week.

Some of the feedback regarding the ward visiting scheme included:

They are not intrusive, that's the thing. They say 'hello' and then just see what happens. (Staff nurse)

They just come in with this calmness and smiling, and I think the way they present themselves just gives the patient that welcoming feeling. (Support staff)

Their presence here is really felt by the patients. (Ward manager)

Because they have been in the system, the patients are more likely to tell them things. (Ward manager)

I think the patients really enjoy having to talk to people who... have the experience of what they are going through and have come out of it and are able to give back. (Staff nurse)

Our peer support services have been cited as an example of good practice in national reports on peer support produced by Together (Faulkner & Kalathil, 2012) and Mind (Faulkner et al, 2013). In addition, guidance for commissioners of mental health services for BAME service users (Joint Commissioning Panel for Mental Health, 2014) describes the Canerows service and recognises that services that are user-led may make a unique contribution to health and wellbeing.

## Managing resistance and overcoming obstacles

As explained above, Canerows Peer Support Services was the idea of Coral Hines, Devon Marston and James Brathwaite, who had themselves struggled to cope in first few days after leaving hospital and wanted to help others find their feet at this critical time. We had a look around for examples of post-discharge services and took advice from Sharon Lawn in Australia (Lawn, Smith & Hunter, 2009). We decided to begin by offering peer support in a less contentious area in order to build trust with the NHS. Devon and Coral negotiated to be allowed to visit one ward once a week informally. They reported back to the team on all aspects of their experiences:

> The surprising thing was that, even though we had both been in
> hospital, going back in a different role, things didn't seem quite what we
> expected. It took some time to adjust.

Key staff were quite welcoming but, no matter how much the work was explained, there were always new staff who appeared not to have been briefed. Even some months into the pilot, Coral and Devon were often kept waiting at the door of the ward while the nursing team discussed whether they could be allowed in.

After about six months of the weekly visits, we attempted to put the service on a more formal footing. Fortunately, the ward consultant psychiatrist, Dr Peter Hughes, was very much in favour of peer support, and brought his whole clinical team to Sound Minds one afternoon to draw up and agree a protocol. The agreement sets out the responsibilities of the partner organisations, the content of training and expectations around recruitment, safeguarding and communication. By this time we had gathered enough experience to offer training for other people who wanted to join the team. With a little money raised from three local sources, we were able to employ someone to co-ordinate the project. We then formalised the training and accredited our own units with the Open College Network. In 2011 we were awarded a three-year grant by Comic Relief and began rolling out the service to other wards.

Forensic visits have taken even longer to establish. From making initial enquiries to the first ward visit took two years of monthly meetings with members of the clinical team, security staff and, occasionally, senior staff. Agreeing a protocol for recruitment and safeguarding was a major hurdle and required discussions beyond our organisations, including involvement of legal representatives from NACRO and the Disclosure and Barring Service itself. We have been fortunate to have a retired professor of forensic psychiatry (Gill Mezey) as a champion, and three highly committed peer support workers, but the project's development has been constantly undermined by staff turnover. Identifying new forensic peer supporters has been slow, as we have been reliant on the forensic outreach service, which has had an almost complete change of staff. For us, these reshuffles have been a bit like playing a fruit machine. We have learnt to be patient and confident that at some point we will have a winning combination of staff again, so we can then move forward a few steps.

The tremendous dedication and commitment from the team stems from their instigation and ownership of Canerows and has been invaluable in its development. The whole team has been fantastic, but I would particularly single out Devon Marston, Coral Hines, Mia Morris OBE and Sandi Grant. From our experience, it is clear that our access to independent funding has allowed us to speak more freely at meetings and helped us gain the trust of local service users. We have been fortunate with fundraising over the past 12 years. My former career in the NHS has certainly been helpful in establishing the credentials of the project and in helping us weave a way through NHS bureaucracy. It requires persistence to identify who or which committee has the responsibility for decision-making and also to recognise how, why and when a decision has been 'parked'. Relentlessness in chasing up actions is important, as is the ability to make your frustrations understood while remaining (usually) respectful and polite.

It has also been a great help to us all that Devon, Coral, James and I also play and rehearse music together regularly as members of Sound Minds reggae group, The Channel One Band. Our long-term friendships and the consistency within the team are key to our creative, organic approach. Together we have performed in a wide range of venues across the UK, and in 2010 we were invited on a mini-tour of the West Coast of Ireland, which resulted in a short film, *The Day We Danced on the Moon*, made for the Berlin Film Festival. The band also won a *Community Care* award for our work in schools in 2004. These are all experiences that unite us. In our small organisation, everyone's individual creativity, opinions and actions can make a real difference in a way that is not possible within the NHS or even in larger charities.

In 2016 Sound Minds and Canerows were awarded a contract by national Mind to run 'Peerfest', an annual conference and celebration of peer support at Rich Mix in London, placing us temporarily at the centre of the national network of peer support. We all gained valuable experience in event management and forged links with other services across England and Wales – links that continue today.

## Future directions

The team receives regular requests to expand the visiting service to other wards and to visit more frequently, and we do our best to respond to these. More peer support input to forensic services is planned, including a befriending service for people detained long-term whose friendships and family relationships in the outside world have fallen away. Also, the need for benefits and welfare advice is huge and our visiting team has now been trained to help people in these areas. We now accompany people to assessments and signpost to other services as required.

Short-term increases in funding can be destabilising to a small organisation and it seems important that any new ideas are introduced slowly. Canerows wishes to retain our independent partnership with the NHS and our autonomy. Independence enables us to maintain our own support systems and ensure that peer supporters develop the resilience required to work within the NHS without being subsumed into the dominant culture.

Has Canerows in turn been able to influence the culture of local mental health services? It would be grandiose to claim that such a small project can offset years of shrinking NHS resources, drive out regimentality or reignite burned-out compassion, but the longevity of the project serves as a constant reminder of the unique value of peer support and of our common humanity:

> Since the service started over 10 years ago, the local NHS has sincerely tried to improve things for people from BAME backgrounds. There are inequalities still to be confronted but we don't see ourselves as primarily a campaigning group. Our strength is that we have never been an angry storm that blows itself out but rather a persistent gentle breeze pushing things forward. (Mia Morris OBE, Project worker)

## References

Bachrach LL (1981). Continuity of care for chronic mental patients: A conceptual analysis. *The American Journal of Psychiatry 138*(11): 1449–1456.

Campbell J, Leaver J (2003). *Emerging New Practices in Organized Peer Support.* Report from NTAC's National Experts Meeting on Emerging New Practices in Organized Peer Support 17–18, 2003, Alexandria, VA. Rockville, MA: Substance Abuse and Mental Health Services Administration.

Care Quality Commission (CQC) (2017). *The State of Mental Health Services, 2014–2017.* London: Care Quality Commission.

Cochinov H (2007). Dignity and the essence of medicine: the A, B, C, and D of dignity conserving care. *British Medical Journal 335*:184.

Csipke E, Flach C, Mccrone P, Rose D, Tilley J, Wykes T, Craig T (2014). Inpatient care 50 years after the process of deinstitutionalisation. *Social Psychiatry and Psychiatric Epidemiology 49*: 665–671.

Faulkner A, Kalathil J (2012). *The Freedom to be, the Chance to Dream: preserving user-led peer support in mental health.* London: Together.

Faulkner A, with Sadd J, Hughes A, Thompson S, Nettle M, Wallcraft J, Collar J, de la Haye S, McKinley S (2013). *Mental Health Peer Support in England: piecing together the jigsaw.* London: Mind Publications.

Fountain J, Hicks J (2010). *Delivering Race Equality in Mental Health Care: report on the findings and outcomes of the community engagement programme 2005–2008.* Project report. Preston: University of Central Lancashire.

Gilburt H, Rose D, Slade M (2008). The importance of relationships in mental health care: a qualitative study of service users' experiences of psychiatric hospital admission in the UK. *BMC Health Services Research 8*: 92.

Henry SG, Fuhrel-Forbis A, Rogers MA, Eggly S (2012). Association between nonverbal communication during clinical interactions and outcomes: a systematic review and meta-analysis. *Patient Education and Counselling 86*(3): 297–315.

Huggett C, Birtel MD, Awenat YF, Fleming P, Wilkes S, Williams S, Haddock G (2018). A qualitative study: experiences of stigma by people with mental health problems. *Psychology and Psychotherapy: theory, research and practice 91*(3): 380–397.

Johnson S, Lamb D, Marston L, Osborn D, Mason O et al (2018). Peer-supported self-management for people discharged from a mental health crisis team: a randomised control trial. *The Lancet 392*(10145): 409–418.

Joint Commissioning Panel for Mental Health (JCPMH) (2014). *Guidance for Commissioners of Mental Health Services for People from Black and Minority Ethnic Communities.* London: Joint Commissioning Panel for Mental Health.

Kings Fund (2015). *Mental Health Under Pressure.* Briefing paper. London: King's Fund.

Lawn S, Smith A, Hunter K (2009). Mental health peer support for hospital avoidance and early discharge: an Australian example of consumer driven and operated service. *Journal of Mental Health 17*(5): 498–508.

Menzies Lyth I (1960). Social systems as a defence against anxiety: an empirical study of the nursing service of a general hospital. In: Trist E, Murray H (eds). *The Social Engagement of Social Science* (vol 1): *the socio-psychological perspective.* Philadelphia, PA: University of Pennsylvania Press (pp439–462).

National Survivor User Network (NSUN) (2018). *The Principles of Peer Support Charter.* [Online.] NSUN. www.nsun.org.uk/peer-support-charter (accessed 26 August 2019).

Penny D (2018). *Defining 'Peer Support': implications for policy, practice and research.* [Online.] Advocates for Human Potential, Inc. http://ahpnet.com/AHPNet/media/AHPNetMediaLibrary/White%20Papers/DPenney_Defining_peer_support_2018_Final.pdf (accessed 14 August 2019).

Repper J, Carter T (2010). *Using Personal Experience to Support Others with Similar Difficulties: a review of the literature on peer support in mental health.* London: Together.

Reynolds D (2010). Human kindness compassion and love: the Ward Visiting Scheme designed and delivered by Canerows and Plaits. *Mental Health and Social Inclusion 14*: 3.

Reynolds D, Seebohm P (2010). Canerows and Plaits Ward Visiting Service and Have Your Say Forum Evaluation. London: Canerows and Plaits. Available from www.soundminds.co.uk (accessed 26 August 2019).

Rose D, Evans J, Laker C, Wykes T (2015). Life in acute mental health settings: experiences and perceptions of service users and nurses. *Epidemiology and Psychiatric Sciences 24*(1): 90–96.

Royal College of Psychiatrists (2010). *No Health Without Public Mental Health: the case for action.* Royal College of Psychiatrists position statement PS4/2010. London: Royal College of Psychiatrists.

Schaufeli W, Maslach C, Marek T (eds) (1993). *Professional Burnout.* London: Routledge.

Star Wards (2009). *Encouraging the Art of Conversation on Mental Health Wards.* [Online.] TalkWell. http://www.mentalhealthsupport.co.uk/documents/talkwell_web.pdf (accessed 14 August 2019).

Thibeault C (2016). An interpretation of nurse–patient relationships in inpatient psychiatry. *Global Qualitative Nursing Research 3*: 1–10.

Wykes T, Csipke E, Williams P, Koeser L (2018). Improving patient experiences of mental health inpatient care: a randomised controlled trial. *Psychological Medicine 48*(3): 488–497.

# Chapter 11

# Place and race: sanctuary, asylum and community belonging

## John Wainwright and Mick McKeown

He who is reluctant to recognise me opposes me. (Fanon, 1967: 218)

This chapter describes the history and mission of Mary Seacole House, an alternative community mental health resource centre in Liverpool. We draw on the findings of a recent participatory action research project involving the members of Mary Seacole House to illustrate important matters of identity associated with space and place. Although these have arisen in a particular place that, arguably, has some unique characteristics, we believe there are more general lessons for wider considerations of the uneasy relationship between race[1] and psychiatry. We focus on individual and collective experiences of racism and mental health for people attending Mary Seacole House and explore how these are bound up with wider struggles in the local Black community.

## The fractious relationship between race and psychiatry

Worse physical and mental health outcomes are associated with both place and ethnicity (Walker, Williams & Egede, 2016), and racism is implicated in some of this (Paradies et al, 2015). Historically, there has been a consistent pattern of disadvantage and anomalies in the delivery of care and treatment in the mental health sector, and this has been reflected in a number of critical reviews (for example, Care Quality Commission, 2018) and the most recent appraisal of UK

---

1. Race is not a satisfactory term as it is a social construction based on negative ethnic characteristics. However, we are using it in this context as a means to articulate differentiation, in order to analyse this difference.

mental health law (Department of Health and Social Care, 2018). People from ethnic minority groups, especially Black men, are substantially over-represented in various diagnostic categories and disproportionately subject to compulsion and coercion in the mental health services. They are more likely to receive high doses of medication, more likely to be placed under section and detained at higher levels of security, more likely to come to psychiatric services via the police or the courts, more likely to be held in seclusion, and less likely to be treated in primary care or receive talking therapies (Bhui et al, 2015; Gajwani et al, 2016; Morgan et al, 2004; Raleigh et al, 2007). Specific policies have been introduced in an attempt to address these inequities, prompted by some high-profile examples of racism in mental health services and deaths of Black men in hospital and in police custody (Department of Health, 2005), reflecting wider public sector policy such as the Macpherson (1999) report dealing with institutional racism. There have also been some broader health policies aimed at promoting recovery, autonomy and respect for users' voices in mental health services (see Mental Health Taskforce, 2016). Nevertheless, Black communities have not achieved self-determination in mental health provision, or had their voice heard in meaningful ways (Department of Health, 2005; Department of Health and Social Care, 2018). Further, the service user/survivor movement itself has faced criticism for a lack of ethnic diversity within its ranks (Wallcraft, Read & Sweeney, 2003).

## Black community-organised alternatives

In reaction to these circumstances, alternative mental health support and lobbying initiatives such as the Black Spaces project have emerged to support Black service users' needs and to ensure their voices and the voice of their communities are heard (BME Voices, 2018; Christie & Hill, 2003; Wright & Hutnik, 2004). A number of alternative approaches to service provision and advocacy have been developed organically by and for Black communities in several cities, including the innovative Bradford transcultural psychiatry centre, and other notable initiatives in London (Hackney and Brixton), Liverpool and Manchester (Francis, 1991; Fernando, 2005; Christie & Hill, 2003). For a period, Mind, the national mental health charity, published *Diverse Minds*, a magazine focused on highlighting racial disadvantages within the mental health system and celebrating alternatives. Nevertheless, many of these positive developments have been undermined by budgetary constraints and have had to navigate the fine line between working alongside mainstream services and being co-opted. In this respect, Fernando has criticised the lack of clarity over what constitutes best practice in multicultural mental health care in the UK (Fernando, 2005). A notable UK government initiative, Delivering

Race Equality, responded to the various identified inequities in the system, using a community development framework (NIMHE, 2003; Department of Health, 2005). Despite this, however, it has been argued that, by focusing on changing practice and attitudes within core mainstream services, an opportunity was missed to galvanise alternative provision in the community and voluntary sector (Fernando, 2010; Bhui, Ascoli & Nuamh, 2012).

Mary Seacole House was established in Liverpool in the 1990s by concerted community campaigning, amid broader struggles within the city focused on race. Therefore, its very existence points up acknowledged anomalies in the mental health system and represents the physical, emotional and historical legacy of the activism of its founders (GCMHG, 2018; Gifford, Brown & Bundy, 1989). The site of Mary Seacole House, near the epicentre of the 1981 Toxteth riots,[2] on Upper Parliament Street, has substantial psychogeographical echoes for the community (Christian, 2008; Boland, 2010) and for Black mental health system survivors (Torkington, 2009). It reverberates with the struggles against racism and racist oppressions within the mental health system, and with the Black community's assertion of control over community mental health, which, in turn, has been damaged by these racisms (Torkington, 1991, 2009; Gajwani et al, 2016; Singh et al, 2007).

Mary Seacole House was one of many BAME[3] organisations in Liverpool, as elsewhere in the UK, that were borne out of these struggles. These struggles were either as a direct consequence of the BAME community finding themselves in conflict with the state through community members challenging, rioting and in physical confrontation with the police (Gifford, Brown & Bundy, 1989; Torkington, 1991; Zack-Williams, 1997), or through specific issues that BAME community activists and/or service users identified as discriminatory in the treatment they received from public services (Gifford, Brown & Bundy, 1989; Ben-Tovim et al, 1986a; Torkington, 1991). This could be in education, immigration, housing, policing, social services or – in the case of Mary Seacole House – mental health services (Gifford, Brown & Bundy, 1989; Torkington, 1991). All of these experiences of the state and/or agencies were framed though racism, in one or more of its various forms (Gifford, Brown & Bundy, 1989; Ben-Tovim et al, 1986a).

---

2. In 1981, the local Black community took to the streets to riot against oppressive and racist policing behaviour, particularly towards young people. The riots were also a response to the local authority's racist and institutionally exclusive practice of economic and political marginalisation of the Black community in Liverpool. See Zack-Williams (1997), Christian (2008), or Boland (2010) for a more detailed discussion.

3. BAME is an acronym for Black, Asian and Minority Ethnic. It is one of several iterations that attempt to be representative of the minority ethnic population in the UK. However, what it includes and the order of the naming by definition excludes and prioritises specific groups. It is, though, a more inclusive term than just using 'Bblack'. See Modood (1994) for a detailed discussion.

Notably, in 1984 the Liverpool Black Sisters and other community activists began a campaign to challenge the local council, health authority and local mental health officials regarding the racism that Black survivors of the mental health system experienced. They established a Heath and Race action research project to provide evidence of this discriminatory treatment, and meetings were held with public sector officials to argue for provision specifically appropriate for the local Black community (Torkington, 1991; Torkington, 2009). This led to the establishment of the Granby Community Mental Health Group (GCMHG), which demanded that the local council and health services provide drop-in and respite facilities for the Black community in the Liverpool 8 area:

> ... where Black people could feel free to discuss their personal anxieties,
> problems and crises in an unstructured and non-judgemental
> atmosphere, a space where they could safely express their frustration
> and anger about the racism they experience in all aspects of their lives.
> (Torkington, 2009: 16)

After protracted, tense and at times emotional negotiations with the local council and health services, Granby Community Health Group established charitable status and secured the resources to lease a three-storey, Georgian building at 91 Upper Parliament Street, in the heart of Liverpool 8, and to employ five staff.[4] Mary Seacole House and its sister organisation, the Advocacy Project,[5] were opened in 1991, providing day care, drop-in and advocacy services for the Black community and a safe haven for BAME service users.

Over the years, Mary Seacole House has developed and grown in response to the demand by BAME service users for emotional and practical support. This has included support in the community for individuals, families and carers; companionship; health and wellbeing services, and advice and consultancy. In response to demand and an increasingly diverse ethnic population in Liverpool, an Asian carers' support group has also been established there. In addition, a peer advocacy support group has been set up and service users have been trained to help fellow users in their struggles within and against the mental health system (Torkington, 2009; GCMHG, 2018). It is now (in 2019) the only BAME voluntary welfare agency in Liverpool that still operates and provides a

---

4. It is important to acknowledge the three Black women who led the struggle to establish Granby Community Mental Health Group and subsequently Mary Seacole House and the Advocacy Project and ensured it continued as a successful Black mental health provision for the local community. They are Protasia Torkington, Yvonne Asige-Rooney and Leonie Nash.

5. Many years later, the Advocacy Project was merged with Mary Seacole House for strategic and financial reasons. However, both of these projects are still in operation.

service for the local community. This is because the other BAME agencies that emerged as a consequence of the 1981 riots have closed down, often because of lack of funding (GCMHG, 2018).

That Mary Seacole House has survived and continues to provide this service to the BAME community in a hostile political and economic environment is a testament to its importance for that community and the local statutory health and welfare services.

## The salience of race, place and space

Urban geographers are developing new thinking about the social and relational dimensions of city living, moving beyond disciplinary interests in spatiality to create new scholarship in geographies of mental health (Parr, 1997, 2000; Wolch & Philo, 2000). For example, by building on scrutiny of aggregates of interpersonal relationships, an interplay between people and the material fabric of cities can be discerned. Through this lens, the cityscape, streets, parks and other spaces can be viewed in terms of their potential for supporting communal, social or political action (Amin, 2008), including health-related action and activism.

Positive affinities for the places we call home have been shown to be associated with positive health, wellbeing and quality-of-life outcomes, and these, in turn, have been linked with access to social capital and levels of civic/ community engagement (Harris et al, 1995; Mesch & Manor, 1998; Brown, Reed & Harris, 2002; Ziersch et al, 2005; Tartaglia, 2013). Attachments to place correlate with better mental health, including within ethnic minority communities, and can buffer against effects of adverse social and physical environments (Becares & Nazroo, 2013; Marcheshci et al, 2015). In contrast, antipathies to place are associated with negative outcomes (Stokols & Shumaker, 1982). Furthermore, communities with strong place attachment, while beneficial for their members, can be exclusionary of outsiders, newcomers and those perceived to be different (Fried, 2000).

Our identities are not fixed; rather, they are perpetually reproduced in response to prevailing systems of representation (Hall, 1998). Much has been made of the ways in which people's attachment to place can constitute an important and valued part of their identity. Any useful consideration of the importance of place for residents of a neighbourhood or city might distinguish between simple affinities for a place (Low & Altman, 1992) and the influence of place on identity (Proshansky, Fabian & Kaminoff, 1983). Similarly, affinities for place can be separated into those that are about the physical environment and those prompted by the relational interactions taking place within it (Bernardo & Palma-Oliveira, 2005).

Liverpool, for example, projects a strong local identity, which reflects historical patterns of work and cultural expression in the city and a strong sense of exceptionalism (Belchem, 2006). Latterly, this has become bound up with efforts to brand the city through its status as the 2008 European Capital of Culture, which was in turn fed by the fame of musicians such as The Beatles and its two local football teams. Commentators such as Boland (2008a, 2008b) draw attention to distinctly social and spatial imaginings of the Liverpool identity that encompass Scouse self-perceptions and externally generated views of Liverpudlians. Hence, a strong sense of local self-regard sits in uneasy juxtaposition to pejorative media stereotypes of, for example, disadvantage and criminality. A valued Scouse identity reflects a humorous, edgy, working-class character replete with urban pride and rebelliousness. This has historically played out in collective resistance to various injustices visited on the city or its citizens by external forces perceived as malign, such as the government or employers (see Beynon, 1984; Taaffe & Mulhearn, 1988), and evident in community responses to the Hillsborough tragedy and its long aftermath (Scraton, 2013).

The city has one of the longest established Black populations in the UK and high proportions of people of dual heritage (Law & Henfry, 1981; Ben-Tovim et al, 1986b; Liverpool Black Caucus, 1986; Small, 1991). Thus, a focus on Liverpool the place – a city where the politics of race and racial disadvantage pivot on a relatively unique set of historical and spatially distributed economic and social relations and where adoption of Scouse identity reflects these divisions – offers opportunities to explore racialised experiences of mental distress and care and support services in relation to place, space and identity. Complex inter-relationships between identities and affinities for place, at both city and neighbourhood levels, have their foundation in a historical backdrop of exclusions and disadvantage and patterns of spatial division in the geography of the city. These remarked-upon socio-historical underpinnings have undoubtedly been influential in patterning health and mental health disadvantage (Torkington, 1991).

## Liverpool 8

Liverpool 8 is the district of the city where ethnic minorities are most obviously concentrated – an area roughly defined by the boundaries of Abercromby and Granby wards, and usually simply referred to as Toxteth. In one sense, Liverpool 8 epitomises an imagined community (Boland, 2010). A sense of belonging to 'The Community' does not insist on knowing everyone in the community; most important is a strong common bond. This certainly involves attachments to the place and community that is Liverpool 8, and notable places within Liverpool 8 boundaries, such as Mary Seacole House.

Liverpool's Black community can be considered to be engaged in a continual struggle against racism, discrimination and multiple social exclusions within the city, with Liverpool 8 being lauded as the 'socio-geographic heart of Liverpool's Black communities' (Lashua 2015: 45). With implied criticism, Liverpool 8 is forever linked in public consciousness to the 1981 riots there, and can be viewed negatively by inhabitants in other areas of the city and region (Gifford, Brown & Bundy, 1989; Ben-Tovim, 1997). Such exclusionary representations have been exacerbated by tendencies to discount the wider importance of the Black community to the city, including the substantial cultural, social and economic contributions it makes to the city 'brand' through activities such as the music scene.

Thus, Black Liverpool residents experience a strong sense of outsider status in their own city; they are daily marginalised from key aspects of city life, including opportunities for rewarding employment and participation in decision-making processes (Zack-Williams, 1997). This has been so much the case that local commentators have previously concluded that:

> Despite its permanency, the Black community of Liverpool 8 can be viewed as one of the most historically deprived in Britain, and more or less constitutes an internal colony with lack of control over its own resources and destiny. (Zack-Williams, 1997: 541)

Faced with exclusion elsewhere in the city, the people of Liverpool 8 have, to some extent, been forced over the years to rely on their own resources and resourcefulness. For example, in response to informal racist door policies operated by mainstream night clubs in the city centre, a number of Liverpool 8 social clubs were developed by and for people with diverse cultural heritage community identities (Small, 1991). Subsequent changes in housing stock ownership and waves of privatisation contributed to further impoverishment of the area and decline of many of the clubs, and a degree of dispersal of residents and communities (Lashua, 2015). Consequent economic disadvantages and disconnection from centres of power clearly contributed to the conditions that drove the aforementioned riots (Ben-Tovim et al, 1986a; Gifford, Brown & Bundy, 1989). Shortcomings of representation have arguably altered little in the intervening decades. This democratic deficit can also be seen in the relative marginalisation of the Black voice within mental health services, despite popular focus on user involvement and co-production. For such reasons, Mary Seacole House has hosted a crucial independent advocacy service from its inception.

Liverpool Black residents, faced with these identified patterns of discrimination and exclusion, have an uneasy relationship with notions of

Liverpool exceptionalism and Scouse identity. With reference to geography and accent, they are certainly Scouse. But the performance of Black Scouse identity involves other heritage, cultural and place affinities, notably to Liverpool 8 (Boland, 2010).

## Identity and attachments within Mary Seacole House

Our qualitative study explored 25 participants' experiences of membership of Mary Seacole House (Wainwright, McKeown & Kinney, in review). It was conducted as part of a bigger participatory project concerned with shaping future directions for the service. Participants were 11 women and 14 men of a range of ethnicities. Part of the study focused on participants' thoughts about Mary Seacole House as a singular space within the geographical place of Liverpool 8, and this is the aspect we are concerned with here. It should be noted that the people who use services offered by Mary Seacole House call themselves 'members'. The commonly used term 'service users' was rejected on the grounds that it implies a transactional distance between staff and people who 'use' services, and so (ironically) is disempowering.

### Attachment and belonging

First, the Mary Seacole House members variously spoke of their sense of attachment to Liverpool 8 and why this was the case. Many identified explicitly with, and took pride in, their local community, combining these affinities with references to heritage and ethnicity, and clearly emphasising place as a crucial factor:

> Roots, because I've got family now who – brothers… who were born in Liverpool, actually live in Liverpool. (Black/dual heritage man)

> We like our area, it's got the most beautiful architecture, people come here to film… we don't want concrete jungles and all that crap. (Black/dual heritage woman)

This attachment to the place that is Liverpool 8 was connected with knowledge and experiences of historical and contemporary struggles, framed by race and racial disadvantage. For these people, the locality represented a territory that had been defended and fought over across generations:

> Well, it's the police isn't it? Whose son, grandson? It is commonplace for our kids to be held by the police. (Black/dual heritage woman)

The sense of belonging to Liverpool 8 was ambivalently tempered by, and enmeshed with, experiences of racism, discrimination and exclusions within the city as a whole. Pride in place was wrapped up with feelings of resistance, staying in power, and survival:

> So I've got family... I've got a Black family, I've got history, I've lived round here for literally hundreds of years... my great-great-grandmother's buried in Smithdown Road Cemetery with... Yeah, yeah, you know what I mean, and so when, when you talk about Mary Seacole, to me it's just a replacement. (Black woman 3)

Attachments to place could be expressed with an air of nostalgia, sometimes tinged with a sense of loss that the area had changed over time:

> Where they all live and they go out the front door, go to work, come back from work, go back into the house and you don't see your neighbours or know your neighbours. It's slowly becoming that way in Toxteth. (Black/dual heritage man)

Some sensed a change in the 'Black community' as a degree of social mobility allowed an advantaged few to move out of Liverpool 8, leaving behind the most vulnerable and disadvantaged.

### Recognition and belonging

Second, participants voiced their appreciation for Mary Seacole House in terms of it being a place and space where they could experience recognition and belonging. The building itself and its décor were felt to be welcoming, with a unique character that enabled a set of social relations conducive to acceptance and wellbeing. This view was often expressed in ways that made clear the contrast with the participants' experiences of mainstream mental health care services.

People felt they belonged in Mary Seacole House, whereas they were more likely to describe feeling alienated in mental health wards. The space offered familiarity and a centredness within the locality, which itself reflected its heritage and culture. This affinity was typically expressed with regard to a sense that Mary Seacole House represented the diversity of the area, both in terms of the staff demographic and the culture, which was seen as connecting with the 'everyday' life experiences of members. This notion of everyday life encompassed key social factors in people's lives locally, such as race and racism, class and poverty. There was also recognition that ethnic and cultural difference was the norm in Mary Seacole House and that the staff knew and understood the life circumstances of the members, including their experiences of racism.

Such acknowledgement was felt to be sorely lacking in other places outside of Liverpool 8 and Mary Seacole House, and especially in mainstream mental health settings. Mary Seacole House staff were described as reflecting and embodying this difference in their own ethnic identity and their understanding of and connection to the Liverpool 8 area themselves. For members, the Mary Seacole House space assumed more salience than its simple physical location; it also constituted a range of relational factors transacted within a milieu of mutual recognition, which they contrasted with negative experiences typically encountered in other, more clinical places:

> No, didn't fancy it at all, didn't know anything about day centres, no,
> don't fancy that like... to be truthful for me, the most important thing,
> the reason I kept coming here was because it was a mix of people, of
> Black and White, because, you know, as I see it, mental illness, it doesn't
> discriminate. (Black/dual heritage man)

In some cases, participants remarked that they might have been at school with some of the staff, placing emphasis on and valuing this interconnectedness within the community. They also appreciated that they were treated as people, as members of the community, rather than clinical cases, and that their struggles against exclusionary institutions, including NHS services, were recognised and empathised with.

This sense of affirmation, recognition and belonging was intimately bound up with a sense of belonging to the local Black community, as well as recognising that the staff also organically belonged there, deepening their capacity for empathic support. Shared understandings of the commonplace aspects of the struggles that Liverpool 8 community residents and members of Mary Seacole House experienced could be taken for granted, as could a shared identity between members and staff.

Members, their families and Mary Seacole House staff share a connection in terms of race, place and history, yet, although race is important in this identification, all ethnicities, including White people, are welcomed in Mary Seacole House. This partly reflects the large numbers of people with dual heritage and in mixed relationships in Liverpool 8. Thus, White Scousers who join the Black community, through relationships or in solidarity with the struggle against racism in the area, become authentically part of the community of Liverpool 8:

I've lived in this area all my life, don't know nowhere else, I've always lived with people of different colours, different nationalities... different religions, and this centre reflects that for me... And there's such mixtures of people, if they ever get round to telling you. (Black/dual heritage man)

## Support and protection

Third, the participants described Mary Seacole House as a supportive and protective space, a port in a storm, and this could include providing sanctuary from oppressive or stigmatising aspects of the community, punitive aspects of mainstream services, and the more obvious discriminations and exclusions already mentioned:

I've never been to another day centre but I've heard of a few, like, and I don't believe they act in the same way as Mary Seacole. It's unique, Mary Seacole House. (Black man)

In contrast to the trauma and pain of mental distress and upsetting encounters with the mental health system, members felt safe and secure at Mary Seacole House and in their relationships with staff, who they experienced as prepared to listen, provide support and be friendly. This could be a welcome contrast to more difficult, less understanding relationships with some family members and neighbours in times of distress:

There's no judgement passed on you here, there's no stigma... when I was labelled, when I was diagnosed with schizophrenia, all of a sudden that word seems to strike terror into people, you find so-called friends disappear into the woodwork. (Black woman)

Mary Seacole House members felt respected and treated as equals by peers and staff alike, and distinctions between the two could be somewhat blurred in their descriptions of friendship and mutual recognition. As explained above, terminology such as 'service users', coined in the mainstream to acknowledge discrepant power differentials, was wholeheartedly rejected in Mary Seacole House because, by differentiating staff who provided services from the people who used them, it was experienced as disempowering. Thus, as explained above, in Mary Seacole House, the chosen term is 'member', which carries a more substantial sense of equality, grounded in shared biography, mutuality of support, acknowledgement of race, belonging, and appreciation of how these factors connect with place and space.

### Shared experience

Fourth, there was an acknowledgement that mental distress does not discriminate, and a common understanding among members that they all shared the pain of mental distress, desperation and loneliness in their lives. For many, disruptions in family relationships could to some extent be redeemed by finding common ground with peers. The indiscriminate impact of mental distress was counteracted within Mary Seacole House by staff and other members' efforts to inculcate an atmosphere based on values of cultural diversity and inclusivity. The sense of community created in Mary Seacole House was felt to generate the supportive quality of the space and help members face the debilitating challenges in their lives.

## Materialities and mundanities of a supportive place

Arguably, this appreciation among members of the importance of place and space in the support provided at Mary Seacole House highlights a broader point about the importance of such matters in the provision of all mental health care. The building itself, its location, the layout of its rooms, the furniture and the artwork produced by members on its walls both give the place a distinctive character that is part of its appreciation and connect with and reinforce the relational aspects of the space – the mutual recognition and sense of belonging (Torkington, 2009). This hints at the ways in which the very fabric of a place can underpin its purpose and be part of the achievement of its ends.

Such material and mundane aspects of a place, often taken for granted, have been remarked upon elsewhere as a crucial part of the experience of mental health care and support, including support offered by peers (Brownlie & Spandler, 2018). The consistent negative experiences of Black people in mainstream mental health services and wider society make the case for literally building into other services some of the characteristics of mutual recognition and reciprocal support found in Mary Seacole House. In a context of widespread stigmatising and exclusionary communities, Pinfold (2000: 210) argues for the creation of 'safe spaces' built 'for, and with, mental health service users and their "unorthodox normalities"'. Arguably, alternative Black services need to be more available (BME Voices, 2018; Francis, 1991) and some of their character should be reproduced across the board in mainstream services. In this sense, exemplar alternatives such as Mary Seacole House operate to prefigure services that could be imagined elsewhere.

When members expressed their connections and affinities with the streets of Liverpool 8, they identified Mary Seacole House at the heart of this.

They also associated this alternative service with resistance to the anomalous treatment of Black people in the mental health system. For the members, a politics of the personal collides with notions of race, place and space in an appreciation of the sanctuary provided by this initiative created by and for the community (Pinfold, 2000; Small, 1991). Within this space is the psychosocial reassurance of a safety where members can securely identify as Black survivors of the mental health system.

## Identity and belonging

There is much debate among BAME welfare agencies about whether service users experience a service as better and more appropriate to their cultural and ethnic needs when the service providers are of the same ethnicity. The central tenet of the argument is that BAME organisations, because of the commonality of experience of the staff, particularly regarding racism, provide an ethos and environment that is much more effective and life-enhancing (Wainwright & Ridley, 2012). This suggests that BAME staff are viewed by service users as *insiders*, because they have a shared ethnicity, cultural experience and/or identify with the struggles against racism (Merton, 1972; Obasi, 2014).

However, this analysis is not without contradiction. For instance, BAME is a homogenising term that places all people of colour together, irrespective of ethnicity, nationality and cultural and political identity – to list just some of many, varying and contested signifiers (Modood, 1994; Anthias, 2010). Ethnic and/or political groupings that use race as a totem with which to identify themselves contain such diverse experiences that, in some contexts, they may themselves represent an *outsider* identity (Modood, 1994; Obasi, 2014). These differences may be constituted through biography, class, gender, sexuality and space (Crenshaw, 2019; hooks, 1984; Obasi, 2014), even before differences of generation and geography are considered. Furthermore, it is possible to be both *insiders* and *outsiders* at the same time, or at different times in different places, different spaces and changing racisms (Merton, 1972; Hall, 1996). This kaleidoscope of difference premised on race, racism and ethnicity constantly leaves the *insider* status of the BAME service open to challenge as being over-simplistic (Hall, 1992; 1996).

Yet, despite these theoretical, political and lived complexities of the insider–outsider binary, Mary Seacole House members were clearly appreciative of the *sense of belonging* engendered in a space they identified as part of the Black community. For them, Mary Seacole House provided more than an ordinary mental health service. Vulnerable and disadvantaged members were better able to relate to staff drawn from their community, with a shared ethnic, cultural and spatial background. The mutual recognition when staff and members looked and sounded alike generated levels of trust and comfort (Wainwright & Ridley, 2012; Ridley & Wainwright, 2010). The support received from Mary Seacole House staff and peers was dependent on this mutual recognition, which was itself built on shared experiences of Liverpool 8, the place, including the negative impact of racism. In this way, identity and belonging assist in forming resilience to the negative psychosocial effects of racism (Christie & Hill, 2003; Wainwright & Ridley, 2012).

Mary Seacole House members share two intersecting experiences: racism and mental distress (Crenshaw, 2019; Nayak & Robbins, 2018). While prejudice and discrimination have resulted in repeated cycles of pain and exclusion, mental distress does not discriminate. Whatever the person's ethnicity or other intersectional characteristics, all members experience a degree of stigma or distancing from (some of) their friends, family or the wider community (Nayak & Robbins, 2018).

They may experience broadly based prejudice on the grounds of ethnic difference and the particular prejudice towards residents of Liverpool 8 from many in the rest of the city. Overlain on this place-specific disadvantage are the many intersecting and contradictory exclusions arising from the confluence of societal racism, the specific discrimination experienced by survivors of the mental health system and other invitations to discrimination and othering furnished by intersecting identities attached to gender, sexuality, class or disability (Nayak & Robbins, 2018). Exclusions and discriminations associated with place are contradictory because their place-centric nature opens up possibilities to imagine place-focused solutions. The establishment of Mary Seacole House stands as an example of this. As *Black Spaces* argues, a place that offers empathic responses forged in a visceral understanding of the racism experienced by Black survivors is likely to be appreciated on those terms (Christie & Hill, 2003). Only in such a place are survivors likely to experience the sense of belonging that shapes feelings of solace and sanctuary.

## Conclusion

This chapter has attempted to identify what it is about place and space that can make a project like Mary Seacole House so particularly healing and holding for its members as a community mental health centre. We have argued that an essential feature is its location in Liverpool 8, within a long-standing Black community that is geographically, politically and socially wrapped around it. Mary Seacole House provides a place where members can feel they belong precisely because it is rooted in the cultural fabric of Liverpool 8's multi-ethnic community (Boland, 2008b; Lashua, 2015). In turn, the relational spaces it offers provide valued respite from the alienation found too often in mainstream care settings, as well as in the wider city and its environs.

The need for better alternatives located deliberately in place and space is as urgent now as it has ever been. In these turbulent global times, austerity measures threaten the few alternative mental health services we have. Moreover, with new influxes of asylum seekers and refugees, race is again at the forefront of critical perspectives on mental health care. More widely within our society, we are hearing a toxic rhetoric espousing exclusionary, place-resonant binaries (Rajan-Rankin, 2015). Places such as Mary Seacole House embody the true meaning of refuge and asylum in more ways than one.

## Acknowledgement

We would like to thank the members and staff of Mary Seacole House for participating in this project. It is their struggle and ongoing commitment that creates the safe space and place to make Mary Seacole House a reality.

## References

Amin A (2008). Collective culture and urban public space. City: analysis of urban trends. *Culture, Theory, Policy, Action 12*(1): 5–24.

Anthias F (2010). Nation and post-nation: nationalism, transnationalism and intersections of belonging. In: Collins PH, Solomos J (eds). *The Sage Handbook of Race and Ethnic Studies*. London: Sage (pp221–248).

Becares L, Nazroo J (2013). Social capital, ethnic density and mental health among ethnic minority people in England: a mixed-methods study. *Ethnicity & Health 18*: 544–562.

Belchem J (2006). *Merseypride: essays in Liverpool exceptionalism*. Oxford: Oxford University Press.

Ben-Tovim G (1997). Why 'positive action' is politically correct. In: Modood T, Werbner P (eds). *The Politics of Multiculturalism in the New Europe. Racism Identity and Community*. London: Zed Books (pp209–223).

Ben-Tovim G, Gabriel J, Law I, Stredder K (1986a). A political analysis of local struggles for racial equality. In: Rex J, Mason D (eds). *Theories of Race and Ethnic Relations*. Cambridge: Cambridge University Press (pp131–152).

Ben-Tovim G, Gabiel J, Law I, Stredder K (1986b). *The Local Politics of Race*. London: Macmillan.

Bernardo F, Palma-Oliveira JM (2005). Place change and identity processes. *Medio Ambiente y Comportamiento Humano 6*: 71–87.

Beynon H (1984). *Working for Ford*. Harmondsworth: Penguin.

Bhui K, Ascoli M, Nuamh O (2012). The place of race and racism in cultural competence: what can we learn from the English experience about the narratives of evidence and argument? *Transcultural psychiatry 49*(2): 185–205.

Bhui K, Ullrich S, Kallis C, Coid JW (2015). Criminal justice pathways to psychiatric care for psychosis. The *British Journal of Psychiatry 207*(6): 523–529.

BME Voices (2018). *BME Voices Talk Mental Health is on a Mission*. [Online.] www.bmevoices.co.uk/about/ (accessed 21 August 2019).

Boland P (2010). Sonic geography, place and race in the formation of local identity: Liverpool and Scousers. *Geografiska Annaler: Series B. Human Geography 92*(1): 1–22.

Boland P (2008a). 'Capital of Culture – you must be having a laugh'. Challenging the official rhetoric of Liverpool as the 2008 European cultural capital. *Social and Cultural Geography 11*(7): 627–645.

Boland P (2008b). The construction of images of people and place: labelling Liverpool and stereotyping Scousers. *Cities 25*: 355–369. doi:10.1016/j.cities.2008.09.003.

Brown GG, Reed P, Harris CC (2002). Testing a place-based theory for environmental evaluation: an Alaska case study. *Applied Geography 22*(1): 49–76.

Brownlie J, Spandler H (2018). Materialities of mundane care and the art of holding one's own. *Sociology of Health & Illness 40*(2): 256–269.

Care Quality Commission (2018). *Monitoring the Mental Health Act: 2016 to 2017. The eighth annual report by the Care Quality Commission on the use of the Mental Health Act 1983.* Newcastle: CQC.

Christian M (2008). The Fletcher report 1930: a historical case study of contested Black mixed heritage Britishness. *Journal of History and Sociology 21*: 213–241.

Christie Y, Hill N (2003). *Black Spaces Project*. London: The Mental Health Foundation.

Crenshaw K (2019). *On Intersectionality: essential writings*. New York, NY: New Press.

Department of Health (2005). *Delivering race equality in mental health care: an action plan for reform inside and outside services, and; The government's response to the independent inquiry into the death of David Bennett.* London: Department of Health.

Department of Health and Social Care (2018). *Modernising the Mental Health Act – final report from the independent review.* London: Department of Health & Social Care.

Fanon F (1967). *Black Skin, White Masks*. New York, NY: Grove Press.

Fernando S (2010). *Mental Health Race and Culture* (3rd ed). Basingstoke: Palgrave Macmillan.

Fernando S (2005). Multicultural mental health services: projects for minority ethnic communities in England. *Transcultural Psychiatry 42*: 420–436.

Francis E (1991). Racism and mental health: some causes for concern for social work. In: Central Council for Education. *Setting the Context for Change: anti-racist social work education.* London: CCETSW (Chapter 10).

Fried M (2000). Continuities and discontinuities of place. *Journal of Environmental Psychology 20*(3): 193–205.

Gajwani R, Parsons H, Birchwood M, Singh SP (2016). Ethnicity and detention: are Black And Minority Ethnic (BAME) groups disproportionately detained under the Mental Health Act 2007? *Social Psychiatry and Psychiatric Epidemiology 51*(5): 703–711.

GCMHG (2018). *Annual Report 2017/18*. Liverpool: Mary Seacole House.

Gifford AM, Brown W, Bundy R (1989). *Loosen the Shackles*. London: Karia Press.

Hall S (1998). Cultural identity and diaspora. In: Rutherford J (ed). *Identity: community, culture, difference* (2nd ed). London: Lawrence & Wishart (pp222–237).

Hall S (1996). Introduction: who needs 'identity'? In: Hall S, du Gay P (eds). *Questions of Cultural Identity*. London: Sage (pp1–17).

Hall S (1992). New ethnicities. In: Donald J, Rattansi A (eds). *Race Culture and Difference*. London: Sage (pp252–259).

Harris PB, Werner CM, Brown BB, Ingebritsen D (1995). Relocation and privacy regulation: a cross-cultural analysis. *Journal of Environmental Psychology* 15(4): 311–320.

hooks b (1984). *Feminist Theory: from margin to center*. Boston, MA: South End Press.

Lashua B (2015). Mapping the politics of 'race', place and memory in Liverpool's popular music heritage. In: Cohen S, Knifton R, Leonard M, Roberts L (eds). *Sites of Popular Music Heritage: memories, histories, places*. London: Routledge (pp45–61).

Law I, Henfrey J (1981). *A History of Race and Racism in Liverpool, 1660–1950*. Liverpool: Merseyside Community Relations Council.

Liverpool Black Caucus (1986). *The Racial Politics of Militant in Liverpool: the Black community's struggle for participation in local politics 1980-1986*. Liverpool: Merseyside Area Profile Group and Runnymede Trust.

Low SM, Altman I (1992). Place attachment: a conceptual inquiry. In: Altman I, Low SM (eds). *Place Attachment*. New York, NY: Plenum Press (pp1–12).

Macpherson W (1999). *The Stephen Lawrence Inquiry: report of an inquiry by Sir William Macpherson of Cluny*. Cm 4262-I. London: Home Office.

Marcheschi E, Laike T, Brunt D, Hansson L, Johansson M (2015). Quality of life and place attachment among people with severe mental illness. *Journal of Environmental Psychology* 41: 145–154.

Mental Health Taskforce (2016). *The Five-Year Forward View for Mental Health*. London: Department of Health.

Merton R (1972). Insiders and outsiders: a chapter in sociology of knowledge. *American Journal of Sociology* 78(1): 9–47.

Mesch GS, Manor O (1998). Social ties, environmental perception, and local attachment. *Environment and Behavior* 30(4): 504–519.

Modood T (1994). Political Blackness and British Asians. *Sociology* 28(4): 859–876.

Morgan C, Mallett R, Hutchinson G, Leff J (2004). Negative pathways to psychiatric care and ethnicity: the bridge between social science and psychiatry. *Social Science and Medicine* 58(4): 739-752.

Nayak S, Robbins R (2018). *Intersectionality in Social Work: activism and practice in context*. London: Routledge.

NIMHE (2003). *Inside Outside: improving mental health services for Black and minority ethnic communities in England*. London: NIMHE.

Obasi C (2014). Negotiating the insider/outsider continua: a Black female hearing perspective on research with deaf women and Black women. *Qualitative Research* 14(1:) 61–78.

Paradies Y, Ben J, Denson N, Elias A, Priest N, Pieterse A, Gupta A, Kelaher M, Gee G (2015). Racism as a determinant of health: a systematic review and meta-analysis. *PloS One* 10(9): 10(9): e0138511. https://doi.org/10.1371/journal.pone.0138511 (accessed 20 September 2019).

Parr H (2000). Interpreting the 'hidden social geographies' of mental health: ethnographies of inclusion and exclusion in semi-institutional places. *Health and Place* 6(3): 225–237.

Parr H (1997). Mental health, public space, and the city: questions of individual and collective access. *Environment and Planning D: Society & Space* 15: 435–454.

Pinfold V (2000). 'Building up safe havens …all around the world': users' experiences of living in the community with mental health problems. *Health and Place* 6(3): 201–212.

Proshansky HM, Fabian AK, Kaminoff R (1983). Place identity: physical world socialization of the self. *Journal of Environmental Psychology 3*(1): 57–83.

Rajan-Rankin S (2015). Anti-racist social work in a 'post-race society'? Interrogating the amorphous 'other'. *Critical and Radical Social Work 3*(2): 207–220.

Raleigh V, Irons R, Hawe E, Scobie S, Cook A, Reeves R, Petruckevitch A, Harrison J (2007). Ethnic variations in the experiences of mental health service users in England. Results of a national patient survey programme. *British Journal of Psychiatry 191*: 304–312.

Ridley J, Wainwright J with Davda P (2010). *'Black' families for 'Black' children? An evaluation of action for children's practice in ethnically matching Black, Asian and dual heritage children for adoption.* London: Action For Children.

Scraton P (2013). The legacy of Hillsborough: liberating truth, challenging power. *Race & Class 55*(2): 1–27.

Singh SP, Greenwood N, White S, Churchill R (2007). Ethnicity and the Mental Health Act 1983: systematic review. *The British Journal of Psychiatry 191*(2): 99–105.

Small S (1991). Racialised relations in Liverpool: a contemporary anomaly. *Journal of Ethnic and Migration Studies 17*(4): 511–537.

Stokols D, Shumaker SA (1982). The psychological context of residential mobility and well-being. *Journal of Social Issues 38*(3): 149–171.

Taaffe P, Mulhearn T (1988). *Liverpool: a city that dared to fight.* London: Fortress.

Tartaglia S (2013). Different predictors of quality of life in urban environments. *Social Indicators Research 11*(3): 1045–1053.

Torkington NPK (ed) (2009). *Their Untold Stories.* Liverpool: Other Publications.

Torkington NPK (1991). *The Racial Politics of Health: a Liverpool profile.* Liverpool: University of Liverpool.

Wainwright J, McKeown M, Kinney M (in review). 'In these streets': the saliency of place in an alternative Black mental health resource centre. *International Journal of Human Rights in Healthcare.*

Wainwright J, Ridley J (2012). Matching, ethnicity and identity: reflections on the practice and realities of ethnic matching in adoption. *Adoption and Fostering 36*(3): 50–61.

Walker RJ, Williams JS, Egede LE (2016). Influence of race, ethnicity and social determinants of health on diabetes outcomes. *The American Journal of the Medical Sciences 351*(4): 366–373.

Wallcraft J, Read J, Sweeney A (2003). *On Our Own Terms: users and survivors of mental health services working together for support and change.* London: The Sainsbury Centre for Mental Health.

Wolch J, Philo C (2000). From distributions of deviance to definitions of difference: past and future mental health geographies. *Health and Place 6*(3): 137–157.

Wright S, Hutnik N (2004). *Black Spaces Project.* London: Mental Health Foundation.

Zack-Williams AB (1997). African diaspora conditioning: the case of Liverpool. *Journal of Black Studies 27*(4): 528–542.

Ziersch AM, Baum FE, MacDougall C, Putland C (2005). Neighbourhood life and social capital: the implications for health. *Social Science & Medicine 60*(1): 71–86.

# Chapter 12

## The PeerTalk Network

### Stephen Normanton

Professional mental health services are under constant pressure to alleviate the emotional distress experienced by a seemingly ever-increasing number of people. The quest continues for a universal quick-fix drug or programme of psychological therapy that achieves outstanding results. Yet it seems more likely that remedies will be found not in complex clinical interventions but in patterns of supportive social interaction (Pfeiffer et al, 2011; Mead & Filson, 2016). A non-judgemental, empathic listening ear can achieve excellent therapeutic outcomes. The primary challenge is to provide the time and space so distressed people can be offered appropriate, open-ended support. The PeerTalk charity has its origins in a project initiated and funded by the Methodist Church in response to this lack of social provision. We aim to deliver a service that effectively and sustainably delivers this time, space and support by organically expanding to reach more and more people.

This chapter describes how the initiative was developed, how obstacles and resistances were overcome, the evidence that it helps, and future directions.

### PeerTalk – the need

Those who attend PeerTalk support groups often express their frustration, and sometimes anger, at their experiences of the mental health services. It seems there is little opportunity in the mainstream care system to tell their stories and receive appropriate support.

Peer support groups are nothing new and PeerTalk doesn't make any claims to be providing innovative or novel therapies. It came into being through a recognition that there aren't enough peer support groups to meet the huge need. PeerTalk aims to be a trusted, reliable, robust and sustainable service that goes some way to filling the current gaps in the statutory mental health provision. Too many community-based, voluntary-sector groups fall by the wayside due to limited organisational capacity. We believe it is essential for professional services to be confident they can signpost people to such groups.

For many who live with depression and other emotional difficulties, an often-repeated pattern of engagement with clinical services begins with a visit to the GP. Although the reported experiences of such visits range from excellent to poor, many perceive that the limitations of time and the convenience of printing prescriptions offer little towards a satisfactory outcome. Some people may be referred to psychological therapy services. Some who attend PeerTalk support groups describe their experiences of such services as very helpful; others say it is a waste of time. Again, limitations on time, and sometimes the relational dynamic with the counsellor or therapist, are what seems to determine the helpfulness of the experience.

Attending an appointment with a GP or psychological/psychiatric clinician carries a significant weight of stigma. Admitting a need for mental health treatment in the first place is a huge step, as many people see this as personal failure or weakness. Having crossed the threshold of the consulting room, people can soon find themselves being offered quick-fix solutions based on risk assessment questionnaires that fail to identify their root needs. This can leave the person feeling they have not been heard or taken seriously. However, some may feel their distress is at least validated if they are prescribed antidepressants, despite a failure to identify an underlying cause.

Asking for time off work to attend a counselling session could set alarm bells ringing for an employer; there is a very real fear for many of being 'found out' as having 'a problem'. One PeerTalk participant told us he missed therapy appointments because he thought his employer would assume he couldn't be trusted to work in people's homes if he was known to have a mental health problem. But even high-flying executives can avoid engaging with workplace counselling services in case they are considered to be a risk to the business.

Even when experiences of psychological therapy services are positive, there is a very long wait to access them and ongoing support following therapy is rare.

People come to PeerTalk meetings with many different stories and experiences, but they tend to have much in common. They have all known times when life can be overwhelming and they have struggled to cope. They also often report that clinicians and therapists 'just don't understand'. One of the strengths of peer-to-peer support is that the people in the group understand each other. Another common experience is the attitude among those around them that they should 'pull themselves together'. We find that, whatever their reason for coming – perhaps they have stopped functioning due to pressures of work or are not coping with the death of a partner or parent – they bring the compounding pressures of feeling that they are failing or weak, that it is their fault. Challenging stigmatising attitudes in society is also one of the PeerTalk aims. Simply being in the company of others who understand provides reassurance that they are not alone in what they are facing, and that in itself can be healing.

## What do we offer?

The idea for PeerTalk came in 2014, after a member of my close family had a brief course of cognitive behaviour therapy to address her feelings of depression. Following the treatment, it became clear that there was little social support in the community to aid the ongoing healing process. Financed with donations from friends and local churches and a grant from the national Methodist church, PeerTalk became a registered charity in October 2016 and established its first group in Bradford, UK, in March 2017.

Being heard is central to the ethos and values of PeerTalk. The posters and fliers advertising PeerTalk support groups include a quote from the life-coach Cheryl Richardson: 'People start to heal the moment they feel heard' (Richardson, 2014). You don't need to have a diagnosis of 'depression' to attend the groups. Some are referred from clinical services and some self-refer after seeing the poster in their local library, unsure whether they 'have' depression or not. All are welcome; a formal diagnosis is not required.

PeerTalk groups offer an anonymous space where people can explore for themselves how they are feeling and talk through their situation. Having time to talk and be heard in a non-clinical environment by others who understand is useful; it can help before accessing clinical services; it can help while accessing clinical services, and it can help after having received clinical services.

Our groups meet in a variety of venues and public spaces, such as church halls, libraries, cafés and even – in one instance – a museum! The main consideration is that the building should be accessible and comfortable, and easy to get to.

The weight of societal stigma and the increased degrees of anxiety associated with depression can make it very difficult for people to take the first steps to attending a support group. Attendees tell us it has sometimes taken three or more attempts to cross a group's threshold, having left home with every intention of doing so. PeerTalk group facilitators try to look out for people outside the door who might be deliberating whether to come in or not, and to offer them an invitation and welcome. Signage indicating where the group meets is important, especially if there are other activities taking place in the same building.

The groups meet weekly and are facilitated by two volunteers. The volunteer facilitators are not there as counsellors, clinicians or advisers; they do not offer opinions of their own or try to 'fix' people. The strength of the groups is that they provide a space where people with lived experience of depression – those surely best-placed to do so – share coping strategies and techniques and offer words of encouragement and support to others attending the group. They are a place where each group attendee can share their story and how they are feeling. Some may choose not to say anything and some talk a lot. The primary role of the facilitators is to manage the time available so that all the attendees are heard.

Meeting on the same day, weekly, all year round provides for continuity. Attendees don't have to think about whether it is the first week in the month or the fourth. Meeting every week is also important to sustain the support that the group produces. There is no limit to the number of occasions a person may attend a group and some do attend nearly every week of the year. The purpose of the group is mutual support. The meetings are not 'drop-ins' for people to talk about the weather or football. The structure to the meetings is the same every week and is the same across all the meetings throughout the PeerTalk network of groups. This provides a familiarity that helps the attendees, as they know what to expect.

The groups are confidential 'in session' and are focused on peer-to-peer support. When the formal meeting ends, we put the kettle on and the conversation becomes informal, phone numbers may be exchanged and meet-ups planned between the group's attendees. The value of the groups can thus extend beyond the weekly meeting itself.

The meetings start with one of the facilitators reading out a standard script that outlines the purpose of the group, the parameters of confidentiality and how the meeting operates. Each attendee introduces themselves by their first name. The lead facilitator then invites all the group members to share if they would like to. As a person talks, the facilitator uses listening skills, clarifies if needed and then reflects and summarises what has been said. The attendee will then be asked if they are OK for the other group members to offer their views on what has been shared. If so, the group will offer encouragement, advice, their own experiences and anything that is supportive of the attendee. The facilitator will then summarise the positive contributions the group has offered and invite the attendee to consider working on one helpful thing during the coming week.

Experience suggests that it takes at least eight volunteers to sustain a support group. The usual commitment for a volunteer is three consecutive weeks in a 12-week cycle. However, such a rota rarely runs as planned as the volunteers often have other commitments. Volunteers have said that the nine-week gap when they're not facilitating makes them feel detached from the group. Group attendees can become unsettled if there are a lot of changes of facilitator, especially if they are new to the group. These issues tend to settle down as the volunteers with that group become a team and group members get to know the volunteers. The volunteers keep in touch with each other between meetings via email or WhatsApp to report how many attended and, without breaking confidentiality, how the meeting went.

PeerTalk recognises that the volunteer facilitators need regular ongoing support and training. In order to deliver this, the volunteers for each group are brought together every two months or so. These gatherings nurture team bonding, as well as opportunity for feedback on how the groups are functioning. The training aims to develop the volunteers' facilitation skills but also to broaden their knowledge of mental health issues.

Often volunteers have connections with someone who lives with depression or they have past personal experience of their own. We recruit volunteers mostly through regional Awareness Day events, where we invite people to give presentations on depression and other emotional difficulties. We try to invite people with different perspectives – usually a clinical perspective delivered by a mental health professional; a personal perspective presented by a known personality who experiences depression; a pastoral perspective on how communities might support those living with depression, and a presentation by actors on how we can challenge the social stigma around mental health. The events are attended by people who are generally interested in mental health, who are often family and friends of people living with depression and are seeking reliable information about how they might be supportive.

A central purpose of these Awareness Day events is to clarify the nature of depression. The clinician highlights that depression is not a disease like cancer or Alzheimer's and, in most cases, is a consequence of adverse life experiences. The personal account describes how the ordinary road of life can sometimes take turns for the worst, without this being a fault or weakness of the person concerned, and that this can affect anyone. The pastoral perspective offers helpful suggestions as to how family and friends can 'be there' for those they care for. The drama component holds up a mirror to many of the stigmatising attitudes to mental health prevailing in society.

The subsequent training programme for the facilitators begins with a professionally qualified mental health worker giving an overview of the possible issues that attendees might bring to a PeerTalk support group. Emotional damage is a common factor. Loss, abuse, pressures of work and problems with family feature in many attendees' stories. The primary purpose of training is to enable the volunteers to fulfil their role as facilitators. They are not trained to offer any kind of counselling or therapy and it is stressed that their role is not to try to fix or rescue attendees. Core skills included in the training include active listening, how to succinctly paraphrase and summarise what they have heard and how to reflect on what has been shared with the group. The training uses role play to familiarise facilitators with the way group meetings are structured and to give them confidence in exercising their facilitation skills. This core training also includes an overview of PeerTalk's policies and procedures – including confidentiality, safeguarding (child and vulnerable adult) and risk management.

After the initial block of training, the volunteer facilitators attend an induction day where the safeguarding policies are explored in more detail, along with the process to follow should concerns be identified. The PeerTalk organisation also has a named safeguarding lead who can be contacted for advice.

What makes a group successful is not the numbers that attend, although too few or too many attendees can make facilitating a group more challenging. A typical PeerTalk group has about seven attendees on any given week, out of a pool of a possible 10 or so. Fluctuations in group numbers occur from week to week and can be influenced by a variety of factors, from what happens to be on television to what the weather is like and what mood an attendee is experiencing at the time. Groups function at their best when a core group of regular attendees has established relationships of trust and they look forward to meeting up with each other. Groups can struggle when the rapport between the peers is poor or when one or more people dominate, to the exclusion of others. The role of the facilitators is critical to a good group experience. When only one or two people come, facilitating a group becomes more of an exercise in holding a conversation that allows for people to share their story and how they are feeling without it becoming a pseudo-counselling session. When groups have larger numbers, the role of the facilitator is to manage the time in such a way that all have opportunity to share something if they choose to do so. This might require the facilitator to politely, but firmly, limit someone who is talking too much.

The desire to try and 'fix' someone who comes along to a group is understandably strong in the hearts and minds of the volunteer facilitators. Some volunteers say how they would just love to go to an attendee's house and do all their washing up and sort out their tidying and cleaning. Some yearn to take a person 'in hand' and sort out their finances or deal with the issues they face for them. This is not the role of a facilitator and is not sanctioned by PeerTalk. It sometimes can be very difficult for volunteers to see someone walk out of the door at the end of a meeting and not know whether they will see them again. PeerTalk emphasises to their volunteers that their support is highly valuable during the time of the meeting but beyond the meeting itself they do not, and should not, hold any obligations to those who attend.

We notice that, as a group becomes established, the potency of the support experienced by attendees increases. Attendees' confidence builds as each person recognises their own story in that of others and they feel less alone. They start to conquer the mountains of distress as they realise that it is OK not to be OK. Being assured that others have been in the same situation and have come through provides hope.

PeerTalk recognises that we are but one of many charities that operate in the voluntary sector and that, together, we provide a network of support within a particular locality. Having information leaflets and fliers available at group venues can be a useful way to signpost participants to other services.

## Managing resistance and overcoming obstacles

Unfortunately, public and private sector professionals can mistrust the capacity of charities such as PeerTalk to offer high standards in the services they deliver. This tendency seems to be particularly prevalent in the mental health services. It is true that being highly motivated and well-meaning doesn't necessarily mean an organisation is competent, skilled and experienced. In order for voluntary-sector agencies to be able to thrive alongside professional services, a relationship of trust needs to be established. Recurrent issues that often undermine the ability for voluntary agencies to deliver a sustainable service are lack of funding and demoralised volunteers. Local community initiatives often start up with vision, enthusiasm and funding but can quickly fail as funds become difficult to source and interest wanes. Public services have good reason to question whether it is appropriate to recommend their users to voluntary groups that might close at any point.

Building relationships with mainstream services is not easy, not least because health professionals can be blinkered to the possible benefits of other pathways to wellbeing. The move to get GPs to use social prescribing is a positive step towards greater inclusivity of alternative approaches (Kings Fund, 2017). PeerTalk gives presentations to local mental health clinical teams with a view to promoting what we offer. These are well received, although the questions from participants are primarily about risk management. Clinicians seem comfortable with what we offer but need assurance that our groups are compliant with stringent safeguarding practices and have the stamp of clinical credibility. This suggests there is a need for some type of Care Quality Commission certificate or charter mark that provides this assurance.

An association with a faith community seems to heighten these suspicions, both among mainstream mental health services and potential funding agencies and trusts. We make it clear that PeerTalk began life as a project of the Methodist Church, with an aim of becoming a charity independent of the faith sector. We are not concerned with matters of faith. Our volunteers come from all faiths and none, and are expected to facilitate the support groups without introducing their own beliefs or opinions. Our shared purpose is to deliver a high quality and valued service to the people who come to our groups.

## Positive benefits

Group attendees soon discover that they are not alone in their struggles and distress. It is often a revelation to an attendee that there are others going through circumstances very similar to their own. For example, two men discovered that they had both recently been bereaved of their mothers and were now struggling to cope with household responsibilities alongside the emotional pain of their grief. Sharing your story with someone else who is going through the same feelings and struggles is cathartic and can improve wellbeing.

In another striking example, a group attendee had had a particular bad week and was considering acting on suicidal thoughts. They had referred themselves to the mental health crisis team who, according to the attendee, had been quite dismissive of their situation and offered no useful help. The attendee phoned one of the other attendees in the PeerTalk group, who talked with them and arranged to meet. When the group next met, the attendee said they believed it was only because of the connection made through attending the group that they were still alive that day.

Knowing that someone else knows what 'it' is like confirms the sense that they are not alone in their experience. This in itself is a very positive benefit for someone attending a peer-to-peer support group. A further, often unrecognised benefit is being able to 'be there' for someone else in their plight and circumstances, which improves the helper's own sense of self-worth and confidence. It is a good feeling for a person to be able to have a sense that their contribution to another is valuable. Peer-to-peer support isn't just about what an individual can get out of the group; being able to offer support and encouragement to others has rich intrinsic benefits for the wellbeing of the giver. This element is widely recognised as one of the five pathways to wellbeing, described as 'Give – look out as well as in' (New Economics Foundation, 2008), and endorsed in government health policy (Foresight Mental Capital and Wellbeing Project, 2008).

Evaluation is so difficult! At a recent meeting with a senior NHS England manager, we were told that 'support' is not really of much interest to healthcare commissioners as it costs money. At the same meeting, however, what was considered of great interest was 'relapse prevention', which saves money. Being able to demonstrate that PeerTalk groups prevent use of clinical services requires a satisfactory method of evaluation. Attendance numbers have little significance for evaluating the effectiveness of a PeerTalk group. Numbers, nevertheless, are hugely significant to the funding bodies and agencies, who mostly calculate whether a cause is worthy of support by how many beneficiaries there are for every pound spent. When evaluating the benefit of wellbeing support, the qualitative measures of its value are also important, as well as head counts of the number of attendees.

Providing indicators of a peer support group's value, whether to funding bodies or clinical agencies, is always going to include elements of subjectivity. A support group attendee may describe improved wellbeing one week and may associate the improvement to having attended the group, but the next week might report experiences of low mood and poor functionality.

PeerTalk aims to evaluate its work through both the narrative descriptions of a person's experience of attending a group and through the use of 'smiley face' indicators that rate how they feel about its worth. In regard to the 'smiley face' method of evaluation, the nature of the question being asked is significant in order for it to be a useful analytical tool. PeerTalk uses the question, 'How likely are you to recommend a PeerTalk support group to someone else who is in a similar situation to you'? The smiley faces represent a range of five possible responses, from 'extremely likely' to 'not at all likely'. Group attendees are invited to make their responses with no expectation placed upon them to do so. Most, but not all, are willing to participate. The result of one such exercise conducted at the same time across nine PeerTalk groups produced results of 29 reporting 'extremely likely', 10 indicating 'likely' and one 'neither likely nor unlikely'. Although it boosted the morale of the volunteers who received this positive feedback, this result didn't necessarily provide convincing data for evaluation purposes.

Much more significant was the invitation to the group attendees to make a response in their own words to the questions, 'What is your experience of the group?' and 'What could we do to improve our groups and the support we offer?' Some typical responses are detailed below.

## What is your experience of the group?

Very positive. I have been going to the group for the past six months and it has improved my mental health a lot. It has provided me with structure and support. I feel less isolated and can relate to other group members well. Unlike many mental health groups, they treat us like intelligent people as well as being non-judgmental and supportive.

I have been to three sessions of the group so far and found it extremely helpful in getting me back on my feet and the support has been fantastic. The volunteers are exceptional, giving their time and always listening and encouraging. I would be lost without them and will continue to attend the sessions for as long as possible.

Since coming to the group I have truly begun to understand the power of peer support. Having the opportunity to share and listen to other people's experiences and realise that I am not alone takes a huge weight off my mind and this is really important.

Amazed by the levels of awareness of others in the group. When I do eventually start to feel better, I feel I will be able to help others more – at the moment though the tank is empty.

## What could we do to improve our groups and the support we offer?

More publicity to gain support for this group.

I don't know. I sometimes like it if there is [sic] few people.

Perhaps have a handout on a practical idea to help with depression that could be referred to.

Two groups for a meeting? Shallow pool, deep pool? Just a thought. Thank you.

PeerTalk recognises the importance of evaluation and its necessity for analysing the benefit of the support groups for the interested agencies and funders, but the true worth of the groups is perhaps most evident to the volunteers who witness the groups week by week. The volunteer facilitators describe their experience of the groups as being extremely fulfilling as they notice the changing circumstances of the individuals who come along. The volunteer support meetings are occasions when the volunteers themselves have the opportunity to share their own experiences of the groups and participate in peer-to-peer support of their own. They enthuse about the quality and depth of sharing the group attendees engage in and the strength of the support that is offered between them. Even on occasions when only one or two people come to a meeting, the volunteer facilitators are often astonished at the amount of trust invested in them as listeners. It is these same qualities of trust and confidence that allow group attendees to share their experiences. Methods for evaluating these qualities and how they benefit peer-to-peer support groups will, most likely, always be inadequate.

Given the high levels of distress and unmet needs within our communities, the organic growth and sustainability of the project are essential. In its first 18 months (and at the time of writing), the PeerTalk charity has established 10 groups. All the groups have received positive evaluations from attendees. Attendance numbers generally fluctuate between five and eight but can be as low as one and as many as 10. During the four days 11–14 March 2019 the total number of attendees across all groups was 56. The 10 support groups are currently facilitated by a national team of 124 volunteers. The recognised benefit of the existing groups has led to invitations to establish further groups, of which six may start in the next 18 months.

## Future directions

PeerTalk aims to be a trusted 'brand' – an organisation that is recognised and respected by mental health professionals and other voluntary sector agencies as a credible partner in supporting those who live with depression and related emotional difficulties. A distinctive characteristic of PeerTalk is that it is a non-clinical agency that normalises people's distress; there is no focus on 'treatment' or therapeutic outcomes. It is through the peer-to-peer sharing of experiences and coping skills that improved wellbeing is realised.

PeerTalk's vision is to be a nationally recognised organisation that sits comfortably alongside state-provided psychological therapies. For that, we need to achieve sustainability, given that local community groups often struggle to survive. From the outset, PeerTalk has recruited, trained and supported its volunteer group facilitators to high standards and ensured that safeguarding policies and procedures are followed.

The volunteer facilitators are key to the success of the charity and their ongoing recruitment is necessary to sustain the groups. New group facilitators sometimes come from those who have attended as peers and have benefited from the groups themselves. The volunteers' contributions of their time make the support groups economically viable. Discounting the organisational overheads, the cost of running a PeerTalk group amounts to local room hire and volunteer travelling expenses. There are no charges for attending a

PeerTalk group. The organisational overheads, however, are not insignificant and include the recruitment and training of the volunteers and their ongoing support and further training. Although difficult to quantify, the overall financial benefit to the state from offering an effective alternative to expensive clinical services is likely to be substantial.

Establishing PeerTalk as a credible, robust charitable organisation has always been a priority. Many hours of time and effort were invested in writing the constitution, producing policies and establishing working practices. The trustees of the charity are supported by a 'hands-on' management committee, who also scrutinise and evaluate the work. Producing policies is one thing but putting them into practice is another, especially in relation to safeguarding issues and confidentiality. Managing potential risk to both volunteer facilitators and group attendees is paramount. To be a credible player alongside professional services demands the highest standards of good practice, which need to be clearly evident throughout the whole organisation.

PeerTalk as a charitable organisation is still in its infancy. The vision is to establish 100 groups across the UK within the next 10 years. We aim to ensure that most people do not have to travel more than 15 miles to attend a group. Such a vision and even greater possibilities are considered realisable should funding be forthcoming. As an organisation, our current priorities are to learn to walk properly before trying to run, and to establish PeerTalk on sound footings as a robust and sustainable agency. The notion of what the future possibilities for PeerTalk might be are nevertheless noteworthy. The strength of peer-to-peer support is always that it is those with a lived experience of a particular aspect of life who are best placed to understand others in similar circumstances. Establishing PeerTalk groups with a particular focus is a potential future development. Hosting groups specifically for people living with post-natal depression could be an option. Other options may be launching groups for people with mental health problems that are not associated with depression but who, nevertheless, would benefit from peer support. Another possibility could be establishing groups in specific locations, such as universities, prisons and workplaces. Key to such a development will be the recognition of the PeerTalk 'brand' as a trusted organisation capable of delivering the highest of standards in both its organisation and delivery of its services.

Life in general is tough for most at the best of times. For some, the worst of times just become overwhelming. The importance of mental wellbeing is increasingly recognised. Improved awareness around mental health will, hopefully, result in more people who are struggling being able to disclose how they are feeling. As more people reach out for support with what are essentially problems of living, it is likely that many will not require traditional psychiatric services. The trend towards more individualised lifestyles and the geographical displacement of families means people tend to have fewer informal societal sources of support. Increased popular consciousness of wellbeing issues will hopefully manifest itself in a greater ability for people to present themselves as needing help. PeerTalk aims to provide the time and space for people to 'be there' for themselves and to 'be there' for others.

The quality of improved wellbeing for those who attend the groups, the economic benefit to the state through saved clinical costs and the gratifying experience of facilitating for the volunteers all suggest that PeerTalk will continue to grow and make a significant contribution to the mental wellbeing of participants. Nevertheless, as with any charity depending on finance, the sustainability of PeerTalk will depend on securing income and the generosity of public support.

*Further information about PeerTalk can be obtained from their website*: www.peertalk.org.uk

### References

Foresight Mental Capital and Wellbeing Project (2008). *Mental Capital: making the most of ourselves in the 21st century*. London: Government Office for Science.

King's Fund (2017). *What is Social Prescribing?* King's Fund; 2 February. www.kingsfund.org.uk/publications/social-prescribing (accessed 13 August 2019).

Mead S, Filson B (2016). Becoming part of each other's narratives: Intentional Peer Support. In: Russo J, Sweeney A (eds). *Searching for a Rose Garden: challenging psychiatry, fostering mad studies*. Monmouth: PCCS Books (pp109–117).

New Economics Foundation (2008). *Five Ways to Wellbeing: the postcards*. https://neweconomics.org/2008/10/five-ways-to-wellbeing-the-postcards (accessed 13 August 2019).

Pfeiffer PN, Heisler N, Piette JD, Rogers MA, Valenstein M (2011). Efficacy of peer support for depression: a meta-analysis. *General Hospital Psychiatry 33*(1): 29–36.

Richardson C (2014). *Life Makeover for the Year 2014. Week 41 – A letter I wish I could send to every 'checked out' healthcare provider*. www.cherylrichardson.com/newsletters/week-41-letter-wish-send-every-checked-healthcare-provider/ (accessed 13 August 2019).

# Chapter 13

# Independent advocacy: challenging human rights restrictions in mental health practice

## Deirdre Lillis

In writing this chapter, I will argue that independent advocacy is part of the bedrock of a human rights-based approach to the care and support of marginalised and excluded people, including those experiencing mental distress. I will also argue that, even where such advocacy is funded by the state, experience to date demonstrates that it is still possible to maintain independence; that independent advocacy has no coercive statutory powers and can be seen, therefore, as genuinely having the interests of the person or group at its heart. I will also discuss how the advocate negotiates the fine line between acting solely on instruction of the client and acting in a way that ensures the client's decisions are fully informed by the information available.

I will argue that there is great potential for independent advocacy to promote the embedding of a human-rights framework in our mental health services. I will also question the move towards 'professionalisation' of independent advocacy and will argue for a model of small, community-based independent advocacy groups, such as the organisation where I work, that can achieve change by building 'networks of solidarity' (Sapouna, 2017) that are inclusive, facilitative and transformational.

I am writing as a practitioner who has worked in independent advocacy in England and the Republic of Ireland for the past 22 years. I currently work for the Social and Health Education Project (SHEP) as the co-ordinator of Cork Advocacy Service (CAS). I work as an independent advocate in part because of my brief but traumatic experience of the psychiatric response to my own distress in the 1980s.

There are numerous forms of advocacy operating across numerous contexts and different legal jurisdictions (see Browne, 2018). It is not within the scope of this chapter to offer a comprehensive overview. I will focus on one country (Ireland) and on the experience at CAS to illustrate how independent advocacy can operate in a particular context and within restricted resources.

## The context

Independent advocacy has its roots in the user/survivor movements of the 1980s and 1990s. In Ireland, the first formal recognition of independent advocacy in the mental health arena began through the work of the Irish Advocacy Network, a peer advocacy organisation that continues to provide access to independent advocacy in inpatient psychiatric services today.

Independent advocacy operates within the context of social justice. In seeking change for individuals and groups, it seeks social change. This is a position I follow, and one that aligns itself to some degree with anti-oppressive social work practice (Dominelli, 2002; Wilks, 2012; Woods, 2013). The significant difference is that the independent advocate holds no coercive statutory powers. This creates a critically different relationship with individuals and groups, as the advocate does not have a role in the removal of a person's liberty or enforcement of treatment.

It is significant that there is no statutory requirement in the Republic of Ireland for the provision of independent advocacy to people subject to mental health legislation. In England and Wales, people subject to detention and treatment under the Mental Health Act are legally entitled to request support from an independent advocate. In Scotland, people receiving mental health services have a right to request independent advocacy even if they are not subject to detention or in psychiatric hospital. The right of access to independent advocacy is also provided for in Northern Ireland capacity legislation.

A right of access to independent advocacy is included at the moment in the forthcoming safeguarding legislation for the first time in the Republic of Ireland. This right means that advocacy services must be funded, by law; it also carries risks, as detailed further below. However, it is important to emphasise that in none of these jurisdictions does the advocate have any decision-making coercive statutory powers: their role is to support the client who lacks capacity or is deprived of their liberty to understand the information given to them and help them express their wishes.

## Independent advocacy

There are many different definitions of independent advocacy. Birmingham (2001: 4) describes it as:

… a rights issue; it should be framed within constitutional and international human rights language and claimed within internal statutes… in an unequal system whereby some people have lesser rights than others, and legal protections are selective, advocacy is a necessary mechanism to name and claim those universal rights.

Independent advocacy constitutes a human rights-based approach, using the language of citizens and rights rather than patients, consumers or service users. In the words of Daniel Blake, in Ken Loach's 2016 film *I, Daniel Blake*:

I am not a client, a customer, nor a service user. I am not a shirker, a scrounger, a beggar nor a thief. I am not a national insurance number, nor a blip on a screen. I paid my dues, never a penny short, and was proud to do so. I don't tug the forelock but look my neighbour in the eye. I don't accept or seek charity. My name is Daniel Blake, I am a man, not a dog. As such, I demand my rights. I demand you treat me with respect. I, Daniel Blake, am a citizen, nothing more, nothing less.

Independent advocacy has emerged from an acknowledgement that paternalism and power imbalances exist within our public services. As noted by the United Nations Special Rapporteur in his report to the UN Human Rights Council 'on the right of everyone to the enjoyment of the highest attainable standard of physical and mental health':

At the clinical level, power imbalances reinforce paternalism and even patriarchal approaches… That asymmetry disempowers and undermines users and undermines their right to make a decision about their health, creating an environment when human rights violations occur. Laws allowing the psychiatric profession to treat and confine by force legitimise that power and its misuse. (Pūras, 2017: 6)

Independent advocacy attempts to redress these power imbalances by being on the side of the disempowered individual or group.

## Cork Advocacy Service

Cork Advocacy Service (CAS) is an initiative of the Social and Health Education Project (SHEP), alongside a number of other initiatives that share the common principles of seeking change through facilitating personal and social transformation. SHEP's vision is to work towards:

> … a socially just world, where all people live in dignity, where we
> cherish and celebrate each other and ourselves and where the integrity
> of the earth is honoured.[1]

Our core values include a belief in each person's dignity, people's potential to grow and transform, the reality of human struggles, and the vulnerabilities and the interdependence of personal wellbeing and community wellbeing.

This is a constantly evolving process, and in SHEP we put effort into reflecting on our core values and how we apply them in what we do. As a community development project, SHEP promotes bottom-up and participatory approaches, fosters community ownership, and works in ways that empower people, groups and communities. We have a particular focus on the importance of facilitation as an enabler of social transformation.

SHEP was founded in 1974. We are part of Ireland's vibrant community and voluntary sector, not the public sector, but we receive significant funding from the state, particularly the Health Service Executive (HSE). We are continually aware that, by accepting funding from the state, we risk having to compromise our philosophies, values and practice in order to survive.

Our training mission statement states:

> SHEP is a values-led organisation that provides quality education
> and training, based on experiential approaches and underpinned by
> humanistic philosophy and theory, to support empowerment and
> appropriate self-acceptance, to enhance health and well-being and to
> promote social justice.[2]

Thus, we work from community development principles, rather than from an individualised, statutory, 'mental health service' position. We do not subscribe to traditional mental health/psychiatric diagnostic labels.

SHEP started out as a social and health education training programme for young people that pioneered a way of working called experiential group work. This approach starts from the life experiences of each individual and aims to support their unique, personal growth. The approach – which we still use in SHEP – enhances opportunities for people to develop the emotional and psychological capacity to relate more creatively and lovingly to themselves and with those around them:

---

1. www.socialandhealth.com/about-us/mission-core-values (accessed 28 April 2019).
2. www.socialandhealth.com/training/shep-learner-charter (accessed 28 April 2019).

We support a holistic approach to well-being, emphasising self-awareness, connecting with others for social justice, and care of the planet we share with others.[3]

As a 2010 evaluation of SHEP notes:

By providing scope and opportunity to participants to identify and realise their potential, SHEP is facilitating them to be independent in their own thinking, to contribute to their own communities and society in ways that actually may not support the status quo in the long term. Thus, it is potentially quite revolutionary as an organisation. (Kearney Consultants, 2010: 17)

Promoting positive mental health and facilitating emotional wellbeing are at the core of all that we do. We participate in personal and social development courses that enhance our understanding of ourselves and our communities. We take responsibility as individuals and communities to enhance transformation through becoming facilitators and community tutors. We provide access to professional, person-centred, low-cost counselling, and we work as independent advocates to secure the rights of and support the voices of marginalised individuals and groups. We believe that all of these routes lead to 'building a supportive, just and sustainable community at a local, national and global level'. It can sound like a lofty aim, and it can sometimes seem an unreachable goal.

We do not define people by diagnoses, labels or individual pathologies. We do not use criteria that erect walls to exclude people. Our aim is to be inclusive of the diversity of human experience; we place a positive value on this diversity rather than seeking to 'other' difference through a language of false narratives of 'us' and 'them'. We believe this is achieved through a belief in humanity, the value of relationships and the value of listening and working from our hearts, while not excluding our heads.

Our intention, then, is to consider the totality of our individual and collective experiences. We subscribe to the concerns raised by Sapouna (2017) about public mental health campaigns that focus on what individuals need to do to adapt to their environment, rather than contextualising human distress, recognising interpersonal and collective responsibility and seeking 'networks of solidarity'.

In summary, the common threads that run through our work are our beliefs in the values of relationships, experience and facilitation, in

---

3. www.socialandhealth.com (accessed 28 April 2019).

social justice, inclusion and equality, and in our responsibility to challenge oppression and discrimination and seek out and respond to grassroots needs.

This organisational context and philosophy provide the framework within which CAS operates.

## How we work

CAS began in 1999 as Cork Older People's Advocacy Service (COPAS), serving older people living in their own homes in a particular geographical area of Cork City. From this beginning, it has developed alongside other advocacy providers (Irish Advocacy Network, Sage, National Advocacy Service and Empowering People in Care are other examples) to establish access to independent advocacy.

As one of the many projects operating within SHEP, we are positioned outside of formally identified mental health services. We do not require people to have labels or diagnoses to use the service. We use instead the language of disability and disempowerment to respond, individually and collectively, to people who may be struggling to get their voices heard and their rights respected. Our resources are small, but we accept the self-definitions of the people who access our services. This fits with the emerging narratives around intersectionality that see people as having multiple elements in our identities.

Our relationship with the person begins by first discussing with them the issue they are concerned about or what has happened to them. It is not about an expert/therapist/professional analysing the person and their internal struggles; we see them in their social/structural environment and from a human rights perspective. The people who come looking for advocacy support are attempting to exert their human rights. Some may argue that individual rights are counterbalanced by individual responsibilities. I believe equality of responsibility is dependent on equality of power. Power is almost always unequal in situations where people are seen as 'lesser than' because of their mental health or disability.

CAS is managed by one part-time advocacy co-ordinator (me), and I also undertake advocacy work and am responsible for advocacy training. We have a panel of 12 advocates who undertake both voluntary work (mostly one-to-one advocacy) and paid work (mostly facilitating group advocacy). The advocates have undergone SHEP training or are taken onto the panel on the basis of prior learning. Continuing personal and professional development is facilitated through regular team meetings, group supervision and external training, conferences and seminars, as resources allow.

We work with individuals and groups who are marginalised through health, disability and/or ageing. We support self-advocacy, provide representative advocacy and facilitate group/collective advocacy. This means an independent advocate may take a number of positions, and potentially different positions, with the same person or group at different times. They include *standing behind* a person, supporting their self-advocacy; *standing beside* a person, as a witness, and *standing before* a person, when speaking up for them and in support of them when they find it too difficult to do that on their own part. These positions also apply in group/collective advocacy.

We do not make assessments and take decisions for people about what is in their presumed best interests. Our work is about listening and supporting the person, sometimes questioning or challenging a decision made about them and sometimes speaking up for them. For SHEP, advocacy is fundamental to our commitment to empowering vulnerable and marginalised groups and communities. We see it as linked to community development, as it plays an important role in developing civil society and bringing about social justice and social transformation.

This may at times present a challenge. Take, for example, a situation where a person is requesting advocacy support to obtain a referral for ECT from a reluctant psychiatrist who does not believe it is effective. The purist advocacy position asserts that the advocate should simply execute the person's stated wishes. At CAS, we recognise that multiple factors may influence those wishes and preferences. In the socio-political context of, for example, class, gender and potential social and cultural inequalities, is this person making an informed decision? Do I invite her to consider the breadth of information about ECT? Do I ask her to consider why the psychiatrist is concerned about this treatment? Some advocates would very clearly say 'no'. Others would say 'yes'. At CAS, we would seek to ensure that she is fully informed, but respect her right to make that decision and to access treatment that, although controversial, is available.

We believe that independent advocacy is about representing a person's or group's wishes according to their will and preference. In the context of human rights-based practice, it is not about acting in the person's or group's presumed best interests. We believe advocacy needs to be independent of other service provision in order to reduce conflict of interest and allow us to hold the position of staying beside the person or group. We believe independent advocates do not make decisions on behalf of others, that we need to be knowledgeable in current laws and policies that inform the rights of citizens using social and health services, and that we need to be patient, persistent, courageous, creative and supported to fulfil our role.

The work we do is illustrated in some of the feedback from people who have used our advocacy service:

The advocate gave me a lot of time and I'm so grateful for that. I would like to thank her for believing in me, listening to me, helping me.

Did not speak for me but rather provided me with the productive things to say and thereby inspiring confidence in myself… she never spoke for me but rather gave me all the support and encouragement needed to speak for myself.

Wrote very good letters to the relevant authorities.

Accessed information… helped me type a letter… accompanied me to [the money advice service]… made enquiries… got the form for me.

I found the advocate… not to be judgemental to me as other people in public services are very judgemental to me.

In CAS we are asked to support people who are in psychiatric units as voluntary patients, where their capacity to consent to their admission may be in question but, because they are not held under section, they have no access to redress or review under the mental health legislation. The advocate will listen to the individual and to the people identified as being supportive of their rights and seek to understand what they want. When verbal language may be limited, communication may be through behaviour, body language and emotional expression. The independent advocate then presents the arguments to those in positions of power. Browne (2018) refers to the skills required of independent advocates as:

> … commitment, courage, competence, compassion and creativity. It also requires an understanding of how to handle challenge, how to communicate aspects of relevant legislation, powers of observation, recording and endless amounts of time and patience. (Browne, 2018: 30)

In seeking to support the human rights of individuals and groups described above, the independent advocate pursues, persists and seeks responses from decision-makers. This can include those responsible for managing budgets, who may be juggling competing demands on scarce resources, and decision-makers in multidisciplinary teams, who are closer to the person but may also be compromised in their ability to uphold their human rights because of budgetary and resource constraints. In seeking responses from the decision-makers, the independent advocate may go to other sources of support, such as (in Ireland) the Irish Human Rights and Equality

Commission, the Mental Health Inspectorate and the HSE Office of the Confidential Recipient. The independent advocate is positioned beside the individual and outside the hierarchy of HSE structures, thus making the approaches to decision-makers possible. This is the critical component in undertaking the work.

In undertaking this work we, as independent advocates, witness the experience of individuals and groups whose human rights have been undermined, in some instances for many years. This may also be happening alongside many positive human and warm relationships with individual members of staff. A successful outcome in these instances is for people to find places to live that offer them a better quality of life. Funding is primarily at the core of the problem. While these transitions can be complex and challenging for individuals, as independent advocates we witness people enjoying new freedoms and opportunities as they grow into their new lives.

As an independent advocate, I often struggle with contradictions between policy and reality, such as the co-opting of the recovery approach from a 'grassroots' model of self-empowerment to a standardised assessment process with goals that may have little to do with the individual's own dreams and aspirations. Such co-option can weaken the activist's energy and undermine challenges to the status quo. The reality of some people's experiences remains far removed from the language of recovery. On the one hand, we hear how recovery will play a part in the cultural shift in mental health services away from practices that restrict our human rights, such as coercion, detention, compulsion and forced treatment. On the other hand, the Irish Mental Health Commission, in its 2017 annual report, states:

> The 2017 inspections have once again highlighted the inappropriate
> use of seclusion and physical restraint in services which have become
> in many instances the normalised response to managing difficult and
> challenging behaviours in the absence of sufficient and skilled staff.
> (p9)

The cultural shift that is being sought also needs to challenge the less explicit forms of coercion, including persuasion, threats, bias, suggested benefits and limited treatment routes offered (Greaney & Lillis, 2017).

It is our experience that independent advocacy is more readily accepted by decision-makers when they agree with our concerns about human rights restrictions. And so, as independent advocates, we chip away at the corners. Sometimes we do this at the request of multidisciplinary teams who have tried to advocate internally with little success.

Our support is particularly necessary when the person or group we are alongside is in opposition to the core beliefs and systems to which psychiatry traditionally subscribes, such as challenges to diagnoses, questions about medication or refusal to take medication. In this respect, our work challenges the biomedical culture, custom and practice that continues to dominate in our mental health services.

## Some critical reflections

Access to independent advocacy remains limited here in the Republic of Ireland, and in the four UK nations, despite its statutory status there. The limited resources of CAS have already been described and are common across the sector in the Republic of Ireland:

> Advocacy services for people with mental health difficulties, which could support people to speak out against these [coercive] practices, are very under-resourced meaning people do not know who to turn to for help in the face of this treatment. (Mental Health Reform, 2018)

There is also competition for the independent advocacy space that is not readily articulated in formal arenas or in writing. One example is when services are being tendered for and different advocacy models are presented as empowering, but some require less resourcing than others (for example, voluntary versus paid advocates, supporting self-advocacy versus representation).

There are other questions that I regularly encounter in my work, including:

- Is independent advocacy being controlled or influenced by the funding agencies through their allocation of grant funding? Do these agencies hold a genuine commitment to human rights and cultural change?

- Is the ownership of independent advocacy being removed from the user/survivor/disability movements? Does a grassroots movement risk being taken over by a 'top-down' professionalisation? For example, does the change of the slogan 'Nothing about us without us' to 'Nothing about you without you' suggest that people already experiencing disempowerment through service responses have been pushed still further away from self-definition and empowerment?

- Would a statutory right to independent advocacy enhance access and provide adequate resources or would it professionalise the role to such a degree that it becomes yet another cog in the multidisciplinary state machine?

- Can independent advocacy impact on cultural and structural change when the work is primarily with the individual and there is no capacity to work at the societal, collective level?

With my glass half empty, I see a fundamental contradiction between human rights-based practice and coercion, both formal and informal, which remains embedded in practice. Cultural and structural change will be slow and compromised if there is no challenge to this fundamental contradiction. The mental health care system will struggle to embrace the genuine values of recovery. Independent advocacy, while playing a part in improving the quality of some people's lives within its limited resources, will continue to tinker around the edges. There is also the ever-present risk of co-option and the professionalisation of independent advocacy, putting group/collective advocacy at risk. Community-based independent advocacy projects, such as CAS, provide vital space for facilitating group/collective advocacy, which can be lost in the fight to win statutory/professional representative advocacy. Such a space is essential both to address the wider determinants that create situations where individual advocacy is needed and to maintain grassroots involvement.

With my glass half full, I hope that independent advocacy can add its energies to the movement for cultural and structural change. I believe that it can help pave the way towards a human rights-based culture in our mental health and social care services, and that it can hold onto its core values and resist professionalisation. I hope that independent advocacy can continue to provide a space where people are heard and their human rights are respected. I believe that this can be achieved through working collectively, as well as supporting and representing individuals, and this in turn will assist in building networks of solidarity (including with those in the professions) (Sapouna, 2017) as we critically reflect on the systems that impact negatively on human wellbeing in the name of 'care'.

In addition, the policy and legislative changes that are happening, while not necessarily 'magic bullets' (Spandler, 2018), can be tools that individuals, groups and independent advocates can use to protect and enhance human rights. Recent examples in Ireland include;

- the Assisted Decision-Making (Capacity) Act 2015, which sets out requirements where a person's capacity to make a particular decision may be compromised. The independent advocate can play a significant role in raising questions as to what efforts have been made to assess the person's capacity, what support they have been given to make a decision and what efforts have been made to establish their will and preferences.

- the Mental Health (Amendment) Act 2018, which removes the word 'unwilling' from the law with regard to permitting forced treatment after a period of three months. (While 'unable' remains in the Act, independent advocates can support a person to question how a decision was made with regard to assessing a person as 'unable' to make a decision.)

- the ratification of the United Nations Convention on the Rights of Persons with a Disability (United Nations, 2006) – in particular Article 12, which requires all signatories to recognise that people with disabilities have the same legal rights as all others in all aspects of life.

- the Mental Health (Renewal Orders) Act 2018, which amends the length of time before a detention order can be reviewed.

- Advance Directives, which do not yet have equal legal status in mental health services as in other areas of health but are a critical tool in providing a person with a voice. Independent advocates can ask how the person's Advance Directive is being incorporated into decision-making and request that any decisions that override a person's stated wishes are recorded in their notes. This in itself can make a professional pause for thought and take proper consideration before an action is taken.

- the Adult Safeguarding Bill (2017), which, for the first time in Ireland's legislation, provides a statutory right to independent advocacy (although, despite seeming a progressive step, it does control and potentially restrict access to independent advocacy).

- changes in language – for example, from 'deprivation of liberty' to 'protection of liberty' – which shift our thinking.

For independent advocates in Ireland, these changes can assist us in our role. It has been my experience, especially where advocates are working as volunteers, that we can be perceived as interfering do-gooders. Structural changes in language, policy and law support us in our work and challenge that perception.

Beyond our own borders, we can learn from the mistakes of other jurisdictions and their potential breaches of human rights – for example, Community Treatment Orders in England, Wales and Scotland – and consider arguments for the abolition of mental health-specific legislation, which is discriminatory by the fact of its existence (see Sidley, 2018).

## Conclusion

I believe there is great potential for independent advocacy in the movement towards establishing a human-rights framework in the mental health arena that would serve us all in working towards cultural change.

In CAS, we emphasise the value of working from the heart and in developing relationships, while at the same time keeping as informed as we can about the legal and policy changes that support the basic human rights we are all entitled to at vulnerable times in our lives. We continue to try to be innovative with our resources and have introduced some important developments in recent years. We are doing more independent facilitation work with self-advocacy groups of people who have been excluded and marginalised from our society and who are trying to find their voices. This work stays close to the people who are seeking to be heard and concentrates on facilitating their voices and supporting their rights, rather than taking a professional representative advocacy role.

We attempt to influence the development of independent advocacy by having a voice in national discussions and, over the past six years, by co-facilitating a space for discussion, debate and shared learning through the annual Independent Advocacy Gathering. In 2019, the focus of our discussions was over-medication, the UK NHS STOMP ('Stop the Over-Medication of People') campaign and the role of independent advocacy here.

A community development orientation that incorporates strong elements of the value of personal development, as SHEP does, can begin by asking people, 'What happened to you?', rather than 'What is wrong with you?' (Longden, 2013). We have the luxury of applying this practice in an organisation that knows where it stands and reflects constantly on its direction and how it maintains its values. This is feasible for others to do if there is a commitment to moving away from the tradition of responding to emotional distress as an internal disorder (a tradition that is still embedded in practice and can be hard to shift in mental health services). Our practice at SHEP aims to challenge this in proactive and innovative ways.

I believe that smaller, community-based independent advocacy groups such as CAS would enhance independent advocacy, provide for local and grassroots involvement in independent advocacy developments, and help to build 'networks of solidarity' (Sapouna, 2017) that are inclusive, facilitative and transformational.

## References

Birmingham D (2001). *Advocacy: a rights issue*. A reflection document. Dublin: Forum of People with Disabilities.

Browne M (2018). *Independent Advocacy in Ireland: current context and future challenge*. A scoping document. Dublin: Safeguarding Ireland.

Dominelli L (2002). *Anti-Oppressive Social Work Theory and Practice*. Basingstoke: Palgrave Macmillan.

Greaney S, Lillis D (2017). *Rights, Coercion and the Yellow Submarine through the Eyes of Advocacy, 'User Involvement' and Peer Support*. Paper delivered at the Annual Critical Perspectives Conference, University College Cork, Cork; November.

Kearney Consultants/West Cork Training (2010). *An Evaluation of the Core Training Programme*. On behalf of the Social and Health Education Project. Bantry: Kearney Consultants/West Cork Training.

Longden E (2013). *The Voices in my Head*. TED2013; February. www.ted.com/talks/eleanor_ longden_the_voices_in_my_head?language=en (accessed 5 January 2019).

Mental Health Commission (2017). *Annual Report 2017*. Dublin: Mental Health Commission.

Mental Health Reform (2018). *Mental Health Reform dismayed by increase in physical restraint in in-patient mental health services*. Press release; 19 October. Dublin: Mental Health Reform. www.mentalhealthreform.ie/news/mental-health-reform-dismayed-by-increase-in-physical-restraint-in-in-patient-mental-health-services (accessed 20 September 2019).

Pūras D (2017). *Report of the Special Rapporteur on the Right of Everyone to the Enjoyment of the Highest Attainable Standard of Physical and Mental Health*. Geneva: United Nations Humans Rights Council.

Sapouna L (2017). *Transforming Mental Health Care: from social perspectives to solidarity networks*. Paper presented as part of the module UW0011: Interdisciplinary Perspectives on Social Justice, Equality, Diversity and Health. Cork: University College Cork; April.

Sidley G (2018). Colluding with prejudice? Mental health nurses and the Mental Health Act. In: Bull P, Gadsby J, Williams S. *Critical Mental Health Nursing: observations from the inside*. Monmouth: PCCS Books (pp106-123).

Spandler H (2018). *Mad Politics Today: some critical reflections*. Keynote presentation. Annual Critical Perspectives Conference, University College Cork, Cork; November. https://ucc.cloud.panopto.eu/Panopto/Pages/Viewer.aspx?id=1f667eb3-2b2e-48cb-95ad-a9a00102f485 (accessed 4 September 2019).

United Nations (2006). *Convention on the Rights of People with Disabilities*. New York, NY: United Nations.

Wilks T (2012). *Advocacy and Social Work Practice*. Maidenhead: Open University Press.

Woods A (2013). Rethinking 'patient testimony' in the medical humanities: the case of Schizophrenia Bulletin's first person accounts. *Journal of Literature and Science* 6(1): 38–54.

# PART 3

---

## The broader context

# Chapter 14

# Reclaiming agency through Oor Mad History

## Anne O'Donnell and Kirsten Maclean

This chapter is about the importance to the service user/survivor movement of remembering and recording our past in order to keep campaigning for future change. It is about Oor Mad History, an innovative community oral history project that was established in Lothian, south-east Scotland, in 2008, and how recording and publishing the recollections of local activists has enabled us to protect our focus and independence from co-option by government bodies and helped fuel and inspire our continuing campaigns for our rights and changes in mental health services.

This chapter is written by one of the people who began the project, Anne O'Donnell, and the community history worker on the project, Kirsten Maclean. We are both still actively involved. The chapter draws on the oral history archive of Oor Mad History, on discussions we have had together and with others, and on personal reflections to describe the project in its different phases. Many of the quotes are taken from the transcripts from the Oor Mad History oral history interviews and book (CAPS, 2010).

First, we explain the Oor Mad History project and the context in which it came about and then outline what it has achieved over the years, our plans for keeping it moving forward and why it is just as urgently needed now as when we started it.

## Oor Mad History project

Oor Mad History is an oral history project launched by mad people in 2008 in Lothian, south-east Scotland, to record the experiences and perspectives of mad people and the history of the activism and collective advocacy of the mental health service user movement in the region. We are based at CAPS Independent Advocacy,[1] which provides independent individual advocacy in East Lothian and Midlothian and collective advocacy across the Lothians, funded by the local health board, NHS Lothian.

The project was conducted by a group of volunteers, who were trained in oral history skills by the Living Memory Association. The volunteers recorded more than 70 oral history interviews, which we transcribed in full. The people involved in the project then read through all the transcripts and highlighted the important quotes to form the basis for a book, *Oor Mad History: a community history of the Lothian mental health service user movement* (CAPS, 2010).[2] The book is divided into two parts. First, we outlined the background to the project, why it is important, what we did and how. We also included pieces by two volunteer interviewers, Jim McGill and Jenifer Booth, and an outline of Powercube, a framework we used that analyses the levels, spaces and forms of power (see below). The second part of the book is made up of images from the archive and quotes from the oral history transcripts, organised into themes such as 'Early Days', 'The Struggle to be Heard – reactions and resistances to advocacy and an emerging user voice', 'What could have been done differently?' and 'The impact of being involved'.

We also collected an archive of paper-based materials and ephemera, including minutes of meetings, posters and t-shirts, from all over Scotland. We have catalogued the paper-based archive and continue to add to it. Some of the archive and all of the recordings have been lodged for safekeeping with the Lothian Health Services Archive.

To launch the book, and the project as a whole, we created an exhibition based on the archive, using objects and images from the archive and artwork by service users connected with the project. But this was just the start; from this, much grew, as we'll explain below.

## History and context

Lothian is a large area in South East Scotland composed of four local authority areas: the City of Edinburgh, East Lothian, Midlothian and West Lothian. NHS Lothian is the regional health authority that covers these four areas.

The NHS and Community Care Act (1990), a UK-wide Act, gave people using health and social care services a greater say in these services. While this was a result of the neoliberal consumerist agenda of the then Conservative administration (Speed, 2007), it provided an opportunity that was seized by

---

1. http://capsadvocacy.org/collective-advocacy (accessed 21 June 2019).
2. http://capsadvocacy.org/lothian-wide-projects/oor-mad-history (accessed 21 June 2019).

mental health service users, among many others, as a way of asserting their right to be heard. CAPS, Oor Mad History's umbrella organisation, emerged from this period, initially as 'The Consultation and Advocacy Promotion Service' with a main focus on promoting consultation with service users and making the case for advocacy. Over time, it became CAPS Independent Advocacy in 2016, and both supports collective advocacy across the Lothian area and provides individual advocacy in East Lothian and Midlothian. As a result of the NHS Community Care Act, subsequent policy changes and the activism of service user groups, user involvement has become standard practice for mental health service funders and providers.

In the years leading up to 2007, when Oor Mad History began, there had been substantial changes in mental health policy and service delivery in Lothian and Scotland generally. Policy developments included the implementation in 2005 of the Mental Health (Care and Treatment) (Scotland) Act 2003, which gave service users the right to access to independent advocacy, the rolling out of the Scottish-wide National Programme for Mental Health and Wellbeing strategy, with its emphasis on challenging stigma and preventing ill health, and the implementation of the national Scottish Delivering for Mental Health plan at NHS Lothian level and the Lothian Mental Health and Wellbeing Strategy.

Alongside there was a new focus on improving access to social and psychological interventions and a move towards shifting the focus of psychiatric treatment from inpatient hospitals to new community teams – notably, a Rapid Response Treatment Service, which would provide an alternative to inpatient assessment and treatment, and a new Crisis Centre in Edinburgh.

Service users from a number of collective advocacy groups had been involved in these changes. For example, the Crisis Centre would not have come about if it were not for the efforts of the Edinburgh Users Forum (EUF) (2003; Maloney, 2005; CAPS, 2010). The right to independent advocacy and other safeguards of detained people's rights in the Mental Health Act are due, to a large part, to the input of service user groups such as EUF and the Highland Users Group (Scottish Parliament, 2002).

But by 2007, we (at EUF) were feeling that our involvement in these changes had been on the terms set by the agendas of decision-making bodies, in particular, the NHS and the Health Department of the Scottish Government (then known as the Scottish Executive). Those of us involved in the different collective advocacy groups found ourselves devoting more and more time and energy to responding to requests for 'user involvement' from the NHS, local authorities, universities and others. We had little time or energy to work on our own priorities.

Jo McFarlane (2002), who was active in both the Lothian Users Forum and the Royal Edinburgh Hospital Patients Council, argued that we needed to question the nature of our involvement and discuss structural issues such as stigma and discrimination, the relationship between psychiatry, the pharmaceutical industry and the government, and the biological model of mental distress. Otherwise, she said, we were just reinforcing the status quo by 'doing user involvement' rather than working for significant change.

Some felt torn between wanting to honour the struggle we had gone through to get a 'seat at the table' and so continuing to engage, and wanting to say no to the demands so we could decide for ourselves our priorities. Cowden and Singh (2007) argue that the discourse of user involvement is contradictory. On one hand, we have the success of service user movements in 'giving service users a voice in decision-making spaces and places' that only a few decades ago would have been unimaginable. However, this advance is opposed by the 'construction of a new hegemony' in which these progressive critiques of a patronising and controlling professional regime have been 'incorporated into a system driven by managerial rather than democratising imperatives' (Cowden & Singh, 2007: 21).

This tension is captured in these comments from some of the Oor Mad History interviews (CAPS, 2010):

I think the whole atmosphere has changed, I think the backdrop against which service user groups are operating now has changed, I think it's far less confrontational, if you like. I think service user groups, service user representatives, are much more welcomed at bigger forums now and I think they're given their rightful place. I don't think you have to battle so much. (Jim McGill)

Well, the NHS has made it clear that they'll listen to us, they'll hear us out and then they'll simply go away and do their own thing anyway. They have absolutely total disregard for what the service users want. So, in answer to your question, service users have absolutely no say, nobody will listen to them. (Veronica Forrest)

I think that it's come a long way since I first went to mental health services, but I think there's a lot of room for improvement. I think we need to continually hammer home the point that we need more say in services and until we're listened to and until it doesnae take years for the things we're campaigning for to come about, until it comes to the point when a group of service users say, this is what we think we need because

> we think this will be better for us… then people look at it seriously rather
> than leaving it for years and years and years and letting somebody else
> come up with the idea and stealing the idea as if it was theirs. (Alistair)

In other words, people involved in collective advocacy locally were experiencing 'consultation fatigue' (Accounts Commission for Scotland, 1998). Through continually being asked their views by the NHS and local authority, they were beginning to lose sight of what mattered to them. This led to people drifting away as they felt collective advocacy no longer gave them space to discuss the issues that they felt needed to change.

Voronka and other critics argue that user involvement itself has been co-opted by the system: that innovations like recovery and peer work, which had emancipatory roots in the user movement, have now been integrated and co-opted by the system (Voronka 2017; Recovery in The Bin, undated).

## What next?

A number of things came together in the mid-2000s: at EUF, we began to reminisce; one of us was researching the potential of oral history for collective advocacy, and we heard about Mad People's History.

As we were beginning to talk about what was happening in collective advocacy, we found ourselves naturally recalling the energy and optimism of the 'early days' of the late 1980s and early 1990s and wondered what we had lost and how. In her oral history interview, Be Morris, an ally of the movement, described this energy in those early years:

> My strongest memories of the early days are how alive and energetic
> it felt and how committed and how exciting it felt. It really felt as if it
> was something major happening. It was a movement along with lots
> of other movements that were very vocal at the time, like the women's
> movement, the Black movement. It felt like at last, folk were standing
> up, forming a strong alliance and making strong statements, that we're
> going to make societal changes.

It also felt important to acknowledge and record our past, especially our contributions to the changes to the mental health system. We also felt that it was important to challenge the policy discourse around user involvement. We wanted to highlight that user involvement and advocacy were not simply a gift from the state; they have been fought for by many groups of people who are recipients of social welfare, and especially the wider disabled people's movement, including mental health service users (Beresford, 2016).

I think that recording our history is a really good idea because when the ones that founded it get on a bit, it'll be great to know it's been recorded and it's not all going to be forgotten about and it's not all been for bugger all really. (Maggie Keppie)

It's 16, 17 years down the road and then, you look back and you think, god, we have got a history, we've done all this stuff. You don't see it necessarily as that when you're involved in the middle of it. I think it's a good point to actually look back and see what we've done and here are our pointers and our purposes. I'm really pleased this is happening. (Adrienne Sinclair Chalmers)

In 2006/07, I (Anne) was studying for my MSc in Community Education at the University of Edinburgh. As a result of the discussions in the user groups, I wrote a dissertation called 'Mad People's History: the potential use of oral history by a collective advocacy group' (O'Donnell, 2007). This started us all thinking concretely about how to make it happen.

At the same time, connections were being made with the mad movement in Canada. Steve Tilley, an ally of the user movement and a lecturer in mental health nursing at the University of Edinburgh, introduced us to developments at Ryerson University in Toronto, where the School of Disability Studies offered a course called Mad People's History, taught by a mad person, David Reville. The course description explained its aim to:

provide an overview of the history of madness from the point of view of people who were, and are, deemed 'mad'... to place the diverse perspectives of people diagnosed as mad, insane or mentally ill as being of central importance in the history of psychiatry, and to address the question: how madness has been viewed by mad people over the centuries. (Ryerson University, undated)

When David and his colleague, Kathryn Church, visited Edinburgh in 2007, Edinburgh Users Forum (EUF) asked him to tell us about his course and invited other collective advocacy groups in the Lothians to come and share what they knew about their history.

We intended to use David's visit as a stimulus to produce our own history of our movement, in order to strengthen our collective advocacy by shaping '[our] sense of collective and communal attachment and the opportunities for further mobilisation' (Harding & Gabriel, 2004: 200). This, we felt, would enable us to resist the user involvement agenda set by government, health and social care providers and professional bodies and re-establish a space where we could collectively set our own priorities and agendas and focus on our own priorities.

David spoke to a packed room at the Drill Hall in Edinburgh, talking about the experience of teaching Mad People's History and about activism in Toronto. People from each of the advocacy projects in Lothian attended and shared their own organisation or group's history and achievements. We found that we shared similar concerns, even though the contexts and structures we worked in were different.

Linda Irvine from NHS Lothian's Mental Health and Wellbeing team had been very supportive of independent collective advocacy and saw the potential for a project. She invited us to submit a proposal for funding, which was successful, and so we were able to begin the work.

## Methods

Oor Mad History was unlike anything CAPS, or most of the individuals involved, had ever done before. Kirsten had experience of working on community history with Gypsy/Travellers but the rest of us had to learn a lot very quickly.

We set up a steering group, which was made up of people with lived experience and of advisors from community and oral history, and in particular John McCaughie from the Living Memory Association and Maggie Mackay from the School of Scottish Studies at Edinburgh University. This gave us the technical expertise we needed in archiving and oral history, as well as support to manage the practical considerations of funding and resources.

Oral history is a powerful tool for reclaiming the histories of groups who have been marginalised by society and by mainstream history. It is one way of democratising history, of putting history in the hands of those who have created it.

Plummer points out that the 'importance of "finding a voice" and "telling one's story" has been well recognised in the politics of the new social movements' (1995: 30). For example, gay men and lesbians have explored their history as a way of resisting discourses that constructed them as sinful, mentally ill or criminal, reframing same-sex attraction as part of the human experience, finding positive role models from the past to counter homophobia and providing a history for LGBT people themselves.

Paul Thompson points out that 'oral history is not necessarily an instrument for change' but that, depending on how and why it is used, it can transform 'both the content and the purpose of history' (Thompson 1998: 22).

We also found inspiration and support from Andrew Roberts and other members of the Survivors History Group. Their website is a digital record of events, people, groups and publications from the survivor/service-user movement, primarily in the UK.[3] Their aim is to 'value and celebrate the contribution that mental health service users/survivors have made and are making to history'. Recently, a global survivor history project, Eurikha, has been set up, with the aim to research 'the emergence of social movements which privilege the rights and perspectives of people who experience severe mental distress, variedly known around the world as users, survivors, consumers, clients, patients, persons with psychosocial disabilities etc'.[4]

We intended that both the content (our history as activists) and the process (our work as oral historians) would challenge dominant constructions of mental health service users as passive recipients of psychiatric services by demonstrating that we are agents in our own lives, individually and collectively.

### Power

Throughout the project, issues of power have been central. We used the Powercube to make sense of our history of advocacy and activism (Cornwall, 2002; Brosnan, 2012). The Powercube is 'a framework for analysing the levels, spaces and forms of power, and their interrelationship'.[5] It comes from the international development work of Johan Gaventa, Andrea Cornwall and others. Brosnan (2012) has applied the Powercube to examine the levels of involvement of mental health service users in Ireland.

To give a very brief overview of something quite complex and dynamic, the Powercube has three dimensions – forms, spaces and levels of power. We initially found it very useful to focus on the spaces of power in order to understand how our activism became subsumed in the user involvement agenda:

> 'spaces' are seen as opportunities, moments and channels where
> citizens can act to potentially affect policies, discourses, decisions and
> relationships that affect their lives and interests.[5]

*Closed* space is where the decisions are made by those in power; *invited* spaces are where those in power invite others to participate on their terms; *claimed* spaces are created by people who have something in common who want to speak up and make changes – that is, collective advocacy.

So, when people come together to work towards change, as the early service user groups did, the spaces within which they collaborate are claimed

---

3. http://studymore.org.uk/mpu.htm (accessed 21 June 2019).

4. www.eurikha.org/about ( accessed 21 June 2019).

5. www.powercube.net/analyse-power/spaces-of-power ( accessed 21 June 2019).

spaces. Closed spaces are found where the big policy and management decisions are made by civil servants, professionals and service planners and providers. User involvement occupies an *invited space*, where those in power invite those who are powerless to be part of the decision-making process. But, as we have already discussed, this has led to service user groups being co-opted. Oor Mad History has been a way for us to reclaim our own space and to refocus on what is important to us.

### Using the word 'Mad'

A CAPS worker, Kirstie Henderson, came up with the project's name before we even got funding. We liked it because it isn't a medical term and it conveyed a sense of energy and agency. It seemed to help us get past the never-ending discussions about terms like service user, survivor, consumer, and mental health problems, mental illness, mental ill health…

> No term in the history of madness is neutral – not mental illness, madness, or any other term. Madness, however, is more respectful of the huge diversity of views within this field over a much longer period than a term exclusively identified with biological determinism that has developed since the early twentieth century. (Reaume, 2006: 182)

It made sense to use 'mad' in the title of the project and to use the most common term in the subtitle, 'a history of the *service user movement* in the Lothians'. We anticipated a lot of anxiety about the word, but in all the talks we have given about the project, we can only remember two negative reactions. Perhaps going to great pains to explain why we use the word has allayed people's concerns.

## Oor Mad History – what we've achieved

The funding from NHS Lothian allowed CAPS to employ a community history worker, Kirsten Maclean. The project was managed by a steering group made up of service users/survivors active in the movement and supporters from the community history field.

The aims of the project were to:

*   remember, record and promote the history of the Lothian mental health service user movement
*   highlight the role service users have played in developing mental health services in Lothian
*   challenge dominant ideas about people who use mental health services

- enable service users to see themselves and to be seen by others as active agents of change
- celebrate the achievements of the movement
- strengthen the service user voice and movement, today and in the future.

In the first two years of the project, we worked with service user volunteers and groups to create the paper-based and oral history archive – unique in Scotland, as we've described earlier in the chapter.

As a result of the book and the exhibition, Oor Mad History became involved in two different activities. The first was the 2010 Scottish Mental Health Arts and Film Festival (SMHAFF[6]). Our exhibition was so successful that we decided to organise another one the following year. Since then, the exhibition, which is now named 'Out Of Sight Out Of Mind' (OOSOOM), has become a key part of the festival. This showed us there was a desire by people with mental health experiences to express their views through art and an audience for this work. We believe that the arts are a powerful tool for advocacy and activism, and OOSOOM is a platform for this work. It now has a distinct identity as 'Arts as Advocacy' within CAPS, with its own dedicated worker.

The other was the development of a course called 'Mad People's History and Identity' at Queen Margaret University, just outside Edinburgh. It seemed important to us to create space for Oor Mad History in a university. With the help of Steve Tilley, we began planning a module at master's level in Nursing Studies. It would be designed and delivered by people with lived experience of mental health issues and there would be places for students from outwith the university.

Throughout this period, we were supported by David Reville and his colleagues in Toronto, in particular Kathryn Church. A small group, including Kirsten and Jim McGill, visited them in 2009, and sat in on David's classes and met people involved in the survivor movement and survivor-led services. In particular, they met Mel Starkman and Geoffrey Reaume from the Psychiatric Survivor Archives of Toronto.[7] In 2012, Anne and Kirsten were invited to take part in 'Mad Positive in the Academy', a small international conference at Ryerson for academics and activists interested in working together. This was where we first heard the term 'Mad Studies'.

Mad Studies is an area of education, scholarship and analysis about the experiences, history, culture, political organising, narratives, writings

6. www.mhfestival.com (accessed 21 June 2019).

7. www.psychiatricsurvivorarchives.com (accessed 21 June 2019).

and most importantly, the PEOPLE who identify as: Mad; psychiatric survivors; consumers; service users; mentally ill; patients, neuro-diverse; inmates; disabled – to name a few of the 'identity labels' our community may choose to use. (Costa, 2014)

We realised that we'd been 'doing' Mad Studies for a long time.

As it was proving difficult to get a course established at the University of Edinburgh, David Reville suggested taking a community development approach. We enrolled one person on the online 'Mad People's History' course at Ryerson, who would follow the course and share their learning with a small group at CAPS.

We were asked to exhibit some of the artwork and material from the archive at Queen Margaret University in 2012. Elaine Ballantyne, a lecturer in occupational therapy, was very interested in our idea of developing a university course on Mad People's History. Again, we were supported by Linda Irvine at NHS Lothian, who provided some funding to the university. The course, which became 'Mad People's History and Identity', was developed by a group of people with lived experience and Queen Margaret University academics. It ran for three years, starting in 2014, took a break for a year while it was being evaluated as part of a Participatory Action Research project, and was then funded for another five years from 2018. The course is open to people with lived experience who are not studying at the university, as part of the university's widening participation work (Ballantyne et al, 2019).

The course at Queen Margaret University and the Arts as Advocacy work occupied our focus from 2011 to 2016. But we were aware that the original purpose of the project – the community history – was being neglected. So, in 2017, when the Queen Margaret University course was taking its break, we began to think about how to revive our core purpose.

By now Anne was working for CAPS, in a different project, and was asked to do some work with the Oor Mad History as Kirsten had gone part time to focus on her PhD. Since the publication of the book in 2010, the user movement in Lothian has had to adapt to changing political and social conditions. These include the devastating impacts of welfare reform since the mid-2000s, cuts to health and social care (Friedli & Stearn, 2015), the co-option of recovery in justifying these cuts (Recovery in The Bin, 2018), and the development of peer support (Christie, 2018) and co-production (Needham & Carr, 2009). These all need to be understood and responded to in more critical ways than we have seen so far. As well, we hadn't even heard of Mad Studies when we started, and now it is a crucial part of how we understand what we are doing.

At the time of writing this, we have just begun to gather the history of this period in a systematic way, by interviewing key actors and by adding to the archive. We are planning to produce another book, covering the period of 2010 onwards. To do this, we have been seeking out people to re-engage with the aims of the original project and to develop the oral history and archiving capacity of the project. Since late 2018, we have been organising workshops with a growing group of old and new activists, many of whom have been through the 'Mad People's History and Identity' course at Queen Margaret University. The workshops include explaining the archive and oral history, as well as developing a timeline of key events and changes since the start of the project in 2008. We also aim to encourage people to explore the archives and research their own interests.

Following a flood at the previous CAPS office, we made the difficult decision to deposit the archive with Lothian Health Services Archive, based at the University of Edinburgh. We are often asked about this decision by people concerned that we do not have physical ownership of the material. Essentially, we had to balance the physical safety of the material against its accessibility, and its safety won out. As a compromise, we have a small archive at the new CAPS office and maintain links with Lothian Health Services Archive. In the past we have organised visits to the archives at both sites and we are planning to make them a regular feature of the project.

As mentioned above, the 'Mad People's History and Identity' course has been funded again, to run until 2022. The last cohort of students in 2018 included some who were new to advocacy and the user movement as well as people who were already active. So, it continues to be a great way of developing the movement as well as providing an opportunity for people to learn and develop.

## Community education and critical pedagogy

CAPS has always had a strong community education (Tett, 2010) ethos to how it works. Community Education in Scotland is now called Community Learning and Development (CLD). It is 'a field of professional practice that enables people to identify their own individual and collective goals, to engage in learning and take action to bring about change for themselves and their communities' (CLD Standards Council, undated).

This has helped our advocacy work to keep a necessary distance from the health and social care fields. The manager of CAPS when Oor Mad History started, Keith Maloney, is a community education graduate, as are Kirsten and Anne. It was Anne's dissertation for her MSc in Community Education that was the basis for the original proposal to NHS Lothian to set up the project.

So, we see Oor Mad History as a whole to be very much an educational project. Our approach is rooted in critical pedagogy, drawing on educationalists such as Paolo Freire and bell hooks, and in a belief that all education is political. We offer space for people to ask questions, learn skills such as interviewing, archiving and presenting, share their knowledge and skills, and collectively work on making the connections between the personal and the political. Our objective is for people to see themselves as active agents for change – as subjects of history, not simply objects of psychiatry and mental health policy.

Fricker's concept of epistemic injustice helps us to understand how people with mental health issues are discredited as knowers (Fricker, 2007). By further breaking down epistemic injustice into ideas of 'testimonial' and 'hermeneutical' injustice, we can better understand how the knowledge, testimony and collective identity-making of mad people is devalued and subjugated (LeBlanc & Kinsella, 2016). Testimonial injustice is when we are not seen as reliable knowers because of our 'mental illness'; hermeneutic injustice is when we are denied the resources to create our own knowledge. As a consequence of testimonial and hermeneutic injustice, perspectives that challenge the biomedical model, and in particular the narratives and analyses of those who identify as mad or as having mental health issues, are excluded from mainstream discourse. Consequently, mental health is de-politicised and constructed as an individual problem, an individual medical issue, to be dealt with privately by keeping on taking the pills.

This is why we believe it is important for us to focus on the history of people with mental health issues as activists, and not on the history of psychiatry or mental health services or on individual stories of distress and recovery. This in itself is challenging to many people, and at the start of the project we had to explain it in detail to those who wanted us to broaden our focus to include individual experiences of distress and using services, the voices of mental health workers or the history of services. One of our aims is to challenge the dominant constructions of people with mental health issues as 'users of services', 'victims of stigma', a statistic, 'perpetrators of gun violence', 'poor souls', 'welfare fraudsters'…

We are writing this in 2019, after more than a decade of austerity, when disabled people, and in particular people with mental health problems, have been subjected to punitive welfare reforms and cuts to services. Professor Philip Alston, the United Nations' special rapporteur on extreme poverty and human rights, has accused the UK government of working 'to reduce benefits by every means available, including constant reductions in benefit levels, ever-more-demanding conditions, harsher penalties, depersonalization, stigmatization, and virtually eliminating the option of using the legal system to vindicate rights' (Alston, 2019). People with mental health issues are particularly affected by this punitive regime (Ryan, 2019).

As people who have experience of using services and/or with experience of madness and distress, we can and do create our own discourses, our own stories and our own alternatives. Social movements have historically used narratives as an integral part of their organising, so creating new narratives and disrupting the dominant one can bolster individual and collective power and potentially lead to political and social change.

## Conclusion

We are left with questions. As we have shown, Oor Mad History has achieved a lot in our 10 years and we are planning to do a lot more. But we, as a project and as a movement, are now in a much more challenging and precarious situation than we were when we started. User-led spaces and organisations are in decline (Beresford, 2019) and the impact of austerity generally on individuals and groups is incalculable.

What role can social movement learning such as Oor Mad History play in opening up spaces where people can come together, engage with alternative views, wrestle with the complexities of the discourse and practice of mental health services, while living in precarious circumstances? And what role can this work play in individual and collective identity making and the developing of critical and political agency?

Oor Mad History is one project in one area. The history of the user movement and of mad people's activism worldwide needs to be recorded and remembered. We are heartened by the ongoing work of the Survivors History Group in the UK and by the setting up of the global research project, Eurikha. We are pleased that we are one small part of that work.

### References

Accounts Commission for Scotland (1998). Focusing on the views of users and carers. *Adult Mental Health Services Bulletin 2*. www.audit-scotland.gov.uk/uploads/docs/report/1998/nr_9801_adult_mental_health_bulletin2.pdf (accessed 21 August 2019).

Alston P (2019). *Report of the Special Rapporteur on Extreme Poverty and Human Rights on his Visit to the United Kingdom of Great Britain and Northern Ireland*. Geneva: United Nations Human Rights Council. https://undocs.org/A/HRC/41/39/Add.1 (accessed 21 August 2019).

Ballantyne E, Maclean K, Collie S, Deeming L, Fraser E (2019). Mad people's history and identity. In: Breeze M, Scandrett E (eds). *Public Sociology Education*. University of Bristol: The Policy Press. Manuscript submitted for publication.

Beresford P (2019). Austerity is denying patients and care service users a voice. [Online.] *The Guardian*; 14 January. www.theguardian.com/society/2019/jan/14/austerity-denying-patients-care-service-users-voice (accessed 21 August 2019).

Beresford P (2016). *All Our Welfare: towards participatory social policy.* Bristol: Policy Press.

Brosnan L (2012). Power and participation: an examination of the dynamics of mental health service-user involvement in Ireland. *Studies in Social Justice* 6(1): 45–66.

CAPS (2010). *Oor Mad History: a community history of the Lothian mental health service users movement.* Musselburgh: CAPS.

Christie L (2018). *Momentum is Growing, the Future is Peer.* [Blog.] Scottish Recovery Network; 31 October. www.scottishrecovery.net/resource/momentum-is-growing-the-future-is-peer/ (accessed 21 August 2019).

CLD Standards Council (undated). *What is Community Learning and Development (CLD)?* [Online.] http://cldstandardscouncil.org.uk/about-cld/what-is-community-learning-and-development-cld/ (accessed 21 August 2019).

Cornwall A (2002). Locating citizen participation. *IDS Bulletin* 33(2): 49–58.

Costa L (2014). *Mad Studies – what it is and why you should care.* [Blog.] Mad Studies Network; 15 October. https://madstudies2014.wordpress.com/2014/10/15/mad-studies-what-it-is-and-why-you-should-care-2/ (accessed 21 August 2019).

Cowden S, Singh G (2007). The 'user': friend, foe or fetish? A critical exploration of user involvement in health and social care. *Critical Social Policy* 27(1): 5–23.

Edinburgh Users' Forum (2003). *Making a Drama Out of a Crisis Service.* The Point. Glasgow: SAMH.

Fricker M (2007). *Epistemic Injustice: power and the ethics of knowing.* Oxford: Oxford University Press.

Friedli L, Stearn R (2015). Positive affect as coercive strategy: conditionality, activation and the role of psychology in UK government workfare programmes. *Medical Humanities* 41:40–47.

Harding J, Gabriel J (2004). Communities in the making: pedagogic explorations using oral history. *International Studies in Sociology of Education* 14(3): 185–201.

LeBlanc S, Kinsella EA (2016). Toward epistemic justice: a critically reflexive examination of 'sanism' and implications for knowledge generation. *Studies in Social Justice* 10(1): 59–78.

Maloney K (2005). *The Development of Mental Health Policy in Scotland: enabling a voice for service users?* Unpublished MEd dissertation, Edinburgh: University of Edinburgh.

McFarlane J (2002). Paying attention to process: a lesson from the mental health service user movement. In: Shaw M, Meaghar J, Moir S (eds). *Participation in Community Development: problems and possibilities.* Leicester: NIACE (pp87–90).

Needham C, Carr S (2009). *SCIE Research Briefing 31: co-production: an emerging evidence base for adult social care transformation.* London: Social Care Institute for Excellence.

O'Donnell A (2007). *Mad People's History: the potential use of oral history by a collective advocacy group.* Unpublished MSc dissertation, University of Edinburgh.

Plummer K (1995). *Telling Sexual Stories: power, change and social worlds.* London: Routledge.

Reaume G (2006). Mad people's history. *Radical History Review* 94: 170–182.

Recovery in The Bin (2018). *Mental Health Peer Workers: our lived experience. Parts 1 and 2.* [Blog.] RITB; 9 November. https://recoveryinthebin.org/category/peer-workers/ (accessed 21 August 2019).

Recovery in The Bin (undated). *RITB – key principles.* [Online.] https://recoveryinthebin.org/ritbkeyprinciples (accessed 21 August 2019).

Ryan F (2019). Welfare 'reforms' are pushing mentally ill people over the edge. [Online.] *The Guardian*; 24 January. www.theguardian.com/commentisfree/2019/jan/24/welfare-reform-mentally-ill-injustice (accessed 21 August 2019).

Ryerson University (2012). *Mad Positive in the Academy.* [Online.] https://www.ryerson.ca/disability-studies/research/mad-positive-in-the-academy/ (accessed 21 August 2019).

Ryerson University (undated). *CDST 504: Mad People's History.* [Online.] https://ce-online.ryerson.ca/ce/calendar/default.aspx?id=5&section=course&mode=course&ccode=CDST%20504 (accessed 21 August 2019).

Scottish Parliament (2002). *Business Bulletin No 150/2002.* [Online.] Scottish Parliament; 25 October. https://archive.parliament.scot/business/businessBulletin/bb-02/bb-10-25h.htm (accessed 26 August 2019).

Speed E (2007). Discourses of consumption or consumed by discourse? A consideration of what 'consumer' means to the service user. *Journal of Mental Health 16*(3): 306–318.

Tett L (2010). *Community Education, Learning and Development.* Edinburgh: Dunedin Press.

Thompson P (1998). The voice of the past: oral history. In: Perks R, Thomson A (eds). *The Oral History Reader.* London: Routledge (pp21–28).

Voronka J (2017). The politics of 'people with lived experience' experiential authority and the risks of strategic essentialism. *Philosophy, Psychiatry, & Psychology 23*(3–4): 189–201.

# Chapter 15

# An alternative to diagnosis: the Power Threat Meaning Framework

## John Cromby

The Power Threat Meaning Framework (PTMF) (Johnstone & Boyle, 2018a) is a meta-framework for conceptualising and identifying patterns in distress and troubled and troubling behaviour. It was co-produced by psychologists and service users/survivors over a five-year period. For the sake of brevity, in what follows the description of the Framework's scope will be shortened to 'distress', but the longer definition applies throughout (especially because some of those given diagnoses will not themselves be distressed, but will be distressing or disturbing to others).

The PTMF was funded by the Division of Clinical Psychology (DCP) of the British Psychological Society (BPS), although it is not official DCP or BPS policy. The impetus for its development was a 2013 DCP position statement (BPS Division of Clinical Psychology, 2013), released when the fifth edition of the American Psychiatric Association's *Diagnostic and Statistical Manual of Mental Disorders* (*DSM-5*) (APA, 2013) was published. The position statement urged clinicians to reject psychiatric diagnosis in favour of psychological alternatives. This chapter will explain why the PTMF was needed and summarise what it involves (including discussions of biology, causality and patterns of distress). It will then consider some possible future developments associated with the Framework, before concluding with some brief critical reflection.

## Why was it needed?

Psychiatric and biomedical understandings of emotional and behavioural difficulties and distress remain prominent in services, research and public understandings. Yet, with respect to the so-called functional psychiatric diagnoses (which include many of the most common diagnoses such as 'schizophrenia', 'depression', 'anxiety disorder', and the 'eating' and 'personality disorders') there is no consistent evidence for the biological aberrations presumed to cause them. In the language of psychiatry, there are no biomarkers for these diagnoses: no biological features that consistently co-vary with them and can assist in making a diagnosis, identifying a treatment, or assessing progress towards a cure.

Advocates of diagnosis sometimes go to quite extraordinary rhetorical lengths to gloss over this problem, but occasionally it gets openly acknowledged. In the press release launching *DSM-5*, Professor David Kupfer (2013), chair of the committee that produced the new diagnostic manual, said:

> In the future, we hope to be able to identify disorders using biological and genetic markers… Yet this promise, which we have anticipated since the 1970s, remains disappointingly distant. We've been telling patients for several decades that we are waiting for biomarkers. We're still waiting.

So, the PTMF was needed because there is no good evidence for the most basic assumption of the diagnostic model: that so-called mental illnesses are illnesses like those in physical medicine.

This is a major reason why psychiatric diagnosis remains unreliable and invalid. The absence of biomarkers means that clinicians must necessarily make judgements about the extent to which feelings, thoughts and behaviours are 'normal', and this must typically be the primary basis of their decisions. This is apparent in the wording of the diagnostic criteria, which includes phrases such as 'excessive guilt', 'inappropriate affect', 'deficient sexual fantasies', 'unusual perceptual experiences' and 'marked impairment in role functioning'. All of these phrases suggest that the person being diagnosed is being compared against some idea of normality. At the same time, of course, precisely what 'normal' looks like is never defined – not in the DSM, nor anywhere else. Indeed, the standard of normality clinicians should use (for example, statistical, medical or sociocultural) goes largely unstated.

Because functional psychiatric diagnosis is insufficiently valid and reliable, all of its claimed benefits – patient reassurance, prognosis, treatment identification, service planning – are compromised. Hence, many who enter mental health services receive biomedical interventions (most commonly, medication) that are modestly efficacious at best and damaging at worst. They end up over-medicated but under-treated (Francesco, 2015). But diagnosis is also problematic because it presumes that a conceptual framework developed to understand body parts and their functions is straightforwardly transferable to persons, their conduct and their experiences. There is no sound reason to make this presumption, and many reasons to question it. As the PTMF notes:

> Our body parts, after all, don't have language, make relationships,
> reminisce about the past or plan the future. Nor do they create symbols,
> stories or social hierarchies, feel love, hate, loneliness or despair. They do
> not attribute meaning to their experiences, influenced by a culture they
> themselves have created. It seems unlikely, then, that people's thoughts,
> feelings and actions, even when distressing, troubling or very difficult to
> understand, will show the same kinds of patterns or follow the same kinds
> of 'rules' as malfunctioning body parts. (Johnstone & Boyle, 2018a: 25–26)

The well-evidenced contribution of culture to the experience and expression of distress provides another reason why an alternative to functional diagnosis was needed. Psychiatry has tended to treat the forms of distress that prevail within non-Western cultures in two different but related ways. On the one hand, it has treated them as exotic or unusual, and so somewhat marginal. On the other hand, in a kind of epistemic colonialism, it has tried to subsume them into the diagnostic categories of the *DSM* or the World Health Organization's equivalent diagnostic manual, the *International Classification of Diseases* (ICD) (WHO, 2018). What both tendencies share is the baseless assumption that the forms of distress that currently prevail in Western cultures are somehow more 'real' than those that occur elsewhere. In place of this assumption, we need to recognise that culture is an integral constituent of all experiences, including those labelled as symptoms of mental illness. But this is not easily possible within a psychiatric diagnostic framework that posits (hypothetical) biological aberrations as the root causes of these experiences, and largely treats culture as mere context.

There are other reasons why the PTMF was needed. Despite the persistent funding disparity in favour of biological research, there is a mass of evidence that social, relational, experiential, biographic, economic, demographic, cultural and historical influences are significant drivers of distress (see Johnstone & Boyle, 2018b). At the same time, there are features of this evidence base that pose challenges in identifying patterns of distress that might inform service delivery, planning, policy and research. The PTMF describes these features, very generally, as:

- 'Everything causes everything' – all types of adversity are associated, on average, with an increased risk of all forms of mental health difficulty
- 'Everyone has experienced everything' – people described as having mental health difficulties have typically been exposed to different combinations of multiple adversities

- 'Everyone suffers from everything' – in diagnostic terms, this is comorbidity, where people may simultaneously fit several different diagnostic categories. At the same time, many 'symptoms', including those typically associated with more severe diagnoses (eg. voice-hearing, dissociation) are also quite common in the general population.

So, a conceptual framework was needed that coherently incorporates and accounts for these 'everythings', and identifies meaningful patterns within them (rather than obscuring them, as diagnosis does).

Finally, the PTMF was needed because, although some service users find psychiatric diagnosis helpful, many do not. Some experience diagnosis as a lifelong mark of shame and deficit, and this damages them quite as much as the life circumstances that brought them into services. Psychiatric diagnoses can be deeply stigmatising and reduce the hope of recovery, while simultaneously fostering passivity, encouraging compliance with potentially harmful psychiatric drug regimes and reinforcing the relevance of a – frequently unhelpful – 'sick role'.

The PTMF was needed to help those who find diagnosis unhelpful but, until recently, lacked a viable alternative. At the same time, it also goes further because it suggests that there is no separate group of the 'mentally ill.' Instead, the PTMF applies, in some respects and some circumstances, to all of us as we struggle to survive in a difficult world.

## What does it involve?

The core of the PTMF can be stated reasonably simply. Imbalances and abuses of power give rise to threats. People react to threats with threat responses. Many (not all) of these threat responses get called symptoms by psychiatry. Instead, the PTMF treats them as potentially intelligible – if sometimes bizarre or self-defeating – reactions to toxic circumstances and events. However, the relationships between threats and responses are not straightforward or predictable. This is because the relations between power, threats and responses are all mediated by meaning, such that all of these elements are intertwined. To better understand the PTMF, then, it will help to now discuss each of its elements separately.

### Power

Power is defined in the PTMF as 'the means of obtaining security and advantage' and as 'influencing people, events and outcomes to suit your own interests and needs' (Johnstone & Boyle 2018a: 94). Power can take many forms – some obvious, some more subtle. These forms include material and financial power, money or wealth; interpersonal power (giving or withholding affection); legal power; coercive power, violence or physical force, and the power that flows from cultural and social capital – from holding and being able to use valued stocks of knowledge or being acquainted with influential, skilled people and being able to draw on them for help.

Stated like this, it is clear that power is unevenly distributed. We live in a deeply hierarchical society where advantages tend to accrue to those who already have the most. That this is not more widely appreciated, or at least not seen by more people as a source of outrage, is largely down to the most influential and pervasive form of power of all: ideological power – the ability to control meaning by imposing terms, setting agendas and influencing flows of information and their perceived legitimacy. Ideological power smooths the operation of other forms of power by conveying subtle and often seemingly innocuous messages – about the thoughts and feelings we should have, how we should behave, the values we should aspire to, how we should relate to others, and the kinds of people we should be. The PTMF considers the imposition of a psychiatric diagnosis to be an example of ideological power.

### Threats and threat responses

Threats arising from imbalances and abuses of power take many forms. What they share is that they all, on some level, represent an actual or potential attack on one or more of our core needs or basic human rights. Threats can, for example, be relational – the threat of rejection, abandonment or isolation. They can be social – the loss of valued roles, community links or status. At the same time, threats can be economic, material or financial, concerning income or access to housing, security or food. For many people, two or more of these forms of threat (and others, such as threats to core values or meanings) frequently coincide.

**Table 15.1: Examples of threat responses**

| |
|---|
| Denial, avoidance |
| Preparing to fight, flee, escape, seek safety |
| Giving up ('learned helplessness', apathy, low mood) |
| Restricting eating, using alcohol |
| Being hypervigilant |
| Having rapid mood changes |
| Having flashbacks, phobic responses, nightmares |
| Holding unusual beliefs |
| Dissociating, hearing voices |

People react to these threats with threat responses. As Table 15.1 suggests, these responses can helpfully be understood as lying along a continuum. Toward one end are responses we mostly experience ourselves as freely choosing, such as preparing to run or hide or appeasing others. Toward the other end are responses we mostly experience as happening to us – as things that our body-brain systems do without conscious intention, such as flashbacks, rapid mood changes, dissociation and hearing voices.

As the examples show, many threat responses are already familiar from the terminology of psychiatric diagnosis, where they are called symptoms. This illustrates how, from a diagnostic perspective, these responses are seen as manifestations of underlying diseases, impairments or disorders. In this sense, they are largely meaningless – just as we do not inquire overly much into the meaning of a sneeze for someone who has a cold.

By contrast, in the PTMF threat responses are seen as (potentially) understandable reactions to adverse circumstances or events. They are manifestations of attempts to adapt, to endure, to survive, even to thrive. In some cases, they are responses that were always going to be problematic if sustained – for example, self-starvation. In others, they are responses that might have been helpful at the time but are less generally adaptive: for example, dissociation as a way of surviving abuse. At the same time, not all threat responses get categorised as psychiatric symptoms; in fact, some are mundane or even socially valued responses such as overwork or ruthless competitiveness. We all use threat responses in some situations.

### Meaning

Threat responses are reactions to the meanings of threats. Meanings mediate threat and threat response at the same time as they permeate and are created by them. For example, we might only appreciate the extent to which the meaning of a situation is anxiety provoking when we notice ourselves engaging in ritual behaviours as it approaches.

With respect to meaning, the role of ideological power – which frequently relies on the control of language and the regulation of agendas – is particularly obvious. However, meaning is also bound up with the operation of power more generally. Consider the different meanings of being either rich or poor, of breaking the law, of having a supportive relationship withdrawn, of being subjected to violence, of acquiring useful social contacts and knowledge, and so on.

As this diversity begins to suggest, meanings are complex and somewhat unstable achievements, always constituted from a range of sources. These sources typically include language, feeling, culture, habit, memory, environments and resources. Vitally, none of these sources are wholly under the control of individuals. Language, for example, pre-exists the individuals who speak it. The discourses and narratives into which it is organised are cultural forms that contribute to shared intelligibility and distribute rights to speak. But sometimes this means that words and phrases have meanings we did not intend, or what we say is not taken seriously. At other times, it means that the words we use simply don't feel adequate – but we must use them anyway, because they are all we have.

In a similar fashion, we cannot simply choose how we feel. Nor can we typically just 'pull ourselves together' when strong feelings threaten to overwhelm us. Feelings can become habitual, tied by association to places, memories, people, activities or events, and in these ways are beyond our control as individuals. In this sense, they are like memories, since we cannot choose precisely what we remember. More crucially still, nor can we choose what we will forget. The past continuously 'gnaws into the present' (as Bergson (1908/1991) put it), and this is likely to be especially the case for memories that are traumatic, shaming or otherwise difficult. And, while their influence is often downplayed in psychology, environments and resources also contribute to meaning. What it means to go without food for an evening will be very different if you have simply forgotten to shop and all the shops are now closed than if you are on benefits and cannot shop because you have no money.

All this shows how meaning is never simply created by individuals. The PTMF does not posit the existence of deviant individuals who persist in producing dysfunctional meanings – for example, because of their (presumed) cognitive deficiencies or biases. Meaning is certainly a personal and, in many ways, private accomplishment. At the same time, the ways in which its different sources arise and come together are mostly not just a matter of individual choice. Put another way, individuals actively make meaning, but they don't do so in circumstances of their own choosing, and nor do they do so with free and equal access to relevant resources.

## Biology

There is no evidence that distress is the outcome of biological illness, disease or aberration (there are no biomarkers). However, this does not mean that the PTMF ignores biology. Instead, the PTMF understands biology in relation to the power imbalances, meanings, threats and responses that form the core of the framework.

From a diagnostic perspective, there is a largely unidirectional and determinate relationship between biology and distress. To illustrate, consider the example of social inequality – a widespread adversity, linked to many forms of distress. Yet by no means everyone exposed to social inequality experiences clinically relevant distress as a consequence. Diagnosis explains this on the basis that the minority who experience distress do so because they also have (hypothetical) biological aberrations. So influence flows from biology to distress – it is unidirectional. At the same time, it is the presumed presence of these biological aberrations that determines who, among the many people exposed to social inequality, experience distress: biology is determinate.

By contrast, the PTMF identifies seven different evidence-based ways of understanding the relationship between biology and distress, none of which depend on hypothetical biological aberrations to determine when distress will occur. While this multiplicity is conceptually difficult to reconcile with the diagnostic model, within the PTMF it is an aspect of the 'everythings' problems outlined above. I will return to this issue below.

The PTMF also summarises the 'lifelines' model of biology formulated by neuroscientist Steven Rose (2005). This process-oriented, dynamic-systems account of gene–environment relations and biological activity is offered as a potential means whereby evidence from biological research can be integrated with findings from social science and psychology to create thoroughly psycho-bio-social explanations of distress. The PTMF illustrates this with a substantial discussion of some of the evidence concerning possible associations between trauma, abuse, distress and biological and neural changes.

The PTMF understands the relationship between biology and distress as primarily one of mediating or enabling. Biological systems are necessary for distress to occur, since they are necessary for all experiences; thus, biology and its potentials are integral to the PTMF. But, rather than (presumed) aberrations being the cause of distress, these biological systems are primarily seen as making distress (and every other kind of experience) possible. We have biological capacities that make it possible for us to feel and to remember. These capacities are immensely valuable, helping us form and monitor relationships and make and orient ourselves toward meaningful plans. Depending on what happens to us, though, these same capacities make it possible to be overwhelmed by feeling, crushed by shaming memories, or disturbed by terrifying flashbacks. Likewise, we have the biological capacity to acquire and use 'inner speech' – the silent self-talk we use to monitor and guide our own activity. But this same capacity can be transformed by traumatic events and adversities so that our self-talk is experienced as coming from someone else: in other words, we hear voices.

This why the PTMF says that threat responses are both evolved and acquired. They are evolved in the sense that they are made possible by biological systems that, over evolutionary time, have become part of our species-nature. And they are acquired in the sense that, in the face of adversity, these systems can be primed or activated in particular ways shaped by our culture, past history and current circumstances and resources. As a result, what were initially purposive adaptations to toxic combinations of adverse circumstances can eventually come to be experienced as bizarre, maladaptive or self-defeating.

## Causality

So the PTMF retains a significant role for biology. At the same time, it removes from biology the false promise of determinate causality – a promise that more than 60 years of relatively well-funded and increasingly technologically enabled research has failed to fulfil. Instead, the PTMF identifies multiple ways of understanding the relation of biology and distress, using a dynamic, process model to relate biological research to evidence from psychology, social science, epidemiology and other relevant fields.

As we have seen, though, this leads to the 'everythings' problems. While epidemiologically it is clear that distress is stratified according to sociological variables such as gender, ethnicity and socio-economic status, it remains impossible to predict in advance the impact of these variables for a given individual. So, in place of the unidirectional, determinate causality upon which diagnosis largely depends, we need a more sophisticated notion. The PTMF describes how causality in distress is contingent and – sometimes – synergistic.

Contingent means that every causal influence is mediated by what are, typically, a whole array of other factors. This contingent notion of causality has actually already been invoked in this chapter, in discussing how differences in meaning mediate between threats and responses. Putting this another way, responses are contingent on the meaning of threats, and not on the threats per se. To explain this more fully, it will help to return to the example of social inequality.

On balance, social inequality makes distress and troubling behaviour more likely among poorer people. Although it is by no means the only adversity that people commonly face, it is widespread and pervasive. But different people do not experience 'the same' level of social inequality in exactly the same ways, and not all become distressed as a result. We cannot predict individual distress from this epidemiological finding.

For functional diagnosis, this is because those who get distressed supposedly have biological aberrations that make them more vulnerable. For the PTMF, this is because the effects of inequality can be ameliorated by many other factors. These include such things as the presence of a trusted confidant; the degrees of love, reassurance and support that family members are able to bestow, and the specific ways in which the threats posed by inequality arise

– for example, their predictability. Conversely, there are other influences that can exacerbate the effects of threats posed by social inequality, so making distress more likely. Most obviously – and most damagingly – these include the simultaneous presence of other threats. They also include factors such as early developmental stage; the absence of close, supportive relationships, and the extent to which threats give rise to a sense of being trapped, betrayed or violated. So, the extent to which social inequality causes distress for a specific individual is contingent on the precise ways that combinations of other causal influences come together in their lives, along with other exacerbating and ameliorating factors.

Causality is also described by the PTMF as synergistic. This means that, as different causal influences come together, their effects can magnify each other. For example, the effects of childhood abuse can be magnified by poverty. Being poorer tends to mean experiencing more social isolation, having fewer opportunities to escape to other environments, and – where abuse takes place in the home – living in smaller, more cramped accommodation. All of these effects of poverty can serve to make contact with the abuser more frequent, more sustained and more intimate. And these qualities, in their turn, will tend to make the effects of the abuse more damaging.

So, the 'everythings' problems reflect the real nature of the multiple causal processes and exacerbating and ameliorating factors that are actually involved in distress. These processes are simultaneously psychological, biological and social. Their contingent and sometimes synergistic intersections mean that, at the individual level, it is impossible to predict with certainty what precise impact adversity will have. Childhood abuse is a risk factor for all forms of distress, but many people who are abused do not have mental health problems. Poverty, discrimination and marginalisation are all risk factors for distress, but again many people exposed to them do not experience clinically significant distress. Using this more sophisticated understanding of causality, the PTMF explains this variation without having to invoke the hypothetical and unproven biological aberrations upon which diagnosis depends.

## Patterns

By addressing the 'everythings' problems, the PTMF establishes a conceptual basis for the identification of patterns of, or regularities in, distress. These patterns emerge not because some people are the bearers of pathologies or aberrations but because our broadly similar biological capacities intersect with power relations and threats that, to some extent, are shared with others. As general embodied capacities intersect with threats distributed by unequal power relations, typical response patterns tend to emerge. However, these patterns are *not* one-to-one replacements for functional psychiatric diagnoses, since they differ from diagnosis in a number of important ways.

First, the patterns do not describe (supposed) illnesses – they describe phenomenological-behavioural efforts to protect, adapt, endure, survive or thrive in the face of adverse circumstances and events. They are things that people find themselves doing, rather than illnesses or conditions they are presumed to have. Second, the threat responses that characterise them (which psychiatry mostly calls symptoms) are understood in terms of the functions they serve: they are patterns of 'embodied, meaning-based threat responses to the negative operation of power' (Johnstone & Boyle 2018b: 10). Third, unlike psychiatric diagnoses, the patterns are not understood as wholly discrete entities: they can be better characterised as modal forms – as 'on average' or typical ways of dealing with particular kinds of threats. This means that their boundaries are necessarily somewhat fuzzy and variable. Fourth, unlike diagnosis, the patterns explicitly locate distress in culture (and therefore history). This is because culture contributes to meaning, and meaning mediates and is permeated by power, threats and responses to them. Fifth, the patterns are described as provisional: there is no expectation that they will remain unchanged, or that they can simply transfer to other cultures. Rather, the PTMF predicts that they will change over time, and that they will vary between cultures. And sixth, the patterns are not presumed to be exclusive to people experiencing clinically significant distress: in attenuated forms, they are present as possible responses to threats among the population more generally.

The PTMF describes a 'foundational pattern' relating power, threat, meaning and threat responses. It then identifies seven provisional general patterns, with titles such as 'surviving rejection, entrapment and invalidation', and 'surviving single threats'. Each describes the typical configurations of meaning, threat and response that might be seen among people facing these particular kinds of challenge. In this way, the PTMF begins to provide a basis for helping people understand their own distress; for clinicians to identify appropriate interventions; for service planners to predict levels of need, and for researchers to explore the character of distress in ways that accurately reflect its origins and character.

## What is the evidence that it helps?

As noted above, the PTMF is a meta-framework that draws on a very wide range of theory, practice and evidence. Much of this is very solidly evidenced – for example, the extensive research supporting the causal role of social factors in distress and the personal impacts of early trauma and adversities.

The impact of the framework itself as a particular way of organising this material is harder to quantify, given that at the time of writing it is less than a year since the PTMF was published. As with any new conceptual model, the PTMF needs to be evaluated in terms of the changes that it implies, so that these in turn can feed back into further development of the perspective. This in itself is complicated, given that the PTMF is a meta-framework, a conceptual tool, a new way of understanding distress. It is not a specific intervention, way of working, service model or research agenda – even though it has potential implications for all of these. Evidence for its helpfulness as an organising framework thus needs to be gathered from a range of sources, both direct and indirect, with a particular focus on service user experiences. The PTMF itself suggests a range of non-diagnostically based research strategies that may be appropriate for these purposes. These could include (but are not limited to) studies of specific experiences (eg. 'hearing voices') linked to biographical and circumstantial information, network analyses of complaints and experiences, use of individually-tailored outcomes in therapeutic outcome research, service user and survivor-led projects (possibly under the aegis of Mad Studies), and the use of narrative methodologies (Johnstone & Boyle 2018a: 308–313).

That said, there is no doubt that the PTMF has already had a striking impact, and this looks set to continue. It is being included in clinical psychology, nursing and social work training courses; it has been particularly strongly welcomed by the British Association of Social Workers, and it has already been incorporated into some social work training and nurse education programmes. In addition to clinical psychology, there has been considerable interest in the PTMF from psychologists and others working in prisons, forensic services and the criminal justice system. The author team has been pleased to hear about the many ways in which the PTMF is starting to influence research projects, clinical practice, charitable organisations and peer support work. A special issue of the practitioner journal *Clinical Psychology Forum* (313, January 2019) describes some of the initial ways that the framework is already being taken up and used in teacher education and social work training, as well as in clinical work with specific populations, including prisoners, young people, and people with intellectual disabilities who have been given autism diagnoses.

## Future directions

The PTMF's influence seems likely to continue and accelerate over the coming years. Again, because it is a meta-framework, the influence of PTMF will necessarily be more diffuse and global than that of a specific intervention. Its primary strength may be its status as a resource that sets out, for the first time, a coherent alternative to functional diagnosis that can be used in services and research to guide practice, formulate hypotheses and develop new ways of working. In this way, it aims to support existing good practice as well as promote new ways forward. As this occurs, the inseparable links the framework makes between power, threat and meaning – and between psychology, biology and social science – should prevent it from easily being co-opted into, or assimilated by, diagnostic ways of thinking and working, although of course this is always a risk.

## Critical perspective

While the PTMF's reception has for the most part been overwhelmingly positive, there has inevitably been some criticism, particularly on social media. Although it is tempting to imagine that all of the critics would be psychiatrists, and all advocates psychologists, the picture has been more complex. Some psychiatrists (and others, such as psychiatric nurses) have very much welcomed the PTMF, including many associated with the Critical Psychiatry Network. Conversely, a handful of psychologists, some of whom have built their careers on research and interventions based on diagnostic categories, have critiqued the framework. More surprisingly, perhaps, a small number of mental health service users have also been critical. Many of these latter criticisms appear to be driven by the wholly understandable fear that, if psychiatric diagnosis is declared invalid, service users might lose their already scant welfare benefits and access to services (see, for example, Anonymous, 2018).

To the great extent that the PTMF is mostly troubling the right people – those who endorse psychiatric diagnosis and its associated practices – criticism could be taken as an inverse marker of success. More constructively, the author team has attended and organised a great many training events, conferences and invitations to speak about the framework: at the time of writing, this includes events in Denmark, Greece, Ireland, New Zealand and Australia, as well as numerous events all over the UK. In this regard, it is relevant too that the PTMF is explicitly presented as a work in progress – a first attempt at producing a more accurate and more helpful way of conceptualising distress than the diagnostic model. Consequently, some aspects of the framework may be revised or clarified as it gets taken up by practitioners and applied by service users.

For example, the framework documents may not describe all of the possible causal influences and exacerbating or ameliorating factors likely to be involved in distress. Evidence is supplied for those that are discussed, and it is probable that all of the influences currently most important in Western culture are included. Nevertheless, the framework remains open to the identification of others, including from other cultures and those that might be important only in specific contexts.

Likewise, the discussion of power does not engage at length with every possible way in which power can be abused or is unequal. The power of psychology itself, for example, is considered in relation to both positivism and neoliberalism, but is not addressed as a separate topic – although the framework remains both conceptually and practically open to its inclusion and critique (as it is to the inclusion and critique of other powers). Similarly, the patterns in distress that the PTMF identifies are explicitly described as provisional, in recognition 1) of their modal or 'on average' character, and 2) that research and application are likely to refine and further elaborate the connections between power, threats, meanings and responses that they begin to specify.

The PTMF is a fundamentally open, dynamic and systemic meta-framework that locates distress in culture, history, circumstances and biographies at the same time as it recognises how distress is mediated and enabled by biological capacities. It eschews the overly simplistic false certainties of the unproven functional psychiatric model, and instead attempts to recognise and account for the messiness and uncertainty of distress as it actually gets produced and lived. As a result, it is also unable to benefit from the ways in which diagnosis has become part of many people's everyday understanding. Inevitably, this means that the PTMF can seem in some ways more complex, or less immediately accessible, than functional diagnosis. This too may be a source of criticism.

In truth, though, distress itself is extremely complex. Distress raises a whole series of interlocking concerns that both recruit and cut across different sets of competing needs and interests – personal, relational, societal, medical, economic, moral, ethical, political and more. Comprehensive explanations of distress therefore must not only be interdisciplinary (ranging across disciplines including psychology, the neurosciences, epidemiology and the social sciences); they must also engage with notions of causality, and with critical analyses of theory and evidence. If the diagnostic model were actually adequate to this great complexity – if it provided reliable and valid descriptions that underpinned humane, effective interventions and were the basis of productive research programmes – then significant progress toward resolving distress would have been made by now. That it has not suggests the need for a better explanation, of the kind that the PTMF supplies.

# References

American Psychiatric Association (2013). *Diagnostic and Statistical Manual of Mental Disorders* (5th ed). Washington: APA.

Anonymous (2018). Will the 'Power Threat Meaning Framework' help survivors on welfare? *Asylum 25*(3): 14.

Bergson, H (1908/1991). *Matter and Memory* (NM Paul, WS Palmer, trans). New York, NY: Zone Books.

BPS Division of Clinical Psychology (2013). *Position Statement on the Classification of Behaviour and Experience in Relation to Functional Psychiatric Diagnoses: time for a paradigm shift.* Leicester: BPS Division of Clinical Psychology.

Francesco S (2015). *Overmedicated and Undertreated: how I lost my only son to today's toxic children's mental health industry.* US: Francesco International.

Johnstone L, Boyle M, with Cromby J, Dillon J, Harper D, Kinderman P, Longden E, Pilgrim D, Read J (2018a). *The Power Threat Meaning Framework: towards the identification of patterns in emotional distress, unusual experiences and troubled or troubling behaviour, as an alternative to functional psychiatric diagnosis.* Leicester: British Psychological Society.

Johnstone L, Boyle M, with Cromby J, Dillon J, Harper D, Kinderman P, Longden E, Pilgrim D, Read J (2018b). *The Power Threat Meaning Framework: overview.* Leicester: British Psychological Society.

Kupfer DJ (2013). Chair of DSM-5 Task Force discusses future of mental health research. *Mad in America*; 3 May. www.madinamerica.com/wp-content/uploads/2013/05/Statement-from-dsm-chair-david-kupfer-md.pdf (accessed 16 August 2019).

Rose S (2005). *Lifelines: life beyond the gene* (fully revised edition). London: Vintage.

World Health Organization (2018). *International Classification of Diseases* (11th revision). Geneva: WHO.

# Chapter 16

# Truth and reconciliation: a radical approach to challenging mental health systems

## Mick McKeown and Helen Spandler

The history of mental health service provision is permeated through and through with state-sanctioned violence and coercive practices. Mental health seems to be the sole area where the medical imperative to 'do no harm' is knowingly flouted and systemic abrogation of human rights is disguised as professional expertise and medical best practice. In recent decades, despite an avowed commitment on the part of statutory mental health systems to user involvement and consultation, coercive practices may even be on the rise (Care Quality Commission, 2018).

We would like to see ways of acknowledging the profound harms that occur in mental health systems. We think this is necessary before those needing care and those charged with providing it can work constructively together to face these systemic problems and begin to imagine, and even realise, sustainable alternatives. Perhaps an effective starting point for healing the hurt experienced in the system is for those of us involved in providing care and treatment to honestly own up to our part in enacting or maintaining harmful systems. This might move towards improved relationships between providers and recipients that, we argue, are necessary not only for effective services but also for the co-operation and alliance-building necessary for wider social change.

Therefore, this chapter builds on previous arguments for supporting a process of truth and reconciliation in mental health services (Slade, 2009; Wallcraft & Shulkes, 2012; Spandler & McKeown, 2017a, 2017b). Truth and reconciliation initiatives have been enacted on a national scale in other contexts as a reparative approach to healing enduring division and conflict. Examples include the Rwandan conflict and South Africa, following the dismantling of the apartheid regime. On a smaller scale, a more grassroots approach has been applied with some success at city or neighbourhood levels – for example, to address divisive, sectarian, ethnic or place-based social problems, including hate crime and adverse policing practices. Both large- and small-scale approaches have been advocated for mental health systems, and have been tried in some jurisdictions, albeit mainly with a focus on the past rather than the present.

We have a particular interest in the contribution such an approach might offer to what we believe are the necessary efforts to build solidarity between survivors, service users and refusers of psychiatric care and the workers in such services. Together, we have been involved in making the case for constructive alliances between these constituencies, including engaging in activism within trade unions, being allies to organised service user and survivor groups, and supporting the radical mental health magazine *Asylum*, and radical groups of professionals such as the Critical Mental Health Nurses' Network.

In this chapter we argue the case for building a grassroots model of truth and reconciliation, anticipate some of the material and political benefits, face up to salient criticisms, and imagine future sites of activism that might benefit from a foundation in truth-telling, healing and reconciliation. This is largely an appeal directed at staff, but we believe that the value of such an approach could be applied in other mental health constituencies, especially service users, refusers and survivors. It would be naïve to expect services to change or to influence the majority of practitioners by merely presenting a one-sided litany of criticisms and failing to attend to the complexities of providing mental health care within contemporary political and economic realities. Therefore, we reflect on some of the complexities of implementing a truth and reconciliation approach in this context.

## Why is a process of truth and reconciliation needed?

We believe that a form of truth and reconciliation is needed to begin to address the abundance of harms and hurtful outcomes that arise within organised mental health care systems. The character of these services has been overly coercive and restrictive and is arguably increasingly so. Coercive and restrictive practices clearly have a number of adverse consequences for service users, resulting in many choosing to refer to themselves as survivors, and others to refuse to make use of services at all. At least in part, the conception of trauma-informed care is driven by recognition of the traumatising and re-traumatising impacts of aspects of mental health services. This can be so much the case that such services have been referred to as to as 'trauma-organised systems' (Bloom & Farragher, 2010; Sweeney et al, 2016).

Routinely occurring practices within services such as forced medication, physical restraint and seclusion are the most noticeable (Cusack et al, 2018; Frueh et al, 2005; McKeown et al, 2019), but there are also everyday subtle actions that reinforce powerlessness, restrict liberty or urge compliance with treatment (Bloom & Farragher, 2010). For example, patterns of medication prescribing are often unsupported by clear-cut evidence, and evidence suggests they precipitate long-term health damage (Whitaker, 2002; Moncrieff, 2013). For critics of the psychiatric system, such treatments are identified as psychiatric harm or 'iatrogenesis' (Breggin, 1991) and are bound up with a system that legitimates epistemic injustice, control and exclusion of people with mental health struggles (Crichton, Carel & Kidd, 2017; Liegghio, 2013). In other words, mental health laws and systems marginalise the individual and collective experiential knowledge of mental health system survivors.

The traumatising effects of mental health systems are cause for particular concern in light of increasing evidence connecting adverse childhood experiences and subsequent mental health problems (Felitti et al, 1998; Varese et al, 2012). In the extreme, patients have been physically and sexually assaulted while under the supposed care of services, including on inpatient wards (Henderson & Reveley, 1996). Moreover, patients who have reported abuse within the system have been disbelieved and silenced (Jennings, 2016; Masson, 1988). In a perverse confirmation of psychiatric logic, victims' reactions to such abuse can be pathologised as symptoms, most commonly as 'borderline personality disorder' (*Asylum*, 2004; Recovery in The Bin, 2016). Even in circumstances where disclosure of abuse is taken seriously, services are poorly set up to provide an appropriately skilled or compassionate therapeutic response (Read, Sampson & Critchley, 2016; Sweeney et al, 2016).

The harmful effects of psychiatric care are not limited to service users; they extend to staff, with many being both physically and psychologically hurt in their roles, not least through operating coercive practices. Stress-related work absences are high among health professional groups (Health & Safety Executive, 2016), and notably among those working in mental health settings (see, for example, O'Connor et al, 2018). For mental health staff, the sources of job stress can include lack of resources and staffing, exacerbated by austerity-driven public service cuts, which can in turn predicate more reliance on coercive practices (McKeown & Foley, 2015). Staff may also become alienated in their work because of concerns over patient welfare, vicarious trauma, or their own vulnerability to violence (Figley, 1995; Rössler, 2012; Sabin-Farrell & Turpin, 2003). Unfortunately, whistleblowing staff who recognise service failings often find themselves victimised by the very system they are seeking to improve (Jackson et al, 2014).

## Does truth and reconciliation work?

Processes of truth and reconciliation usually involve some sort of collective gathering that allows for respectful attention to testimony and dialogue aimed at restorative rather than retributive justice. These forms of transitional justice are as much about forming new, respectful relations between people as repairing wrongdoing and harm. They start from an optimistic view of humanity and the potential for progressive change (Seidel & Abu-Nimer, 2015). Creating sufficient space for personal testimony to be heard and attended to can be the engine for healing, recognition, compassion, community building, consciousness raising and, ultimately, accountability. Public communication of private pain is seen as key to translating the 'personal experiences of victims into a far deeper statement of *collective* suffering and injustice' (Rose, 2015: 71).

Truth and reconciliation has not been extensively tried in mental health services; evidence for its effectiveness needs to be sought in other contexts. In such settings, there may be a trade-off between the benefits of reconciliation for the wider community, which may be less for individual participants, such as those who give testimony. The most well-known example of the approach is the large-scale South African Truth and Reconciliation Commission, which was established to facilitate healing and lay the foundations for nation building after the dissolution of the apartheid regime (Clark, 2012; Rose, 2015). Perhaps its most notable effect was to inculcate a deep sense of empathy and common humanity and sustain a more compassionate national consciousness (Rose, 2015) within a collective act of 're-humanization' (Androff, 2010: 274). But for individuals, recounting and revisiting traumatic experiences in public may have no such therapeutic benefit and may even add to the distress or sense of violation in victims (Rose, 2015; Stein et al, 2008). Furthermore, survivors may be disappointed if the pace of change is slow, there is no access to compensation, or they feel pressured to 'forgive' perpetrators (Jeffery, 2015). Hence, any such process should be accompanied by sensitive support for those giving testimony, with no insistence on interpersonal forgiveness or disclosure of victimhood (Rose, 2015). In this way, truth and reconciliation processes may move towards a more reciprocal, critical, self-reflective exchange.

Legally sanctioned examples of truth and reconciliation often guarantee amnesty for perpetrators and seek to provide reparations for victims. The quest for reconciliation is typically sought through public apology, 'bearing witness to the past' and 'truth-telling and forgiveness' (Stein et al, 2008: 463). The alternative to such large, national commissions is a grassroots approach at neighbourhood or locality level (Androff, 2010; Inwood, 2012). Androff (2010) argues that truth and reconciliation approaches have shown themselves to be adaptable to application in a range of contexts and circumstances. Indeed, these processes could help redress notable failures in healthcare organisations, such as Stafford Hospital (Francis, 2013) and Winterbourne View (Department of Health, 2012). Following similar reasoning, the NHS has been urged to adopt no-blame investigation systems, with the aim of fostering honest disclosure rather than evasion (Bromiley, 2009). Indeed, Mersey Care NHS Trust, which primarily provides mental health care, has, with the support of trade unions, initiated a 'just and learning' culture that starts from these assumptions.[1] It is thus our view that truth and reconciliation could be translated into mental health services for the mutual benefit of both service users and staff.

## A movement for truth and reconciliation?

Ours is not the first call for a truth and reconciliation process for mental health services. There have been previous persuasive demands for public apologies for psychiatric harm. For example, a case for truth and reconciliation has been made by advocates for recovery-oriented systems (Slade, 2009) and survivor activists (Harris, 2014; Wallcraft, 2010; Wallcraft & Shulkes, 2012). Slade (2009) points out that ideals of 'partnership' in mental health care may be meaningless without service providers first apologising for their noted failings.

The Canadian survivor magazine *Our Voice (Notre Voix)* has featured demands for a public apology (LeBlanc, 2016). In the UK, the survivor activist Jan Wallcraft initiated a petition, drawing on the UN Convention of the Rights of Persons with Disabilities (CRPD), to call for official international apologies and reparations in the form of specific demands, including the repeal of discriminatory forced-treatment legislation and the establishment of alternative, non-coercive services, such as user-led or Soteria crisis houses.[2]

Psychiatrists and governments have usually fallen short of apologising for general care and treatment wrongs committed by the profession. Psychiatrists have, however, offered expert testimony in truth and reconciliation processes in some national contexts. However, these have focused on the negative experiences of, for example, indigenous populations at the hands of colonial and post-colonial systems, rather than directly on psychiatry (eg. van Rensberg, 2015). Where psychiatry itself has been the focus, truth and reconciliation has typically been applied retrospectively – for example, to make reparative efforts for the profession's complicity in Nazi abuses (Wallcraft & Shulkes, 2012); the

1.  www.merseycare.nhs.uk/about-us/just-and-learning-culture-what-it-means-for-mersey-care/just-and-learning-culture-our-journey (accessed 17 August 2019).

2. www.ipetitions.com/petition/truth_and_reconciliation_in_psychiatry (accessed 17 August 2019).

use of aversion therapy to 'treat' homosexuality in the UK (Carr & Spandler, 2019), or historical aspects of care in New Zealand (Department of Internal Affairs, 2007; Kavanagh-Hall, 2013).

## A practical grassroots approach

Formal truth and reconciliation commissions are usually set up when there have been notable gains made by oppressed groups and significant shifts in power relationships and social structures. This has yet to happen to any significant degree in relation to mental health system survivors. As such, public apologies for systematic wrongdoing in mental health systems are unlikely to be forthcoming in the near future, as contemporary services continue to be challenged for violating human rights. Therefore, we propose that a grassroots approach to truth and reconciliation may be best suited. Indeed, in the absence of formal apologies and commissions in other fields, some grassroots organisations have explored 'bottom-up' approaches to transitional justice and reconciliation, acknowledging past experiences of harm amid discussions about challenging contentious issues in the present (see, for example, in relation to racism, abortion and LGTB rights, Inwood & Alderman 2016; Inwood, 2012).

These smaller-scale, local initiatives also carefully consider issues such as setting, inclusion and the discursive and dialogic means by which apology, truth-telling, listening, healing and alliance-building might be best advanced. These approaches concern themselves with creating particular spaces conducive to supporting and sustaining forms of dialogue appropriate to the healing task in hand. For the advocates of such spaces, these communication practices exist externally to the regime of contention, such as psychiatry, and are essential to underpin action for change:

> One of the first keys in justice activism is getting participants to sit down with one another to engage fully in a process that can create the conditions necessary for organising work to occur. (Inwood & Alderman, 2016: 59)

There have been a few examples in the mental health context. For example, a number of grassroots organisations in the US, including *Rethinking Psychiatry* and the *Icarus Project* came together to convene a series of truth and reconciliation events in reaction to the negative experiences of many survivors and service users in mental health services (Levy, 2016a; 2016b). This initiative was inspired by varied experiences, including lessons learnt from other politically divisive issues where antagonistic standpoints have typically been advanced (eg. abortion, LGBT rights). Indeed, one of the organisers had previously been involved in truth and reconciliation initiatives in other contexts. Practices used by community traditions of indigenous peoples were used, such as 'healing circles' (Androff, 2010). The organisers also took into account progressive modern developments in mental health services, especially those that foreground the importance of communicative dialogue in healing distress, such as the Open Dialogue approach (Seikkula & Arnkil, 2013).

Healing circles are methods used to create an enabling space that is open to hearing previously ignored, neglected or silenced voices, such as stories of harm that aren't usually voiced, heard or shared. Seating is arranged in two concentric circles, with the chairs in the inner and outer circles facing each other. Participants are allocated to the circles according to whether they identify as staff or survivor/service user (they can, in theory, be in either at different times). Then the people in each circle take turns to listen attentively and respectfully to the other's stories of experiences within the system, taking care to allow full airing of these narratives without interruption – that is, without argument, justification or contention. This is followed by time for questions, clarification and discussion.

The experiences in these healing circles reveal some of the mutual and reciprocal value of a restorative approach. Care is taken to respectfully attend to all stories, whether they are palatable, agreeable or not. Even though the starting point is people's experiences of harm within the psychiatric system, there is also space for participants to identify valued and appreciated aspects of help and support within the system. They can also attend to the accounts of those who have experienced harm from people with mental health problems – narratives that are seldom heard without being framed as sensationalised stories of dangerous madness.

Participants are able to be involved in a process of genuine dialogue. The impacts may be small but perhaps represent more profound shifts in consciousness, involving, at the very least, a raised awareness of the experiences of others. Staff participants reported changing their practice in regard to informing people about medication, moving away from the simplistic orthodoxy of promoting psychotropic prescriptions as 'just like' medication for physical illnesses towards offering more honest, balanced information. While such examples do not represent wide-scale change, these small steps could lead to more significant and long-lasting changes over time.

## Building alliances from the start

We have attempted to build interest in the idea of truth and reconciliation in mental health care by discussing it in a variety of settings with different audiences. We have brought the ideas presented in this chapter to meetings of practising and academic nurses and social workers, mixed groups of critically minded practitioners and service users, such as the Annual Critical Perspectives Conference at University College Cork and trade union delegate conferences, such as Unison's annual health care service group conference. We have also engaged in discussions with local-level, grassroots activist groups and union branches, and posted blogs on relevant critical sites (Spandler, 2016), including the Critical Mental Health Nurses' Network.[3]

For example, with the support of Unison's national Nursing Sector Committee, and in conjunction with the survivor activist Jan Wallcraft, we hosted a fringe meeting at the 2017 Unison Health Conference. Beforehand, we had some anxieties that the idea might receive a hostile reception from some quarters in the union, or that the debate might take an antagonistic or defensive turn. All things considered, the actual event went well and the truth and reconciliation idea was, we believe, respectfully attended to and given a more-than-fair hearing. Questions and contributions from the delegates demonstrated that there was some interest in the idea, but perhaps less understanding about how to make it work in practice. There were also individual acknowledgements and understanding of the harms caused by aspects of mental health services. Subsequent feedback suggests that the audience for this fringe meeting was appreciative of having the opportunity to get to grips with a contentious idea. At least one delegate told the Nursing Sector Committee that it was the best such event they had been to at a Unison conference. Before we get carried away with this largely positive experience, it is worth noting that the event was attended by around 70 delegates – not at all bad for a fringe meeting at this event, but this was out of more than 1,000 delegates and visitors to the conference.

Up to now, we have largely focused on attempting to persuade constituencies of workers and trade unionists of the potential value of truth and reconciliation. This is due to a number of factors. First, we are more able to reach these groups because of our academic and trade union roles. Second, and perhaps the flip side of the first point, we do not claim a service user or survivor identity, so do not believe it is correct for us to target this constituency for persuasion. Preferably, if service users, survivors and refusers are taken with the idea (and, after all, it was as a user-led initiative that it first caught our attention), then better placed activists can advance and shape the idea within their own movements. Third, we believe that, because the majority

3.  https://criticalmhnursing.org/2018/03/29/bread-and-roses-activist-imaginings-for-the-future-of-mental-health-nursing/#more-1374  (accessed 17 August 2019).

of harm within the system is brought about by staff and staff complicity with its subtler forms, then staff should be in the vanguard of organising opportunities for healing, including beginning with an apology. To a large extent, workers in the system need to make the first move, and this needs to be associated with a credible demonstration that such moves are made in good faith. We have taken up this point in other arguments for solidarity alliances between trade unionists and survivor activists (McKeown, Cresswell & Spandler, 2014), so naturally extend this thinking to the organising task of truth and reconciliation.

Various social media posts or tweets in response to writings about the idea of truth and reconciliation in the mental health context demonstrate the importance of staff making the first move. Much of this online discourse reflects scepticism about staff motivations or disbelief that mental health workers, especially psychiatrists, are capable of, possess the necessary insights or are indeed in any way willing to apologise for their role or to listen and learn from service users' narratives of hurt at the hands of the system. Indeed, on many occasions, to identify oneself as a mental health practitioner within certain critical survivor twitter streams is to invite ridicule and questioning of the veracity of any claimed commitments to alliance or solidarity. For us, this reinforces the potential value of truth and reconciliation and taking proper care over the communicative process therein, rather than undermining or negating this. Nevertheless, the extensiveness and degree of antagonisms and hurts suggests that organising for truth and reconciliation will be difficult, and in our view further strengthens the case for bottom-up, grassroots initiatives rather than top-down approaches, which may be even more distrusted.

The editors of a new critical mental health nursing book, Stephen Williams, Jonathan Gadsby and Pete Bull (2018: ii), have taken on board the importance of acknowledging collective responsibilities, publishing an apology for 'the many historical and present ways in which mental health nurses in general have contributed to ... distress and disempowerment'.

This offering has been well-received and reviewed, with particular appreciation for the apology:

> As a mental health nurse, the introduction and apology get to the heart of the matter, if not the mind. All of what [mental health nurses] do is tinged with coercion; whether with people on locked wards or those in their own home. The list of what mental health nurses are party to is a long one and makes difficult reading. (Jones, 2019: 1)

Yet, not all mental health nurses are ready for such an apology, and even some who acknowledge shortcomings within the system have said this is a step too far, or accuse the authors of a form of arrogant omnipresence to presume to speak on behalf of all nurses (personal communication). Again, we feel that this sort of disputation furthers the case for truth and reconciliation, rather than hinders it. One nurse's humility may be another's arrogance, but this clearly, in our view, needs to be unpacked and debated, civilly and democratically, with the hope of greater understanding and appreciation of different viewpoints. We are optimistic that people who would willingly engage in such a project would be open-minded enough to accept there is much still to learn on all sides.

Moreover, alliances between workers and mental health system survivors are certainly not the only route to progressive change. While we have primarily focused on the use of truth and reconciliation in relation to mental health workers and service users/survivors, there is no reason why similar processes could not be used with other related constituencies where related fault lines have opened up. For example, they could apply with service users/survivors, family members and so-called carers, and between survivors and activists who may take different, even radically opposing positions in relation to mental health care. However deployed, it would be foolish to assume that truth and reconciliation offers any easy solution to the abject failures of mental health services and the harms visited upon those within them. Therefore, the next section outlines some potential difficulties with this approach.

## Facing up to the complexities of truth and reconciliation

During the last few years when we have been actively promoting this idea, we have encountered several legitimate concerns. We take this opportunity to reflect on these here. While largely supportive of the idea, Carr and Taggart (2017) note a lack of service user involvement in its active promotion. While we have heard some calls for a truth and reconciliation process from individual service user activists, we acknowledge that this hasn't been taken up by organised service-user groups. When it has been, discussion has largely focused on the demand for wholesale apologies from governments or psychiatry, which certainly seems unlikely at the present time. Without a good section of the survivor community on board with this idea, it is unlikely to progress. This lack of engagement may relate to the other issues raised.

Carr and Taggart (2017) are also concerned about our highlighting the harm experienced by staff as well as service users. They suggest that our case for truth and reconciliation, while appropriately attending to interpersonal harms, neglects structural injustices that are writ large within psychiatry, with staff having much more access to power within the system. Moreover, they argue, staff have a 'choice to work [in services], [are] not subject to containment and compulsion, and [can] leave the hospital at the end of the working day' (Carr & Taggart, 2017: 1). They point out that, without recognising these important structural inequalities, a focus on truth and reconciliation can arguably mean that both staff and service users can claim that they are 'victims' of the system. This, they argue, is one of the reasons that a truth and reconciliation process has been less successful in Northern Ireland, as both Nationalists and Unionists felt some claim to victimhood.

This important point suggests that truth and reconciliation can be especially difficult in contexts where issues of power and victimhood are still highly contested and unresolved. This is certainly still the case in mental health services. While we suggest that these very issues could be helpfully reflected on in a truth and reconciliation context, we agree that, without careful and skilful facilitation, these processes could merely exacerbate underlying tensions, rather than resolve them.

Russo (2017: 19) raises a related objection. She suggests that our calls could merely reinforce the focus on staff and service users' 'roles' within the system, without an appreciation of the serious power imbalances and potential conflicts of interest between 'those whose job is to provide care and those who receive it'. Moreover, she highlights the potential problem of a process that seems to invite a focus on resolving service users' (assumed) 'hurt' within the system and their need for healing, rather than on resolving systemic failings. These systemic failings, she suggests, may relate to the assumed need for these distinct 'staff' and 'service user' roles in the first place. In turn, this could result in a one-sided focus on the emotional 'hurt' of survivors and service users, rather than revealing any accompanying emotions or motivations of staff.

Russo warns against any truth and reconciliation process being led by mental health professionals, lest it merely reproduce, rather than acknowledge and understand, the impact of power differences in the system. We would suggest that, by focusing on staff as well as service user hurt, the truth and reconciliation process could actually begin to break down staff/service user distinctions by revealing shared, if unequally distributed, hurt and harms. This might help us begin to move away from current unhelpful systems and begin to forge different kinds of communications and relationships, based on a shared humanity. This clearly requires a willingness of the part of staff *and* service users to fully engage in this process, rather than the onus being on service users and survivors.

Cresswell (2017) highlights several objections to our case for truth and reconciliation, which we will consider in detail here. First, he suggests that our call for truth and reconciliation rests on the assumption that mental health care is an example of a human rights abuse and questions whether psychiatric harm is equivalent to other human rights abuses. This is another fair point. Indeed, not all service users are antipathetic to mental health care systems, including aspects of compulsion and coercion (Katsakou et al, 2012). Simply framing these as human rights violations may be problematic as it glosses over the immense complexities of providing support to people in potentially life-threatening situations who may refuse intervention (Plumb, 2015). Arguably, this makes mental health systems tangibly different to more straightforwardly oppressive regimes like apartheid. However, while mental health services might not be a monolithic system of harm, there are plenty of current objections to psychiatric practice, and plenty of examples of injustice and harm, both historical and contemporary. There are enough, we suggest, to warrant a process to attempt to understand and acknowledge the harmful aspects of the system. Moreover, it might help us to understand the similarities *and* differences between psychiatric harm and other systems of oppression.

Cresswell's second point is that the proposed grassroots approach would not have the legitimacy of a more formal, legalistic process and thus would risk failing to engage participants. Indeed, it may be that service users and survivors are put off by the informality of grassroots approaches, fearing a lack of authority and legitimacy to influence real change. But it could also be the case that a less formal, voluntary engagement would be facilitated by the sorts of bottom-up approaches we advocate, and that, by avoiding top-down imposition, they could equally work to promote engagement. In addition, because truth and reconciliation is presented as a form of transitional justice, it may act as a necessary stepping stone to eventually realising more formal sanctions or restitution.

Cresswell's next objection is that any truth and reconciliation process would likely be merely 'preaching to the converted'. In other words, it would involve staff who are already critically minded and would fail to engage staff who might gain most from the process in terms of learning and shifting perspective, or place the least blameworthy staff in the front line of criticism. The point about only engaging those who are already critically minded is a fair one. However, we note that most progressive initiatives for social change begin with more engaged activists for social change, who are then able to bring in more participants from wider constituencies. Moreover, it is worth saying that implicit in this critique is a misunderstanding of the essence of truth and reconciliation, which is as much about listening and learning from each other as 'preaching' to the converted. As we have suggested, the privileging of dialogue, rather than monologue, both contrasts with the undemocratic character of the forms of psychiatry most objected to and opens up unique possibilities for mutual learning. It doesn't assume that any particular expert (by profession or even by experience) contains the 'correct position' or the final word about mental suffering, or indeed mental health services.

Cresswell's fourth objection is that truth and reconciliation processes orient themselves to consensus rather than disagreement, debate and contestation. Cresswell suggests that this fundamentally ignores an important element of democracy: namely, that the working out of antagonism and conflictual positions is an important driver of democratic action and motivator for seeking progressive change. However, we suggest that truth and reconciliation does not need to proceed on the basis of consensus seeking and that there should be plenty of room for conflicting viewpoints, disagreement and contention. At the same time, we would hope that a more sensitive and deeper understanding of the distress experienced by protagonists is achieved and remedies are considered within an atmosphere of tolerance and respect for difference and diversity. Indeed, it is likely, and desirable in our view, that a successful truth and reconciliation process would allow for the contemplation and imagining of a plurality of alternative approaches for supporting people in mental distress, with no need for everyone to agree with all of them. Instead of working towards unanimity, our ambition for truth and reconciliation is that it can lay the foundations for civil, deliberative democratic relations that would be essential for forging the solidarity required for building effective alliances.

Moreover, making a virtue of antagonistic relationships risks amplifying the harm that underpins a lot of mental health distress, and is surely not in the interests of either staff or service users. Any forum that brings together mental health service staff and service users runs the risk of revisiting the conflictual relationships inherent within psychiatry but also holds the potential for transcending them. Arguably, the reinvention of abusive, conflictual relations within social media discourse, or the equally self-defeating retreat into self-confirmatory or self-congratulatory virtual echo chambers, demonstrates the danger of unmitigated antagonistic standpoints. Effective social movements can be seen to model alternative, democratic, appreciative, anti-oppressive, non-violent communication and decision-making processes. These more deliberative democratic forms are available to us for deployment within truth and reconciliation approaches, and can, if successfully enacted, further build capacity for strengthening activism and organising, rather than undermining them.

Finally, Cresswell suggests that truth and reconciliation may be a waste of activist energies and a distraction from efforts to achieve practical transformational or revolutionary social change. No seeker of transformative change wants to believe they are working against the potential for that change. However, we do not think that working on transitional justice goals and more explicit political activism are necessarily mutually exclusive. Contrary to seeing truth and reconciliation as an alternative to activism, we actually think it may be necessary to it. We feel that truth and reconciliation can assist in feeding into broader activist strategies and thus making them more, not less, effective. Indeed, if activism for a better, fairer society neglects to pay attention to harmful social relations, then they may simply become reinvented within any new care and treatment systems, or indeed any activist movements themselves. In other words, without the foundation of mutual understanding, compassion and cooperation, we are unlikely to be able to replace compulsions and coercions within interpersonal relationships both inside and outside of mental health services.

We think that some of the objections or misgivings attached to truth and reconciliation can be avoided by envisaging smaller-scale, local grass-roots initiatives rather than systemic grand commissions, which in any event are unlikely to be sanctioned by governments or psychiatry. It is hoped that meaningful truth-telling and reconciliation might be better supported at a local level and more readily translate into building movements and alliances that could sustain and expand these practices and benefits throughout the system. In this way, ideally with beneficial consequences being spread incrementally, activist enthusiasm and iteratively fresh troubling of the system and its harmful effects would counter co-option, assimilation and dilution. In addition, any such process would need to be carried out carefully, sensitively and skilfully to avoid reproducing, rather than ameliorating, underlying power dynamics and conflicts. With this in mind, rather than being led by so-called mental health experts, truth and reconciliation is probably best facilitated by people who have considerable experience in working with it in other contexts and settings.

## What next?

Truth and reconciliation is an idea waiting to happen in mental health, and perhaps its time is coming. It is certainly not the only route to progressive social change, but radical change in mental health seems increasingly necessary, yet simultaneously hard to achieve. The required solidarity for sustaining the sort of activist alliances necessary for effective social change will not emerge fully formed from nowhere.

A number of burning issues and associated campaigns are bubbling away, including debates about the best way to combat the wholesale neoliberal assault on public welfare and services and its disproportionate impact on disabled people and people living with mental health problems. Debates about key issues in mental health care such as psychiatric compulsion, diagnosis and medication continue unabated and unresolved. Unfortunately, many service users find themselves caught in a crossfire between rival ideologies and positions. The way these debates are often framed – in binary or oppositional terms – seems to undermine, rather than support, solidarity.

Moreover, the quick-fire responses favoured by new social media technologies do not promote genuine dialogue. We may, indeed, need to reinvent our capacity for respectful, two-way communication that the truth and reconciliation process embodies (Turkle, 2016). After all, it is, at least in part, systemic communication breakdown that results in much mental distress in the first place. Developing grassroots truth and reconciliation forums might start to address the dis-ease that results from our collective neglect of dialogue. Promoting dialogue is especially important in wider settings where debates and discussions around mental health politics (and politics in general) too readily become polarised and monologic, rather than dialogic. A grassroots truth and reconciliation process could be one modest way of creating a more solid basis for solidarity between survivors, workers and other activists. Similarly, recent suggestions that mental health nurses exercise a right to conscientiously object to forced treatment of mental health service users represents another potential catalyst for solidarity.[4]

There is an emerging body of knowledge about how to organise truth and reconciliation, and this needs to be open to further learning and refinement along the way. We recognise this is no panacea. Any grassroots truth and reconciliation process, however successful 'internally', won't necessarily directly feed into policies, resource allocation and service planning. Moreover, any such initiative is likely to be turbulent and unsettling, as we all open ourselves up to 'inconvenient truths'. However, we don't believe that mental health services can be reformed or revolutionised without improving our ways of engaging with disagreement and dissent. After all, communication and engagement must be at the heart of organising effective mental health support. To borrow an organising slogan from the wider labour movement, we ask: 'If not now, when?'

---

4. https://criticalmhnursing.org/2018/09/26/conscientious-objection-from-enforcing-treatment (accessed 17 August 2019).

## References

Androff D (2010). 'To not hate': reconciliation among victims of violence and participants of the Greensboro Truth and Reconciliation Commission. *Contemporary Justice Review 13*: 269–285.

*Asylum* (2004). Special issue: Women at the margins – women and borderline personality disorder. *Asylum 14*(3).

Bloom S, Farragher B (2010). *Destroying Sanctuary: the crisis in human service delivery systems.* New York, NY: Oxford University Press.

Breggin P (1991). *Toxic Psychiatry: why therapy, empathy and love must replace the drugs, electroshock, and biochemical theories of the 'new psychiatry'.* New York, NY: St. Martin's Press.

Bromiley M (2009). Would you speak up if the consultant got it wrong?... and would you listen if someone said you'd got it wrong? *Journal of Perioperative Practice 19*(10): 326–329.

Care Quality Commission (2018). *Mental Health Act: the rise in the use of the MHA to detain people in England.* London: Care Quality Commission.

Carr S, Spandler H (2019). Hidden from history? A brief modern history of the psychiatric 'treatment' of lesbian and bisexual women in England. *Lancet Psychiatry 6*(4): 289–290.

Carr S, Taggart D (2017). *Do We Need a Truth and Reconciliation Process in Psychiatry?* [Blog.] The Mental Elf; 9 August. www.nationalelfservice.net/populations-and-settings/ service-user-involvement/do-we-need-a-truth-and-reconciliation-process-in-psychiatry (accessed 24 March 2019).

Clark J (2012). Reconciliation via truth? A study of South Africa's TRC. *Journal of Human Rights 11*(2): 189.

Cresswell M (2017). Truth and reconciliation in psychiatry: a response to Spandler and McKeown. *Mental Health Review Journal 22*(4): 324–331.

Crichton P, Carel P, Kidd I (2017). Epistemic injustice in psychiatry. *BJPsych Bulletin 41*(2): 65–70.

Cusack P, Cusack F, McAndrew S, McKeown M, Duxbury J, (2018). An integrative review exploring the physical and psychological harm inherent in using restraint in mental health in-patient settings. *International Journal of Mental Health Nursing 27*: 1162–1176.

Department of Health (2012). *Transforming Care: a national response to Winterbourne View Hospital.* Department of Health Review: final report. London: Department of Health.

Department of Internal Affairs (2007). *Te Āiotanga: report of confidential forum for former in-patients of psychiatric hospitals June 2007.* Wellington, New Zealand: DIA.

Felitti V, Anda R, Nordenberg D, Williamson DF, Spitz AM, Edwards V Koss MP, Marks JS (1998). Relationship of childhood abuse and household dysfunction to many of the leading causes of death in adults: the Adverse Childhood Experiences (ACE) study. *American Journal of Preventive Medicine 14*(4): 245–258.

Figley C (1995). Compassion fatigue: towards a new understanding of the costs of caring. In: Stamm BH (ed). *Secondary Traumatic Stress: self-care issues for clinicians, researchers, and educators.* Lutherville, MD: Sidran Press (pp3–27).

Francis R (2013). *Report of the Mid Staffordshire NHS Foundation Trust Public Inquiry.* London: Stationery Office.

Frueh B, Knapp R, Cusack K, Grubaugh A, Sauvageot J, Cousins V, Yim E, Robins C, Monnier J, Hiers T (2005). Special section on seclusion and restraint: patients' reports of traumatic or harmful experiences within the psychiatric setting. *Psychiatric Services 56*(9): 1123–1133.

Harris L (2014). *Psychiatry: we need a truth and reconciliation commission in mental health.* [Blog.] Mad in America; 5 May. www.madinamerica.com/2014/05/psychiatry-admit-wrong-mental-health/ (accessed 24 March 2019).

Health and Safety Executive (2016). *Work-Related Stress, Anxiety and Depression Statistics in Great Britain 2016.* London: HSE. www.hse.gov.uk/statistics/causdis/stress.pdf (accessed 24 March 2019).

Henderson C, Reveley A (1996). Is there a case for single sex wards? *The Psychiatrist 20*(9): 513–515.

Inwood J (2012). Righting unrightable wrongs: legacies of racial violence and the Greensboro Truth and Reconciliation Commission. *Annals of the Association of American Geographers 102*(6): 1450–1467.

Inwood J, Alderman D (2016). *How grassroots truth and reconciliation commissions can help activists to reclaim their communities and advance social justice.* [Blog.] LSE US Centre; 17 June. http://blogs.lse.ac.uk/usappblog/2016/06/17/how-grassroots-truth-and-reconciliation-commissions-can-help-activists-to-reclaim-their-communities-and-advance-social-justice/ (accessed 24 March 2019).

Jackson D, Hickman L, Hutchinson M, Andrew S, Smith J, Potgieter I, Cleary M, Peters K (2014). Whistleblowing: an integrative literature review of data-based studies involving nurses. *Contemporary Nurse 48*(2): 240–252.

Jeffery R (2015). The forgiveness dilemma: emotions and justice at the Khmer Rouge tribunal. *Australian Journal of International Affairs* 69(1): 35.

Jennings A (2016). On being invisible in the mental health system. In: Harris M, Landis C (eds). *Sexual Abuse in the Lives Of Women Diagnosed with Serious Mental Illness.* Abingdon: Routledge (pp161–180).

Jones P (2019). Book review. *Critical Mental Health Nursing: observations from the inside. Hodges' Model: Welcome to the QUAD;* 28 January. https://hodges-model.blogspot.com/2019/01/book-review-i-critical-mh-nursing.html (accessed 24 March 2019).

Katsakou C, Rose D, Amos H, Bowers L, McCabe R, Oliver D, Wykes T, Priebe S (2012). Psychiatric patients' views on why their involuntary hospitalisation was right or wrong: a qualitative study. *Social Psychiatry and Psychiatric Epidemiology 47*(7): 1169–1179.

Kavanagh-Hall E (2013). Forgotten hospital abused petition for apology. [Blog.] *Newswire;* 13 May. http://www.newswire.co.nz/2013/03/forgotten-hospital-abused-petition-for-apology/ (accessed 24 March 2019).

LeBlanc E (2016). Where is our apology? *Our Voice/Notre Voix 1*(November): 53–64.

Levy R (2016a). *Truth and reconciliation: an evening of sharing and healing.* [Blog.] *Mad in America;* 14 May. https://www.madinamerica.com/2016/05/speaking_truths_-sharing_healing/ (accessed 24 March 2019).

Levy R (2016b). Truth and reconciliation in psychiatric, mental health services. Commentary: healing circle to connect receivers and providers of psychiatric treatment. [Blog.] *StreetRootsNews;* 10 March. http://news.streetroots.org/2016/03/10/truth-and-reconciliation-psychiatric-mental-health-services (accessed 24 March 2019).

Liegghio M (2013). A denial of being: psychiatrization as epistemic violence. In: LeFrancois B, Menzies R, Reaume G (eds). *Mad Matters: a critical reader in Canadian mad studies.* Toronto: Canadian Scholars' Press (pp122–129).

Masson J (1988). *Against Therapy: emotional tyranny and the myth of psychological healing.* New York: Atheneum.

McKeown M, Cresswell M, Spandler H (2014). Deeply engaged relationships: alliances between mental health workers and psychiatric survivors in the UK. In: Burstow B, LeFrancois BA,

Diamond SL (eds). *Psychiatry Disrupted: theorizing resistance and crafting the revolution.* Montreal, QC: McGill/Queen's University Press (pp193–216).

McKeown M, Foley P (2015). Reducing physical restraint: an employment relations perspective. *Journal of Mental Health Nursing* 35(1): 12–15.

McKeown M, Scholes A, Jones F, Aindow W (2019). Coercive practices in mental health services: stories of recalcitrance, resistance and legitimation. In: Daley A, Costa L, Beresford P (eds). *Madness, Violence and Power.* Toronto: University of Toronto Press (pp263–285).

Moncrieff J (2013). *The Bitterest Pills: the troubling story of antipsychotic drugs.* Basingstoke: Palgrave Macmillan.

O'Connor K, Muller Neff D, Pitman S, Plumb A (2018). Burnout in mental health professionals: a systematic review and meta-analysis of prevalence and determinants. *European Psychiatry* 53: 74–99.

Plumb A (2015). UN Convention on the Rights of Persons with Disabilities: out of the frying pan into the fire? Mental health services users and survivors aligning with the disability movement. In: Spandler H, Anderson J, Sapey B (eds). *Madness, Distress and the Politics of Disablement.* Bristol: Policy Press (pp183–198).

Read J, Sampson M, Critchley C (2016). Are mental health services getting better at responding to abuse, assault and neglect? *Acta Psychiatrica Scandinavica* 134: 287–294.

Recovery in The Bin (2016). A simple guide on how to avoid receiving a diagnosis of 'personality disorder. *Clinical Psychology Forum* 279(March): 13–16.

Rose E (2015). Twenty years since democracy in South Africa: reconsidering the contributions of the Truth and Reconciliation Commission. *Melbourne Journal of Politics* 37: 61–77.

Rössler W (2012). Stress, burnout, and job dissatisfaction in mental health workers. *European Archives of Psychiatry and Clinical Neuroscience* 262(2): 65–69.

Russo J (2017). It's not about past hurt. It's about the way you call for alliances. *Asylum Magazine* 24(1): 18–19.

Sabin-Farrell R, Turpin G (2003). Vicarious traumatization: implications for the mental health of health workers? *Clinical Psychology Review* 23(3): 449–480.

Seidel T, Abu-Nimer M (2015). Peace and reconciliation processes. In: Stone J, Hou X, Dennis R, Rizova P, Smith A (eds). *The Wiley-Blackwell Encyclopaedia of Race, Ethnicity and Nationalism.* Oxford: Wiley Blackwell (pp1–3).

Seikkula J, Arnkil T, (2013). *Open Dialogues and Anticipations: respecting otherness in the present moment.* Teema: THL.

Slade M (2009). *Personal Recovery and Mental Illness.* Cambridge: Cambridge University Press.

Spandler H (2016). Healing the rifts between mental health workers and psychiatric survivors. [Blog.] *LSE Business Review;* 21 November. http://blogs.lse.ac.uk/businessreview/2016/11/21/healing-the-rifts-between-mental-health-workers-and-psychiatric-survivors/ (accessed 24 March 2019).

Spandler H, McKeown M (2017a). Exploring the case for truth and reconciliation in mental health. *Mental Health Review Journal* 22(2): 83–94.

Spandler H, McKeown M (2017b). Response to Mark Creswell: truth and reconciliation: a welcome dialogue. *Mental Health Review Journal* 22(4): 332–334.

Stein D, Seedat S, Kaminer D, Moomal H, Herman A, Sonnega J, Williams D (2008). The impact of the Truth and Reconciliation Commission on psychological distress and forgiveness in South Africa. *Social Psychiatry and Psychiatric Epidemiology* 43: 462–468.

Sweeney A, Clement S, Filson B, Kennedy A (2016). Trauma-informed mental healthcare in the UK: what is it and how can we further its development? *Mental Health Review Journal* 21(3):174–192.

Turkle S (2016). *Reclaiming Conversation: the power of talk in a digital age*. New York: Penguin Books.

van Rensburg BJ (2015). Reconciliation and psychiatry in South Africa. *BJPsych International* *12*(3): 62–64.

Varese F, Smeets F, Drukker M, Lieverse R, Lataster T, Viechtbauer W, Read J, van Os J, Bentall R (2012). Childhood adversities increase the risk of psychosis: a meta-analysis of patient-control, prospective-and cross-sectional cohort studies. *Schizophrenia Bulletin 38*(4): 661–671.

Wallcraft J (2010). *Truth and Reconciliation in Psychiatry*. [Online.] www.ipetitions.com/petition/truth_ and_reconciliation_in_psychiatry/ (accessed 24 March 2019).

Wallcraft J, Shulkes D (2012). Can psychiatry apologise for crimes against humanity? *Open Mind* January/February: 12–13.

Whitaker R (2002). *Mad in America: bad science, bad medicine, and the enduring mistreatment of the mentally ill*. Cambridge, Mass: Perseus Publishing.

Williams S, Gadsby J, Bull P (2018). Our apology. In: Bull P, Williams S, Gadsby J (eds). *Critical Mental Health Nursing: observations from the inside*. Monmouth: PCCS Books (pp ii–iii).

# Contributors

**Paul Brewer** joined an architecture course from school but dropped out owing to mental health issues. He began working in the NHS in 1976 as a hospital porter and, following a brief interlude in Australia, trained as an occupational therapist. He qualified as a group analyst at the Institute of Group Analysis London but no longer practises. Paul left the NHS in 2003 to work at Sound Minds, where he remains CEO. He lives in London.

**Anne Cooke** is Clinical Director of the Doctoral Programme in Clinical Psychology at the Salomons Centre for Applied Psychology, Canterbury Christ Church University. For many years she worked as a consultant clinical psychologist in the NHS, leading psychology services in mental health teams. She was named British Psychological Society Practitioner of the Year in 2017, in particular for her work to make available good-quality public information about mental health. Anne edited the BPS public information report, *Understanding Psychosis*, leading a group of 24 contributors. The report explores alternatives to the disease-model approach to 'schizophrenia' and argues that even the most severe distress and the most puzzling behaviour can often be understood psychologically. Anne is also engaged with colleagues in the 'Discursive of Tunbridge Wells' project, which aims to open up debates about key issues in mental health via a blog and podcast.

**John Cromby** is Professor of Psychology at the University of Leicester. He is interested in how psychological phenomena get produced when social and bodily influences come together. This has meant conducting research in mental health, learning disability and drug addiction settings, and being especially interested in feeling, embodiment and emotion. He has published 11 books, more than 70 academic journal articles, and more than 30 book chapters. His co-authored textbook, *Psychology, Mental Health and Distress,* was a 2014 British Psychological Society Book of the Year, and he is a contributing author to the Power Threat Meaning Framework.

**Jonathan Gadsby** is a mental health nurse, co-founder of the Critical Mental Health Nurses' Network and research fellow at Birmingham City University. He holds a master's in philosophy and ethics of mental health. Before that, he worked in various mental health teams, mostly in Bristol, mostly in community roles. On some days, he wonders if he would be more effective superglued to Waterloo Bridge than reading, thinking, writing and teaching. He does not like coercion and, given all of the problems with 'nature' and 'degree', thinks that the Mental Health Act ought to be almost impossible to apply. He thinks democracy has much more to offer in the future.

**Harry Gijbels** has worked in the area of mental health nursing for more than 40 years. He retired in 2017 as a senior lecturer in the School of Nursing and Midwifery at University College Cork, Ireland, but he continues to be actively engaged through his involvement with the Hearing Voices Network Ireland, and, with Lydia Sapouna, in the organisation of the Annual Critical Perspectives Conference at University College Cork. Harry's work in teaching, activism and supporting innovative projects is informed and influenced by dominant discourses, issues of power, expertise, human rights and social justice in mental health.

**Eoin Gorman** is programme director and lecturer in the Department of Occupational Science and Occupational Therapy at University College Cork. Clinically, Eoin has worked across various psychosocial settings, including adult and older adult inpatient and community mental health and youth and young adult community mental health. Eoin's educational and career pathway is heavily influenced by his interest in psychosocial concepts and issues, including gender and sexuality, mental health and Madness, death and dying, spirituality, human rights-based healthcare and social justice. He is particularly interested in social trends, attitudes and critical perspectives towards mental health and service user-led movements. Eoin is currently pursuing his PhD exploring the lived experience of transgender people in Ireland.

**Dr Anjula Gupta** is a clinical tutor on the Doctorate in Clinical Psychology Programme at University of Hull. She has been interested in this area of psychology since her clinical training, pursuing her interest by completing a community psychology master's degree. She offers community psychology placements to trainee clinical psychologists from the Leeds clinical psychology programme and co-ordinates and teaches on the community psychology placements at Hull University. She has worked in the NHS for 26 years, currently as a consultant clinical psychologist in the assertive outreach and rehab inpatient services at Leeds and York Partnership NHS Foundation Trust. An important aspect of her work in the NHS involves influencing the system from the inside to benefit service users, their families, local communities and service providers.

**Joan Hamilton** was born in Jersey and relocated and settled in Co Cork in 1967 with her husband, Gerry, and their six children. It was the experience of her youngest daughter that led to the setting up of Slí Eile. Joan witnessed her daughter's increasing torment and isolation when, from the age of 16, she had numerous admissions to psychiatric hospital over a 14-year period. Her daughter eventually ended up in a long-stay facility, with no hope of recovery. Driven by a huge sense of injustice, Joan, with the support of many others, set up Slí Eile Housing Association and Support Services, to offer her daughter, and many others like her, caught in the revolving door of the psychiatric system, 'another way' ('slí eile') to recovery. Until her retirement in 2017, Joan was the CEO of the first social housing project, Villa Maria, which opened in 2006, and of the Slí Eile Farm project, which opened in 2012, both of which demonstrated that there are 'other ways' to support people in distress.

**Deirdre Lillis** is currently the co-ordinator of Cork Advocacy Service, a service within the Social and Health Education Project, an Irish, not-for-profit, community training and development organisation. Deirdre has worked as an independent advocate for the past 23 years – 10 years in the UK and 13 years in Ireland – in voluntary organisations such as Mind in the UK and Shine in Ireland and for one user-led service, Users Support Service, in the UK. Deirdre has supported individuals and groups as an independent advocate, facilitated user involvement, user-led service monitoring and research, and facilitated advocacy training. Deirdre is committed to working in critically reflective ways. She is influenced and informed by her own experience of the psychiatric response in her early 20s and by her learning from others who share a commitment to challenging injustice in constructive and innovative ways.

**Kirsten Maclean** comes from a background in community education, working alongside a range of community groups over more than 20 years. Her work is informed by her political and personal values and experiences as well as a commitment to working collectively for change. Kirsten has been part of the Oor Mad History project, which is based at CAPS Independent Advocacy, Scotland, for 10 years as a community history worker. Currently she is a also a PhD candidate at Strathclyde University's Centre for Health Policy, Glasgow. Her research is looking at educational spaces, 'citizenship', and personal and political agency in both the US and Scotland in a context of mental health and madness.

**Dr Bryan McElroy** works as a general practitioner with a special interest in psychiatry and the spectrum of human psychological and emotional experiences. He qualified from University College Cork medical school in 2009 and obtained a diploma in clinical psychiatry during his GP training, which finished in 2015. He has been attending the Annual Critical Perspectives Conferences at University College Cork since 2010, and has found them to be an invaluable source of inspiration and vitally important information. He also has training and experience in the work of Byron Katie, the 'three principles' of Sydney Banks, Eye Movement Desensitisation Reprocessing and the Alexander Technique. In his spare time he enjoys dancing and spending quality time outdoors.

**Mick McKeown** is Professor of Democratic Mental Health, School of Nursing, University of Central Lancashire and a trade union activist with Unison. He is a founding member of Preston Cooperative Development Network, encouraging trade union support for cooperative development in the region. Mick is a longstanding member of Unison's National Nursing Sector Committee, arguing for union organising to extend to alliance formation with service users/survivors, and relational approaches to union organising and workplace democracy in the healthcare sector.

**Shirley McNicholas** is the founder of Drayton Park Women's Crisis House and developed the Drayton Park model. She did this in close collaboration with women who have used services and colleagues who have worked in the service over the years. Shirley has worked in mental health services for 35 years and has campaigned for women-only provision throughout this time. She has delivered training on a range of issues such as domestic and sexual abuse. She has been women's lead for Camden and Islington NHS Trust for more than 10 years and is also a freelance consultant and trainer in trauma-informed approaches and women's mental health. Shirley's work is central to her life and politics and she is committed to changing how services are provided to all.

**Revd Stephen Normanton** is the Chief Executive of the PeerTalk Charitable Foundation, a charity that he, with the support and encouragement of many others, founded in 2016. Stephen has been a Methodist Church minister since

1990, serving in Cumbria, West Yorkshire, London and North Yorkshire. Stephen's church ministry has always maintained strong involvement in a wide range of community-based projects. Before church ministry, Stephen worked for three years in the remote far-west of Nepal, in a development project, plying his then trade as an electrician. Stephen has a degree in International Studies with the Open University and maintains an interest in global affairs. Stephen is married to Philippa and they have two grown-up children, Robert and Susannah.

**Anne O'Donnell** has been involved in collective advocacy/service user activism in Scotland since the mid 1990s. She was one of the founders of Oor Mad History and is currently working for CAPS Independent Advocacy as co-ordinator of LEARN, an education project that offers mental health courses developed and delivered with people who have lived experience of mental health issues. She is interested in the intersections between collective advocacy, activism and transformative education; the history of survivor activism, and in how mental distress and madness are understood and responded to under capitalism.

**Andie Rose** is a mental health campaigner and activist. She helps train staff in understanding how trauma affects our lives. She has been a member of the women's strategy group within Camden and Islington NHS Foundation Trust for many years, helping to write policies, advocating for women-only crisis houses and helping to improve services and systems. She has been using services for more than two decades.

**Lydia Sapouna** is a lecturer in the School of Applied Social Studies, University College Cork. Her teaching, research and community contributions are primarily in the area of critical mental health, education and practice. She is very interested in the politics of mental health and the role of social activism in changing power imbalances in mental health systems. At the same time, she is managing the tension between her commitment to social justice and the expectation to prepare students for practice in a predominantly biomedical and often coercive context. Over the years she has worked collaboratively with service users/survivors in the areas of advocacy and human rights, but she is increasingly concerned about the co-option of user involvement by mainstream institutions, including education. With Harry Gijbels, she has organised the Annual Critical Perspectives Conference at University College Cork, since 2009. This free, two-day conference draws an annual attendance of more than 500 delegates, and is now considered one of the most significant events of its kind, nationally and internationally.

**Dr Gary Sidley** is a freelance writer, trainer, blogger and conference speaker. In 2013, he opted for early retirement from his post of Professional Lead/ Consultant Clinical Psychologist, after 33 continuous years of employment in the UK's National Health Service. Gary's NHS career began in 1980 as a psychiatric nurse, and he qualified as a clinical psychologist in 1989. In 2000, he obtained his PhD for a thesis exploring the psychological predictors of suicidal behaviour. He is a vocal critic of bio-medical approaches to mental health, illustrating his concerns with anecdotes drawn from his extensive experience of working within the psychiatric system. His book, *Tales from the Madhouse: an insider critique of psychiatric services*, was published by PCCS Books in February 2015. More recently, he has been involved in promoting recovery-orientated services and his writings and training sessions have addressed a variety of issues that highlight the pernicious nature of current Western psychiatry. His articles can be found on his blog: http:// talesfromthemadhouse.com and on hubpages http://gsidley.hubpages.com. Gary also regularly tweets about mental health issues at https://twitter.com/ GarySidley

**Helen Spandler** is Professor of Mental Health at the University of Central Lancashire, Preston. Helen has published widely in the area of critical mental health politics, history, policy and practice. She is also the Managing Editor of *Asylum*, the radical mental health magazine (http://asylummagazine.org).

**Dr Iseult Twamley** is a clinical psychologist and Open Dialogue trainer/ supervisor. Since 2012 she has been clinical lead of Cork Open Dialogue Implementation, Ireland, implementing Open Dialogue (OD) as part of the adult mental health service, initially as a pilot and since 2015 as a routine mental health care pathway. She is co-lead with Dr Maria Dempsey of the OD research programme at University College Cork. Iseult's experience in Ireland has given her a particular interest in supporting OD implementations in their specific context and culture, and she has trained and supervised OD practitioners in the UK, Australia, Israel, Italy and the Netherlands. As a trauma survivor herself and a family member of a psychiatric service user, Iseult is passionate about approaches to mental health that address collaborative and co-productive practices. She credits her involvement with the Hearing Voices Network and trialogues as challenging her previous 'education' and ethics and continues to seek opportunities to hear and learn from non-professional sources of wisdom. Iseult would like to note that all views and any errors in the chapter are hers alone.

**Fiona Venner** is the Chief Executive of Leeds Survivor Led Crisis Service, an organisation she has led since 2005. Fiona has worked in mental health since the early 1990s, always in the voluntary sector and predominantly in acute settings. This has included working with homeless people with mental health problems in London and managing the Suicide and Self-Harm Team at 42nd Street, a Manchester-based charity supporting young people. Fiona was the Deputy Chief Executive of Leeds Mind before her current job and has worked as a volunteer therapist in various Leeds counselling services. Fiona is also a marathon runner and a Labour councillor on Leeds City Council, representing Kirkstall ward in West Leeds, where she lives with her collection of rescued ragdoll cats.

**Dr John Wainwright** is a senior lecturer at the University of Central Lancashire (UCLan). He is a Health and Care Professions Council-registered social worker and, before entering academia, spent several years working with children, young people and their families in youth justice and community settings. Alongside his professional experience in the youth justice system, he was a co-founder of the service user-led organisation in Liverpool, Black and In Care , which worked with and advocated for Black and minority ethnic young people who were in the care system. He has an ongoing involvement in research focusing on ethnicity, youth justice, adoption and mental health. John is the lead for the Youth and Justice strand of the Criminal Justice Partnership at UCLan.

# Name index

# Subject index